Chemopreventive Activities
of Phytochemicals

Chemopreventive Activities of Phytochemicals

Special Issue Editor

Toshio Morikawa

MDPI • Basel • Beijing • Wuhan • Barcelona • Belgrade • Manchester • Tokyo • Cluj • Tianjin

Special Issue Editor
Toshio Morikawa
Kindai University
Japan

Editorial Office
MDPI
St. Alban-Anlage 66
4052 Basel, Switzerland

This is a reprint of articles from the Special Issue published online in the open access journal *International Journal of Molecular Sciences* (ISSN 1422-0067) (available at: https://www.mdpi.com/journal/ijms/special_issues/phytochemicals1).

For citation purposes, cite each article independently as indicated on the article page online and as indicated below:

LastName, A.A.; LastName, B.B.; LastName, C.C. Article Title. *Journal Name* **Year**, *Article Number*, Page Range.

ISBN 978-3-03936-503-6 (Hbk)
ISBN 978-3-03936-504-3 (PDF)

Contents

About the Special Issue Editor

Toshio Morikawa is Professor at the Pharmaceutical Research and Technology Institute, Kindai University, Japan. He was born in Kyoto Prefecture, Japan in 1972 and received his Ph.D. under the supervision of Professor Masayuki Yoshikawa at Kyoto Pharmaceutical University in 2002. In 2001, he started his academic career at Kyoto Pharmaceutical University as an Assistant Professor. He became a Lecturer in 2005, an Associate Professor in 2010, and a Professor in 2015 at the Pharmaceutical Research and Technology Institute, Kindai University. He received The Japanese Society of Pharmacognosy (JSP) Award for Young Scientists in 2005 and The JSP Award for Scientific Contributions in 2018. His current research program focuses on the search for bioactive constituents from natural resources and the development of new functional foods for the prevention and improvement of lifestyle diseases. He has published over 200 papers in peer reviewed journals and is currently serving on the editorial board members of Journal of Natural Medicines, Traditional & Kampo Medicine, Japanese Journal of Food Chemistry and Safety, and Molecules. He was also served thrice as Guest Editor for IJMS.

Preface to "Chemopreventive Activities of Phytochemicals"

Phytochemicals, naturally occurring products produced by plant resources, are classified as polyphenols, terpenoids, phytosterols, and alkaloids, etc. It is well-recognize that several phytochemicals have shown to exhibit chemoprevention and chemotherapeutic effects in not only experimental in vitro and in vivo trials but in clinically [1]. Inflammation is caused by a variety of stimuli including physical damage, UV irradiation, microbial invasion, and immune reactions. The classical key features of inflammation are redness, warmth, swelling, and pain, and their cascades can lead to the inflammatory bowel disease and psoriasis. Many of the inflammatory diseases are becoming common in aging society throughout the world. The clinically used anti-inflammatory drugs suffer from the disadvantage of side effects and high cost of treatment in case of biologics [2]. Therefore, researches on new anti-inflammatory molecules and elucidation of their molecular mechanisms are actively conducted. This book titled "Chemopreventive Activities of Phytochemicals" is intended to offer anti-inflammatory active natural products as candidates and/or leads for pharmaceuticals, based on the publication of 11 papers in the Special Issue in International Journal of Molecular Sciences.

Ranjan et al., summarized several natural products, such as capsaicin, cucurbitacin B, isoflavones, catechins, lycopenes, benzyl isothiocyanate, phenethyl isothiocyanate, and piperlongumine, targeting different signaling pathways involved in cancer progression, suggesting their potential to be successful anti-cancer agents [3]. Gao et al., described that using recent phenotypic drug discovery tools such as in silico Screening with Connectivity Map, we can finally be in the position to uncover novel functions of phytochemicals which could be both chemopreventive and therapeutic toward many chronic diseases caused by cellular stresses [4]. As for potential implications in cardio-protection, Ferenczyove et al. reviewed that quercetin and its derivatives may represent promising substances for prevention/treatment for wide range of cardiac disease [5]. Musial et al., addressed beneficial properties of green tea catechins, one of the most popular functional phytochemicals. This review summarized that the beneficial effects of the main catechin of green tea, epigallocatechin 3-O-gallate, brings promising results in prevention of breast, lung, prostate, stomach, and pancreatic cancers and can be used an adjunct [6]. Ramirez et al., summarized overview and future perspective of functional ingredients obtained from *Brassicaceae* species [7]. Shen and co-workers investigated anti-inflammatory effect of d-tocotrienol, an important component of vitamin E, against lipopolysaccharide-stimulated macrophages via mitogen-activated protein kinase (MAPK) and peroxisome proliferator-activated receptor (PPAR) signaling pathways [8]. He and co-workers demonstrated that a traditional medicine, Citrus aurantium L., and its flavonoid constituents showed significant regulatory effects on 2,4,6-trinitrobenzene sulfonic acid-induced inflammatory bowel disease rats through anti-inflammation and inhibition of intestine muscle contraction [9]. Huang and co-workers investigated that an alkamide, spilanthol [(2E,6Z8E)-N-isobutylamide-2,6,8-decatrienamide] obtained from Spilanthes acamella Murr., can improve atopic dermatitis (AD) symptoms via regulation of Th1/Th2 balance, inhibition of mast cell hyperplasia, and suppression of the mitogen-activated protein kinase signaling pathways ameliorated 2,4-dinitrochlorobenzene-incuded AD-like skin inflammation in mice [10]. Chen and co-workers examined the phytochemical characterization of Sapindus mukorossi seed oil and effects on in vivo and in vitro wound healing activities. The results suggest that S. mukorossi seed oil could be a potential source for promoting skin wound healing [11]. Morikawa and co-workers demonstrated that an acylated flavonol glycoside helichrysoside showed glucose tolerance-improving activity in mice as well as structural requirement of the related flavonoids for promoting glucose and lipid metabolism in hepatocytes [12]. Chiaino and co-workers investigated apoptotic-enhancing effects of Acacia catechu Willd. heartwood extract in human colon cancer cells [13].

I have put together as a guest editor of Special Issue titled "Chemopreventive Activities of Phytochemicals" in Bioactives and Nutraceuticals section of *International Journal of Molecular Sciences* and hope it will be of use to many researchers. I would like to acknowledge all the authors for their valuable contributions and the reviewers for their constructive remarks. Special thanks to the publishing stuffs of *International Journal of Molecular Sciences* at MDPI for their professional support in all aspects of this Special Issue.

Author Contributions: T.M. wrote this preface. The author has read and agreed to the publication version of the manuscript.

Funding: This research received no external funding.

Conflicts of Interest: The authors declare no conflict of interest.

Guest Editor Name 1, Guest Editor Name 2, Guest Editor Name 3
Guest Editors

References

1. Altemimi, A.; Lakhssassi, N.; Baharlouei, A.; Watson, D.G.; Lightfoot, D.A. Phytochemicals: extraction, isolation, and identification of bioactive compounds from plant extracts. *Plants* **2017**, *6*, 42.
2. Gautam, R.; Jachak, S.M. Recent developments in anti-inflammatory natural products. *Med. Res. Rev.* **2009**, *29*, 767–820.
3. Ranjan, A.; Ramachandran, S.; Gupta, N.; Kaushik, I.; Wright, S.; Srivastava, S.; Das, H.; Srivastava, S.; Prasad, S.; Srivastava, S.K. Role of phytochemicals in cancer prevention. *Int. J. Mol. Sci.* **2019**, *20*, 4981.
4. Gao, Y.; Kim, S.; Lee, Y.-I.; Lee, J. Cellular stress-modulating drugs can potentially be identified by *in silico* screening with connectivity map (CMap). *Int. J. Mol. Sci.* **2019**, *20*, 5601.
5. Ferenczyova, K.; Kalocayova, B.; Bartekova, M. Potential implications of quercetin and its derivatives in cardioprotection. *Int. J. Mol. Sci.,* **2020**, *21*, 1585.
6. Musial, C.; Kuban-Jankowska, A.; Gorska-Ponikowska, M. Beneficial properties of green tea catechins. *Int. J. Mol. Sci.* **2020**, *21*, 1744.
7. Ramirez, D.; Abellán-Victorio, A.; Beretta, V.; Camargo, A.; Moreno, D.A. Functional ingredients from *Brassicaceae* species: overview and perspectives. *Int. J. Mol. Sci.* **2020**, *21*, 1998.
8. Shen, J.; Yang, T.; Xu, Y.; Luo, Y.; Zhong, X.; Shi, L.; Hu, T.; Guo, T.; Nie, Y.; Luo, F.; Lin, Q. d-Tocotrienol, isolated from rice bran, exerts an anti-inflammatory effect *via* MAPKs and PPARs signaling pathways in lipopolysaccharide-stimulated macrophages. *Int. J. Mol. Sci.* **2018**, *19*, 3022.
9. He, W.; Li, Y.; Liu, M.; Yu, H.; Chen, Q.; Chen, Y.; Ruan, J.; Ding, Z.; Zhang, Y.; Wang, T. *Citrus aurantium* L. and its flavonoids regulate TNBS-induced inflammatory bowel disease through anti-inflammation and suppressing isolated jejunum contraction. *Int. J. Mol. Sci.* **2018**, *19*, 3057.

10. Huang, W.-C.; Huang, C.-H.; Hu, S.; Peng, H.-L.; Wu, S.-J. Topical spilanthol inhibits MAPK signaling and ameliorates allargic inflammation in DNCB-induced atopic dermatitis in mice. *Int. J. Mol. Sci.* **2019**, *20*, 2490.

11. Chen, C.-C.; Nien, C.-J.; Chen, L.-G.; Huang, K.-Y.; Chang, W.-J.; Huang, H.-M. Effects of *Sapindus mukorossi* seed oil on skin wound healing: *in vivo* and *in vitro* testing. *Int. J. Mol. Sci.* **2019**, *20*, 2579.

12. Morikawa, T.; Nagatomo, A.; Oka, T.; Miki, Y.; Taira, N.; Shibano-Kitahara, M.; Hori, Y.; Muraoka, O., Ninomiya, K. Glucose tolerance-improving activity of helichrysoside in mice and its structural requirements for promoting glucose and lipid metabolism. *Int. J. Mol. Sci.* **2019**, *20*, 6322.

13. Chiaino, E.; Micucci, M.; Durante, M.; Budriesi, R.; Gotti, R.; Marzetti, C.; Chiarini, A.; Frosini, M. Apoptotic-induced effects of *Acacia catechu* Willd. Extract in human colon cancer cells. *Int. J. Mol. Sci.* **2020**, *21*, 2102.

International Journal of
Molecular Sciences

Review

Role of Phytochemicals in Cancer Prevention

Alok Ranjan [1], Sharavan Ramachandran [1,2], Nehal Gupta [1], Itishree Kaushik [1,2],
Stephen Wright [1,3], Suyash Srivastava [1], Hiranmoy Das [1], Sangeeta Srivastava [4], Sahdeo Prasad [2]
and Sanjay K. Srivastava [1,2,*]

[1] Department of Biomedical Sciences, Texas Tech University Health Sciences Center, Amarillo, TX 79106, USA;
    alok.ranjan@nih.gov (A.R.); sharvan.ramachandran@ttuhsc.edu (S.R.); nehal.gupta@ttuhsc.edu (N.G.);
    i.kaushik@ttuhsc.edu (I.K.); stephen.wright@ttuhsc.edu (S.W.); suyash.srivastava17@gmail.com (S.S.);
    hiranmoy.das@ttuhsc.edu (H.D.)
[2] Department of Immunotherapeutics and Biotechnology, and Center for Tumor Immunology and Targeted
    Cancer Therapy, Texas Tech University Health Sciences Center, Abilene, TX 79601, USA;
    sahdeo.prasad@ttuhsc.edu
[3] Department of Internal Medicine, Texas Tech University Health Sciences Center, Amarillo, TX 79106, USA
[4] Department of Chemistry, Lucknow University, Mahatma Gandhi Road, Lucknow, UP 226007, India;
    sangeetas.lu@gmail.com
*   Correspondence: sanjay.srivastava@ttuhsc.edu; Tel.: +325-696-0464; Fax: +325-676-3845

Received: 13 September 2019; Accepted: 8 October 2019; Published: 9 October 2019

Abstract: The use of synthetic, natural, or biological agents to minimize the occurrence of cancer in healthy individuals is defined as cancer chemoprevention. Chemopreventive agents inhibit the development of cancer either by impeding DNA damage, which leads to malignancy or by reversing or blocking the division of premalignant cells with DNA damage. The benefit of this approach has been demonstrated in clinical trials of breast, prostate, and colon cancer. The continuous increase in cancer cases, failure of conventional chemotherapies to control cancer, and excessive toxicity of chemotherapies clearly demand an alternative approach. The first trial to show benefit of chemoprevention was undertaken in breast cancer patients with the use of tamoxifen, which demonstrated a significant decrease in invasive breast cancer. The success of using chemopreventive agents for protecting the high risk populations from cancer indicates that the strategy is rational and promising. Dietary components such as capsaicin, cucurbitacin B, isoflavones, catechins, lycopenes, benzyl isothiocyanate, phenethyl isothiocyanate, and piperlongumine have demonstrated inhibitory effects on cancer cells indicating that they may serve as chemopreventive agents. In this review, we have addressed the mechanism of chemopreventive and anticancer effects of several natural agents.

Keywords: chemoprevention; capsaicin; cucurbitacin B; benzyl isothiocyanate; phenethyl isothiocyanate; piperlongumine; isoflavones; catechins; lycopene

1. Introduction

Cancer is a disease, which involves abnormal growth of cells with the potential to invade and metastasize to other parts of the body. Among several factors that are involved in cancer initiation include changes in the genes that regulate normal functions of the body. Given the steady increase in cancer incidence worldwide, together with escalating problems with drug resistance, there is increasing interest in various strategies for cancer prevention.

Chemoprevention is the use of natural, synthetic or biological agents to prevent, suppress or to reverse the initial phase of carcinogenesis or to prevent the invading potential of premalignant cells [1]. The interest in the area of chemoprevention has largely increased with growing understanding of the biology of cancer, identification of molecular targets, and success in breast, prostate, and colon cancer prevention [2]. At the molecular level, cancer chemoprevention has been distinguished by alteration of multiple pathways, which play a critical role in the three basic steps of carcinogenesis, that is, initiation, promotion, and progression [3]. Recently, FDA has approved ten new agents for treating precancerous lesions and for reducing the risk of cancer [4].

Clinically, chemoprevention has been categorized into primary, secondary, and tertiary. Primary chemoprevention is suitable for the general population with no cancer, as well as populations at high risk of developing cancer in their lifetime. Secondary chemoprevention is intended for patients with pre-malignant lesions, which may progress to invasive cancer. Generally, primary and secondary chemoprevention has been categorized under primary chemoprevention. Examples of primary chemopreventive agents are dietary phytochemical and non-steroidal anti-inflammatory drugs (NSAID). On the other hand, tertiary chemoprevention is to prevent the recurrence of cancer [5]. For instance, the administration of tamoxifen is an example of tertiary chemoprevention in breast cancer [6].

2. Capsaicin

Capsaicin (trans-8-methyl-N-vanilly l-6-nonenamide) is a pungent alkaloid and active component of chili pepper belonging to the plant genus called *Capsicum* [7,8]. The heat associated with chili pepper is measured in Scoville Heat Units (SHU), which is the factor by which a chili extract is diluted to reduce its heat. The concentration of capsaicin is proportional to the SHU in any given hot chili pepper. The concentration of capsaicin varies from 0.1–1.0% in different peppers.

Capsaicin has been reported as a chemopreventive, tumor suppressing, radiosensitizing, and anticancer agent in various cancer models [9–11]. Topical application of capsaicin is used to reduce pain or may represent an effective treatment to alleviate the symptoms of osteoarthritis when oral non-steroidal anti-inflammatory drugs are not used due to side effects [12]. Capsaicin binds to a subfamily of receptor called transient receptor potential cation channel subfamily V member 1 (TRPV1). TRPV1 receptor is also known as capsaicin receptor [13]. In general, anti-cancer activity of capsaicin is not mediated by binding with TRPV1. However, a few studies have demonstrated an increase in intracellular calcium leading to apoptosis upon binding with TRPV1 [13]. Capsaicin treatment blocks the activation of activator protein 1 (AP-1), nuclear factor kappa B (NF-κB), and signal transducer and activator of transcription 3 (STAT3) signaling pathways that are activated and responsible for tumor growth [11]. It has also been shown that capsaicin generates reactive oxygen species (ROS), depolarizes mitochondria or may cause cell cycle arrest leading to apoptosis [11]. Capsaicin reduces bladder cancer cell migration by direct binding with sirtuin 1 (SIRT1) followed by down-regulation of SIRT1 deacetylase [14]. We have demonstrated that capsaicin-induced apoptosis in pancreatic cancer cells was associated with inhibition of β-catenin signaling. Oral administration of 5 mg/kg capsaicin significantly suppressed the growth of implanted pancreatic tumors in mice. After oral administration, within an hour, maximum concentration of capsaicin is achieved in blood and maximum distribution in several organs such as kidneys, lungs, and intestine [15].

Capsaicin inhibits the activity of carcinogens, through numerous pathways, and induces apoptosis in several cancer cell lines in vitro and in rodents [7,16,17], and thus may be considered for cancer therapy. The anti-cancer mechanisms of capsaicin are listed in Table 1. However, there have been reports of tumor formation in animals receiving natural capsaicin [18,19]. Studies suggest that compounds contaminating natural capsaicin from peppers may have been responsible for the tumor formation [16]. The cancer enhancement in studies with tumor promoters and carcinogens may have been secondary to the irritating property of capsaicin and may have induced increase blood flow, which may have in turn increased the absorption of the promoters and carcinogens, and thus increased their levels, leading to tumor formation [16]. Direct application with >98% pure capsaicin showed no tumor formation on the skin and all the mice were normal [20]. Several small epidemiological studies suggest a link between capsaicin consumption and stomach or gall bladder cancer, but contamination of capsaicin-containing foods with known carcinogens renders their interpretation problematic [16]. The postulated ability of capsaicin metabolites to damage DNA and promote carcinogenesis remains unsupported [16]. Thus, pure capsaicin appears to be safe and efficacious in animal models, and thus can be evaluated in humans for safety and efficacy against cancer.

In 2014, a phase 2 clinical trial study (NCT02037464) associated with the chemopreventive effect of capsaicin was started. However, the outcome and results of this trial have not been published yet (https://www.clinicaltrials.gov/ct2/show/NCT02037464). The purpose of this study was to evaluate the chemopreventive properties of capsaicin in prostate cancer patients who are enrolled in an active surveillance program or patients scheduled to undergo radical prostatectomy.

3. Catechins

Catechins are natural polyphenols and dietary phytochemicals present in green tea and other beverages [21,22]. Lower incidence of cancer associated with dietary consumption of polyphenols present in plants has been reported [23]. Catechin (C), epicatechin (EC), epigallocatechin (EGC) and epigallocatechin-3-gallate (EGCG) are the major components of green tea [24]. Their concentrations in green tea infusion vary from 9.03–471 mg/L [25]. Catechin is an antioxidant and prevents cardiovascular disease [26,27]. Additionally, catechins have been shown to provide protection against oxidative stress induced by tertbutylhydroperoxide [28,29]. Epigallocatechin gallate (EGCG) is one of the most abundant catechins present in green tea [24]. Furthermore, EGCG has been shown to sensitize cancerous cells to apoptosis induced by anti-cancer drugs and to protect non-cancerous cells from harmful effects of ultraviolet radiation exposure [30]. The anti-cancer effects of catechins are listed in Table 1.

Table 1. Summary of the mechanisms of action of various phytochemicals in various cancer models.

Compound	Source	Cancer	Proposed Anticancer Mechanism	Reference
Capsaicin	Chilli pepper (Capsicum)	Pancreatic cancer	Blocks AP1, NF-κB and STAT3 signaling, cell cycle arrest, inhibition of β-catenin signaling	[7,11]
Catechins	Green tea and other beverages	Neuroblastoma, Breast cancer, Prostate cancer	Cell cycle at G2 phase, protection against oxidative stress, Affecting STAT3-NFκB and PI3K/AKT/mTOR pathways	[27,31]
Lycopene	Tomatoes, papaya, pink grapefruit, pink guava, red carrot	Prostate cancer, Breast cancer, cervical cancer	Dietary Antioxidant, Affecting NF-κB signal transduction, Antiangiogenic effect, Inhibition of Wnt-TCF signaling	[32,33]
Cucurbitacin B	Medicinal plants (Cucurbitaceae family)	Colorectal cancer, Lung cancer, Neuroblastoma, Breast cancer, Pancreatic cancer	Inhibitors of JAK-STAT3, HER2-integrin, and MAPK signaling pathways	[34–36]
Benzyl isothiocyanate (BITC)	*Alliaria petiolata*, pilu oil, papaya seeds	Leukemia, Breast cancer, Prostate cancer, Lung cancer, Pancreatic cancer, Colon cancer, Hepatocellular carcinoma	G_2/M Cell cycle arrest and apoptosis, down-regulation of MMP-2/9 through PKC and MAPK signaling pathway, inhibition of PI3K/AKT/FOXO pathway, STAT3 mediated HIF-1α/VEGF/Rho-GTPases inhibition	[37–40]

Table 1. *Cont.*

Compound	Source	Cancer	Proposed Anticancer Mechanism	Reference
PEITC	Cruciferous vegetables	Glioblastoma, Prostate cancer, Breast cancer, Cervical cancer, and Leukemia	ROS Activation, G2/M cell cycle arrest, and apoptosis, down regulation of HER2 and STAT3 signaling,	[41,42]
Isoflavone	Soy, lentils, beans, and chickpeas	Leukemia, Lymphoma, Gastric, Breast, Prostate, Head and Neck carcinoma, and Non-Small Cell Lung Cancer	Inhibition of c-erB-2, MMP-2, and MMP-9 signaling pathways, Affecting IGF-1R/p-Akt signaling transduction	[43,44]
Piperlongumine	Roots of long pepper	Multiple myeloma, melanoma, Pancreatic cancer, colon cancer, Oral squamous cell carcinoma, Breast cancer, and Prostate cancer	Autophagy-mediated apoptosis by inhibition of PIK3/Akt/mTOR	[45]

Dextran-Catechin, a conjugated form of catechin was demonstrated to have better serum stability and was more active against neuroblastoma than unconjugated catechin [46]. Mechanistically, dextran-catechin was observed to induce oxidative stress by decreasing the intracellular glutathione level and by disrupting copper homeostasis [46]. Moreover, catechin extract and nanoemulsion of catechin have been shown to inhibit prostate cancer cells by arresting the cell cycle in *S*-phase, with the half maximal inhibitory concentration being 15.4 µg/mL and 8.5 µg/mL respectively [27]. Additionally, catechins, particularly EGCG, inhibit the proliferation of breast cancer cells by generating reactive oxygen species [29]. EGCG has been demonstrated to have maximum relative efficiency of cellular DNA breakage whereas catechin was reported to possess minimum efficiency [47]. In another study, ribosomal protein S6 kinase (RSK)-2 has been established as a novel molecular target of EGCG using computational docking screening methods [48]. Other studies have suggested that the combination of EGCG and green tea extracts inhibit tumor growth in a xenograft mouse model of several human cancer cell lines. Also, studies have revealed that green tea has chemopreventive properties [49]. In a 10 year prospective cohort study, Drs. Nakachi and Imai showed that drinking 10 cups (120 mL/cup) of green tea everyday delays cancer onset by 7.3 years and 3.2 years in females and males, respectively [50]. Overexpression of ErbB in both normal and mutated forms has been established to play role in cancer metastasis [51]. The study demonstrated that EGCG acts directly or on downstream of ErbB signaling such as mitogen-activated protein kinase (MAPK), STAT and phosphoinositide 3-kinases (PI3K)/AKT/mammalian target of rapamycin (mTOR) pathways [51]. Side effects and acquired resistance associated with conventional platinum based chemotherapy for ovarian cancer is a major drawback [52]. Interestingly, theaflavin-3,3′-digallate (TF3), a monomer present in black tea was demonstrated to induce potent inhibitory effect on cisplatin resistant ovarian cancer cells. Additionally, G2 arrest was shown to be involved in TF3 induced apoptosis in resistant ovarian cancer [31]. Upregulation of p53 via Akt/mouse double minute 2 homolog (MDM2) pathway might be involved in TF3-induced G2 arrest and apoptosis [31].

EGCG was reported to enhance the anti-cancer activity of several anti-cancer drugs such as retinoids [53]. AM80 is a synthetic retinoid that is a clinically used drug for relapsed and intractable acute promyelocytic leukemia patients [53]. A recent study demonstrated that the combination of EGCG and AM80 synergistically induced apoptosis as well as upregulated expression of DNA damage inducible genes such as (GADD153), death receptor 5 (DR5) and p21^{wafl} in lung cancer. Furthermore, downregulation of histone deacetylase 4, -5, and -6 was observed as a mechanism for synergistic induction of apoptosis in lung cancer by EGCG and AM80 [53].

Since catechins prevent or slow the growth of prostate cancer, a clinical trial was conducted using green tea catechins for treating patients with prostate cancer undergoing surgery to remove the prostate

(NCT00459407). Although the trial started in 2007, results have not been published yet. The primary objective of the study was to estimate the bioavailability of green tea extract in the prostate of patients after the treatment of green tea extract. Furthermore, one of the several secondary objectives was to determine the effect of green tea extract on matrix metalloprotein (MMP)-2 and MMP-9 in prostate cancer patients.

4. Lycopene

Lycopene is a member of the carotenoid family, which is mainly found in tomatoes and other food products such as watermelons, papaya, pink grapefruit, pink guava and red carrot [54,55]. It is a naturally occurring pigment that contributes to the red color in these food products. Lycopene is a potent dietary antioxidant and because of its antioxidant effect, it is known to have a protective effect on several diseases such as cardiovascular diseases, neurodegenerative diseases, hypertension, osteoporosis, diabetes, and cancer [56,57]. The anti-cancer effects of lycopene against a variety of malignancies have been previously discussed by Farzaei et al. [58]. There are about 250 articles available so far on the anti-cancer effects of lycopene. Several anti-cancer mechanisms of lycopene are listed in Table 1. A recent study has been conducted to access the effect of dietary lycopene on prostate cancer. In this study Zu. et al. demonstrated that higher intake of lycopene was associated with lower incidence of prostate cancer. In addition, they found that expression of tumor tissue biomarkers related to angiogenesis, apoptosis, cell proliferation, and differentiation were less in patient samples with higher lycopene intake indicating that lycopene suppresses tumor development by inhibiting tumor neo-angiogenesis [59]. It has been reported that lycopene tends to preferentially accumulate in prostate tissue as compared with other tissues, which might be responsible for its anti-prostate cancer activity [54]. Several other studies have shown that lycopene causes cell cycle arrest and apoptosis in prostate cancer cells [60,61]. Moreover, lycopene inhibits the growth of prostate and breast cancer cells by inhibiting NF-κB signaling [62]. A study by Chen et al. showed the anti-angiogenic activity of lycopene in both in vitro and in vivo models, proposing that the mechanism of action may involve modulation of PI3K-Akt and ERK/p38 signaling pathways [32].

Several studies have shown that lycopene in combination with melatonin shows strong chemopreventive activity via antioxidant and anti-inflammatory activities [63–65]. Lycopene also enhances the effect of quinacrine on breast cancer cells by inhibiting Wnt-TCF signaling [33]. Oral administration of 16 mg/kg lycopene for 7 weeks significantly inhibited prostate tumor growth by 67% when compared to control in athymic nude mice. The study also showed that lycopene reduced the expression of proliferating cell nuclear antigen (PCNA) and VEGF in tumor tissues and plasma respectively [66].

Several clinical trials have been commenced to investigate the chemopreventive and chemotherapeutic effects of lycopene on the progression of prostate cancer. Nonetheless, studies report conflicting beneficial effects of lycopene in reducing prostate enlargement and decreasing serum prostate-specific antigen (PSA) levels whereas others studies have null findings. (NCT00006078, NCT01443026, NCT00068731). In a randomized clinical trial, administration of 15 mg lycopene every day for 6 months in benign prostate hyperplasia patients resulted in reduced disease progression with decreased serum PSA concentrations [67].

5. Cucurbitacin B

Cucurbitacins are tetracyclic triterpenoids that are found in traditional Chinese medicinal plants belonging to the cucurbitaceae family. Among eight different types of Cucurbitacins, Curcubitacin B (CuB) is the most active component against cancer and showed promise in various cancer models [68].

The effective concentrations of CuB in vitro range from 20 nM–5 μM and in vivo therapeutic doses range from 0.1–2 mg/kg [69]. Various anti-cancer mechanisms of CuB are mentioned in Table 1. Several studies have shown that CuB inhibits STAT3 signaling in various cancer models such as colorectal cancer [34], lung cancer [70], neuroblastoma [35], acute myeloid leukemia [71], pancreatic cancer [72] and breast cancer [36]. Recent studies have established the anti-angiogenic effects of CuB associated with inhibition of VEGF/FAK/MMP-9 signaling in highly metastatic breast cancer cells [73]. In non-small cell lung cancer, the anti-metastatic effect of CuB was achieved by targeting the Wnt/β-catenin signaling axis [74]. A study from our laboratory demonstrated that CuB inhibits breast tumor growth by inhibiting HER2-intergrin signaling. The inhibition of HER2-integrin signaling was associated with down regulation of integrin α6 and integrin β4 that are overexpressed in breast cancer cells [36]. In addition, it has been reported that CuB reduces invasion and migration of hepatoma cells by modulating PI3K/Akt signaling [75]. Furthermore, several studies demonstrated the potentiating effect of CuB with other chemotherapeutic agents. In pancreatic cancer, CuB augmented the anti-proliferative effects of gemcitabine by inhibiting JAK-STAT pathway [76]. CuB was also shown to sensitize cisplatin-resistant ovarian cancer cells to apoptosis when combined with cisplatin, a standard chemotherapeutic agent for ovarian cancer [77]. Another study demonstrated that CuB in combination with docetaxel or gemcitabine synergistically suppressed the growth of breast cancer cells [78]. Interestingly, combination of CuB with curcumin in hepatoma cells reversed multidrug resistance by modulating P-gp [79].

Studies have been conducted to compare the pharmacokinetic profile of CuB with that of CuB loaded solid lipid nanoparticles. The plasma AUC of CuB loaded nanoparticles was 2.47 μg·h/mL, which was almost 2-fold higher than plasma AUC of CuB (1.27 μg·h/mL) after an intravenous dose of 2 mg/kg. It was observed that CuB loaded nanoparticles showed 3.4 fold increased uptake in tumor cells when compared with CuB and exhibited better tumor suppressive effects [80]. CuB was mainly distributed in organs such as spleen and liver. Another study has demonstrated that CuB loaded modified phospholipid complex improved therapeutic efficacy, bioavailability and targeted drug delivery for cholangiocarcinoma [81].

6. Benzyl Isothiocyanate (BITC)

Isothiocyanates (ITCs) are natural compounds of high medicinal value that are present in cruciferous vegetables such as broccoli, watercress, Brussels sprouts, cabbage, cauliflower and Japanese radish [82]. They are present as conjugates in the genus *Brassica* of cruciferous vegetables [38]. ITCs are well-known for their chemo-preventive activity and mediate anti-carcinogenic activity by suppressing the activation of carcinogens and increasing their detoxification [82]. The high content of glucosinolates, which store ITCs in cruciferous vegetables confer anti-cancerous effects. ITCs suppresses tumor growth by induction of oxidative stress mediated apoptosis, inducing cell cycle arrest, inhibiting angiogenesis and metastasis [82].

Benzyl isothiocyanate (BITC) is one of the major classes of ITCs that exert potential health benefits to humans. It is extensively found in *Alliaria petiolata*, pilu oil, water cress, garden cress and papaya seeds [83]. BITC found in *Salvadora persica* has been shown to exert anti-bacterial activity against Gram-negative bacteria [84]. BITC influences several key signaling pathways which are considered to be the hallmarks of cancer. In addition, BITC sensitize tumors to chemotherapy and has substantial anticancer effects against various human malignancies like leukemia [85], breast cancer [86], prostate cancer [87], lung cancer [88], pancreatic cancer [89] colon cancer [38] and hepatocellular carcinoma [90] as mentioned in Table 1. A published study demonstrated that BITC induces DNA damage in human pancreatic cells. It was also shown that DNA damage causes G_2/M Cell cycle arrest and apoptosis [37]. Another study established BITC mediated inhibition of the migration and invasion of human colon cancer cells. The anti-invasive effect of BITC was through down-regulation of MMP-2/9 and urokinase-type plasminogen activator (uPA) linked to protein kinase C (PKC) and MAPK signaling pathways [38]. In our previous study, we have shown that BITC induces apoptosis in pancreatic cancer cells but not in normal human pancreatic ductal epithelial cells. The induction of apoptosis by BITC was through inhibition of STAT3 signaling. In the same study, oral administration of 12 μmol BITC significantly suppressed the growth of BxPC3 pancreatic tumor xenograft in athymic nude mice [89]. In another study, we have demonstrated that BITC suppressed pancreatic tumor growth by inhibiting

PI3K/AKT/FOXO pathway [39]. We have also demonstrated that BITC suppresses angiogenesis and invasion in pancreatic tumors by inhibiting STAT3 mediated HIF-1α/VEGF/Rho-GTPases [40]. BITC also displayed antitumor effects by potentiating p53 signaling in breast cancer cells. p53 activation was through the activation of p53-LKB1 and p73-LKB1 axes. In the same study, it was also reported that BITC suppressed the mammosphere –forming capability of breast cancer cells [91].

Our studies have shown that BITC possesses therapeutic selectivity towards cancer cells and does not affect normal human pancreatic epithelial cells. BITC was detected in pancreatic tumors and plasma, indicating that the therapeutic concentration can be achieved by oral administration [39]. The concentration of BITC achieved in tumor tissue and plasma was 7.5 μmol/g and 6.5 μmol/L respectively after oral administration of 12 μmol BITC in athymic nude mice [39]. In one of our published studies, nano-emulsion BITC was prepared to enhance its dissolution and solubility. The entrapment efficiency of BITC nano-emulsion was observed to be 15–17 mg/mL leading to increased accumulation in the tumor cells [92].

7. Phenethyl Isothiocyanate

Phenethyl isothiocyanate (PEITC) is another isothiocyanate mainly present in cruciferous plants. PEITC is one of the active ingredients of cruciferous vegetables that have been extensively studied for its anti-cancer effects in glioblastoma, prostate cancer, breast cancer and leukemia [36] and listed in Table 1. Several studies have indicated that consumption of cruciferous vegetables such as broccoli, watercress, and garden cress leads to chemoprevention in various rodent models [93]. A study demonstrated RASSF1A reactivation by PEITC, which is known to have tumor suppressive functions by promoting G2/M cell cycle arrest and apoptosis in prostate cancer cells [42]. Our study established for the first time the anti-metastatic potential of PEITC in a breast cancer model. Our results showed that oral administration of 10 μmol PEITC for 10 days suppressed the metastasis of breast tumor cells to the brain [94]. Another study by us indicated HER2 as a potential target of PEITC in breast carcinoma. PEITC exhibited synergistic effect when combined with doxorubicin and was associated with down regulation of HER2 and STAT3 [41]. PEITC was also shown to induce ROS generation in p53-deficient chronic lymphocytic leukemia cells (CLL) and therefore could be effective for treatment of CLL patients with p53 mutations [95]. Interestingly, the combination of PEITC and paclitaxel synergistically potentiated the anti-proliferative effects of paclitaxel on breast cancer cells.by inducing apoptosis and cell cycle arrest [96]. It has been reported that PEITC in combination with adraimycin or etoposide causes caspase 3 and 8 activation by modulating PKCs and telomerase and thus sensitizes the cervical cancer cells [97]. A recent study showed chemopreventive effects of PEITC and curcumin combination in prostate cancer xenografts [98]. Our lab has shown the immune modulation by PEITC in mice bearing breast tumor xenografts. We observed that PEITC treatment significantly suppressed breast tumor growth by reducing myeloid derived tumor suppressor cells (MDSCs) and T regulatory lymphocytes [99].

PEITC is fairly lipophilic in nature with a molecular weight of 163.2 g/mol [100,101]. Pharmacokinetics of PEITC is well established in rodents as well as in humans. Ji et al. [102] performed a detailed pharmacokinetic study of PEITC in Sprague-Dawley rats. At a dose of 10 μmol/kg (1.63 mg/kg), oral bioavailability of PEITC was 115%. The apparent volume of distribution (V_d) and clearance were 1.94 $\pm$ 0.42 L/kg and 0.70 $\pm$ 0.17 L/h/kg, respectively at the dose of 2 μmol/kg PEITC. In another clinical study, 100 g of watercress was given to four human volunteers and plasma concentration was determined using one-compartment pharmacokinetic model [103]. The highest plasma concentration (C_{max}) attained was 928.5 nM as estimated by LC-MS/MS with Tmax and $T_{1/2}$ around 2.6 h and 4.9 h, respectively.

A phase II clinical trial study (NCT00691132) for chemopreventive effects of PEITC against lung cancer started in 2009 and completed in the year 2013. The primary end point of this study was to determine whether PEITC is effective in preventing lung cancer in cigarette smokers. The metabolic activation of tobacco carcinogen 4-(methylnitrosamino)-1-(3-pyridyl)-1-butanone (NNK) was reduced by 7.7% with PEITC treatment in smokers [104]. Another study started in year 2011 by National Cancer Institute (NCT01265953) to evaluate the chemopreventive effects of PEITC against prostate cancer. From this clinical trial, it was found that isothiocyanate inhibits histone deacetylase (HDAC) activity in human colorectal and prostate cancer cells.

8. Isoflavones

Isoflavones are naturally occurring isoflavonoids present in plants belonging to the leguminosae family [105]. Isoflavones are extensively present in soy, lentil, bean, chickpeas and have profound importance as phytoestrogens in mammals. Soy is an abundant source of isoflavones, such as, genistein, glycitein, and daidzein, the concentration of which varies between 560 and 3810 mg per kg of soy [106]. Isoflavones are present in inactive form as glycosides in plants and are activated to bioactive aglycones by hydrolyzation to beta-glucosidases in the intestine. The aglycones are conjugated to liver glucorinides and excreted in urine [107]. Interestingly, the active form of isoflavones has a greater absorption rate than inactive form.

Isoflavones exert potential health benefits and are widely used in the treatment of hormone dependent conditions like menopause, cardiovascular disease, osteoporosis, and cancer [105]. Isoflavones derived from soy, such as genistein, have been established to have significant anti-cancer effects against leukemia, lymphoma, gastric, breast, prostate and non-small cell lung cancer [44]. Several studies have reported the anti-cancer effects of genistein in various cancer models such as prostate cancer [108], breast cancer [109], lung cancer [110] and head and neck squamous cell carcinoma [111], cervical cancer [112], ovarian cancer [113], renal cancer [114], bladder cancer [115], liver cancer [116] as shown in Table 1. Induction of apoptosis by genistein treatment was shown through inhibition of IGF-1R/p-Akt signaling in breast cancer [43]. Another study demonstrated anti-angiogenic and anti-metastatic effects of genistein by inhibiting c-erbB-2, MMP-2, and MMP-9 in breast carcinoma [44]. Genistein has been reported to induce differentiation in breast cancer stem cells by interaction with ER+ cells. This differentiation effect of genistein is mediated by the PI3K/Akt pathway [95]. Soy isoflavones are capable of sensitizing the cells to radiotherapy, thereby improving the efficacy of current treatment [117]. It has been demonstrated that soy isoflavones overcome radiotherapy resistance by inhibiting the altered activation of APE1/Ref-1, NF-κB, and HIF-1α [118]. Additionally, genistein has also been reported to induce anti-oxidant properties [113,119,120]. Isoflavones such as genistein and daidzein have minimal clinical toxicity [121].

A clinical trial using purified isoflavones was started in 2009 (NCT01036321) and completed in 2018. The main focus of this trial was to compare safety, effectiveness, and mechanism of action of purified isoflavones in African American and Caucasian Mento with prostate cancer. Change in percent Ki-67 was evaluated in prostate tumor tissues after 3–6 weeks of intervention with purified isoflavones (40 mg daily) vs. Placebo. On the basis of this clinical trial outcome, isoflavones could be developed as a potential chemotherapeutic and chemopreventive agent.

9. Piperlongumine

Piperlongumine or Piplartine (5,6-dihydro-1-[(2E)-1-oxo-3-(3,4,5-trimethoxyphenyl)-2-propenyl]-2 (1H)-pyridinone) is a phytochemical alkaloid extracted from the roots of long pepper Piper longum L., a member of the Piperaceae family. Long peppers have profound medicinal importance in Indian Ayurvedic medicine and Latin American folk medicine [122]. Piperlongumine was used to treat various diseases such as bronchitis, malaria, viral hepatitis, cancer, and melanogenesis [123]. The key therapeutic features of piperlongumine are its anti-inflammatory, anti-nociceptive, anti-bacterial, anti-fungal, anti-diabetic, anti-tumor, and anti-depressant properties [122]. Overall, piperlongumine has significant chemotherapeutic and chemopreventive potential making it an effective treatment option for cancer.

Piperlongumine has been found to be effective against several cancers such as multiple myeloma [124], melanoma [125], pancreatic cancer [126], colon cancer [127,128] oral squamous cell carcinoma [129], non-small-cell lung cancer [130], gastric cancer [131], biliary cancer [132], and prostate cancer [133]. The mechanism of the anti-cancer effects of piperlongumine is listed in Table 1. Piperlongumine induced ROS generation leads to oxidative stress mediated DNA damage in pancreatic cancer cells [126]. The study reveals that piperlongumine induces autophagy-mediated apoptosis by inhibition of PI3K/Akt/mTOR in lung cancer [45]. It also inhibits inflammation by suppressing inflammatory transcription factors NF-κB [127]. We have demonstrated that piperlongumine inhibits STAT3 and its activation to suppress anoikis resistance resulting in inhibition of metastatic potential of pancreatic cancer and melanoma [125,134]. Furthermore, piperlongumine has been reported to display synergestic effect with paclitaxel or cisplatin in human ovarian cancer cells [135].

The toxicity and pharmacokinetic profile of piperlongumine have been well established. Piperlongumine treated rats and mice with doses varying from 100–3000 mg/kg did not show any signs of toxicity. After oral administration of 5 mg/kg and 10 mg/kg piperlongumine, the $t_{1/2}$ was found to be 1.42 h and 0.84 h and Cmax was 884.31 μg/L and 201.42 μg/L respectively [122]. Our lab has shown that nano-emulsion of piperlongumine enhanced its bioavailability and efficacy [136]. In conclusion, piperlongumine has been established to be an effective agent for cancer treatment.

10. Conclusions

Chemoprevention is a relatively safe and cost effective approach because cancer can be prevented by changing dietary habits [137]. This approach has gained momentum after the approval of tamoxifen and raloxifen by US Food and Drug Administration for breast cancer risk reduction [138]. Various epidemiological and preclinical studies have convincingly argued the role of several dietary agents to be involved in preventing occurrence of cancer as well as its treatment. Several clinical trials associated with chemopreventive properties of above discussed natural compounds are ongoing. Drug associated toxicity is a significant barrier for currently available chemotherapeutic drugs. However, use of natural compounds for cancer prevention may mitigate associated toxicity. However, bioavailability is the biggest problem with most of the naturally occurring chemopreventive agents. Overall, this review summarizes natural compounds targeting different signaling pathways involved in cancer progression, suggesting their potential to be successful anti-cancer agents (Figure 1).

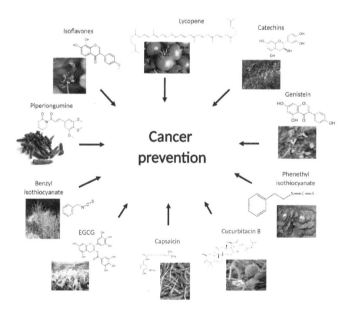

Figure 1. Phytochemicals in cancer chemoprevention.

Acknowledgments: This work was supported in part by R01 grant CA129038 (to Sanjay K. Srivastava) awarded by the National Cancer Institute, NIH.

Conflicts of Interest: The authors declare no conflict of interest.

References

1. Sporn, M.B. Approaches to prevention of epithelial cancer during the preneoplastic period. *Cancer Res.* **1976**, *36*, 2699–2702. [PubMed]
2. Golemis, E.A.; Scheet, P.; Beck, T.N.; Scolnick, E.M.; Hunter, D.J.; Hawk, E.; Hopkins, N. Molecular mechanisms of the preventable causes of cancer in the United States. *Genes Dev.* **2018**, *32*, 868–902. [CrossRef] [PubMed]
3. Pitot, H.C. The molecular biology of carcinogenesis. *Cancer* **1993**, *72*, 962–970. [CrossRef]
4. Vogel, V.G.; Costantino, J.P.; Wickerham, D.L.; Cronin, W.M.; Cecchini, R.S.; Atkins, J.N.; Bevers, T.B.; Fehrenbacher, L.; Pajon, E.R.; Wade, J.L., 3rd; et al. Update of the National Surgical Adjuvant Breast and Bowel Project Study of Tamoxifen and Raloxifene (STAR) P-2 Trial: Preventing breast cancer. *Cancer Prev. Res.* **2010**, *3*, 696–706. [CrossRef] [PubMed]
5. De Flora, S.; Ferguson, L.R. Overview of mechanisms of cancer chemopreventive agents. *Mutat. Res.* **2005**, *591*, 8–15. [CrossRef] [PubMed]
6. Ball, S.; Arevalo, M.; Juarez, E.; Payne, J.D.; Jones, C. Breast cancer chemoprevention: An update on current practice and opportunities for primary care physicians. *Prev. Med.* **2019**, *129*, 105834. [CrossRef]
7. Pramanik, K.C.; Fofaria, N.M.; Gupta, P.; Ranjan, A.; Kim, S.H.; Srivastava, S.K. Inhibition of beta-catenin signaling suppresses pancreatic tumor growth by disrupting nuclear beta-catenin/TCF-1 complex: Critical role of STAT-3. *Oncotarget* **2015**, *6*, 11561–11574. [CrossRef] [PubMed]
8. Sung, B.; Prasad, S.; Yadav, V.R.; Aggarwal, B.B. Cancer cell signaling pathways targeted by spice-derived nutraceuticals. *Nutr. Cancer* **2012**, *64*, 173–197. [CrossRef]
9. Venier, N.A.; Colquhoun, A.J.; Sasaki, H.; Kiss, A.; Sugar, L.; Adomat, H.; Fleshner, N.E.; Klotz, L.H.; Venkateswaran, V. Capsaicin: A novel radio-sensitizing agent for prostate cancer. *Prostate* **2015**, *75*, 113–125. [CrossRef]
10. Chapa-Oliver, A.M.; Mejia-Teniente, L. Capsaicin: From Plants to a Cancer-Suppressing Agent. *Molecules* **2016**, *21*, 931. [CrossRef]
11. Oyagbemi, A.A.; Saba, A.B.; Azeez, O.I. Capsaicin: A novel chemopreventive molecule and its underlying molecular mechanisms of action. *Indian J. Cancer* **2010**, *47*, 53–58. [CrossRef] [PubMed]
12. Guedes, V.; Castro, J.P.; Brito, I. Topical capsaicin for pain in osteoarthritis: A literature review. *Reumatol. Clin.* **2018**, *14*, 40–45. [CrossRef] [PubMed]
13. Sharma, S.K.; Vij, A.S.; Sharma, M. Mechanisms and clinical uses of capsaicin. *Eur. J. Pharmacol.* **2013**, *720*, 55–62. [CrossRef] [PubMed]
14. Islam, A.; Yang, Y.T.; Wu, W.H.; Chueh, P.J.; Lin, M.H. Capsaicin attenuates cell migration via SIRT1 targeting and inhibition to enhance cortactin and beta-catenin acetylation in bladder cancer cells. *Am. J. Cancer Res.* **2019**, *9*, 1172–1182. [PubMed]
15. Suresh, D.; Srinivasan, K. Tissue distribution & elimination of capsaicin, piperine & curcumin following oral intake in rats. *Indian J. Med. Res.* **2010**, *131*, 682–691. [PubMed]
16. Bley, K.; Boorman, G.; Mohammad, B.; McKenzie, D.; Babbar, S. A comprehensive review of the carcinogenic and anticarcinogenic potential of capsaicin. *Toxicol. Pathol.* **2012**, *40*, 847–873. [CrossRef] [PubMed]
17. Pramanik, K.C.; Srivastava, S.K. Apoptosis signal-regulating kinase 1-thioredoxin complex dissociation by capsaicin causes pancreatic tumor growth suppression by inducing apoptosis. *Antioxid Redox Signal.* **2012**, *17*, 1417–1432. [CrossRef]
18. Bode, A.M.; Dong, Z. Toxic phytochemicals and their potential risks for human cancer. *Cancer Prev. Res.* **2015**, *8*, 1–8. [CrossRef]
19. Ko, E.Y.; Moon, A. Natural Products for Chemoprevention of Breast Cancer. *J. Cancer Prev.* **2015**, *20*, 223–231. [CrossRef]
20. Liu, Z.; Zhu, P.; Tao, Y.; Shen, C.; Wang, S.; Zhao, L.; Wu, H.; Fan, F.; Lin, C.; Chen, C.; et al. Cancer-promoting effect of capsaicin on DMBA/TPA-induced skin tumorigenesis by modulating inflammation, Erk and p38 in mice. *Food Chem. Toxicol.* **2015**, *81*, 1–8. [CrossRef]

21. Noberini, R.; Koolpe, M.; Lamberto, I.; Pasquale, E.B. Inhibition of Eph receptor-ephrin ligand interaction by tea polyphenols. *Pharmacol. Res.* **2012**, *66*, 363–373. [CrossRef] [PubMed]
22. Prasanth, M.I.; Sivamaruthi, B.S.; Chaiyasut, C.; Tencomnao, T. A Review of the Role of Green Tea (*Camellia sinensis*) in Antiphotoaging, Stress Resistance, Neuroprotection, and Autophagy. *Nutrients* **2019**, *11*, 474. [CrossRef] [PubMed]
23. Pandey, K.B.; Rizvi, S.I. Plant polyphenols as dietary antioxidants in human health and disease. *Oxid Med. Cell Longev.* **2009**, *2*, 270–278. [CrossRef] [PubMed]
24. Reygaert, W.C. Green Tea Catechins: Their Use in Treating and Preventing Infectious Diseases. *BioMed Res. Int.* **2018**, *2018*, 9105261. [CrossRef] [PubMed]
25. Reto, M.; Figueira, M.E.; Filipe, H.M.; Almeida, C.M. Chemical composition of green tea (*Camellia sinensis*) infusions commercialized in Portugal. *Plant. Foods Hum. Nutr.* **2007**, *62*, 139–144. [CrossRef] [PubMed]
26. Babu, P.V.; Liu, D. Green tea catechins and cardiovascular health: An update. *Curr. Med. Chem.* **2008**, *15*, 1840–1850. [CrossRef] [PubMed]
27. Tsai, Y.J.; Chen, B.H. Preparation of catechin extracts and nanoemulsions from green tea leaf waste and their inhibition effect on prostate cancer cell PC-3. *Int. J. Nanomed.* **2016**, *11*, 1907–1926. [CrossRef]
28. Maurya, P.K.; Rizvi, S.I. Protective role of tea catechins on erythrocytes subjected to oxidative stress during human aging. *Nat. Prod. Res.* **2009**, *23*, 1072–1079. [CrossRef]
29. Farhan, M.; Khan, H.Y.; Oves, M.; Al-Harrasi, A.; Rehmani, N.; Arif, H.; Hadi, S.M.; Ahmad, A. Cancer Therapy by Catechins Involves Redox Cycling of Copper Ions and Generation of Reactive Oxygen species. *Toxins* **2016**, *8*, 37. [CrossRef]
30. Ng, C.Y.; Yen, H.; Hsiao, H.Y.; Su, S.C. Phytochemicals in Skin Cancer Prevention and Treatment: An Updated Review. *Int. J. Mol. Sci.* **2018**, *19*, 941. [CrossRef]
31. Tu, Y.; Kim, E.; Gao, Y.; Rankin, G.O.; Li, B.; Chen, Y.C. Theaflavin-3, 3′-digallate induces apoptosis and G2 cell cycle arrest through the Akt/MDM2/p53 pathway in cisplatin-resistant ovarian cancer A2780/CP70 cells. *Int. J. Oncol.* **2016**, *48*, 2657–2665. [CrossRef] [PubMed]
32. Chen, M.L.; Lin, Y.H.; Yang, C.M.; Hu, M.L. Lycopene inhibits angiogenesis both in vitro and in vivo by inhibiting MMP-2/uPA system through VEGFR2-mediated PI3K-Akt and ERK/p38 signaling pathways. *Mol. Nutr. Food Res.* **2012**, *56*, 889–899. [CrossRef] [PubMed]
33. Preet, R.; Mohapatra, P.; Das, D.; Satapathy, S.R.; Choudhuri, T.; Wyatt, M.D.; Kundu, C.N. Lycopene synergistically enhances quinacrine action to inhibit Wnt-TCF signaling in breast cancer cells through APC. *Carcinogenesis* **2013**, *34*, 277–286. [CrossRef] [PubMed]
34. Yar Saglam, A.S.; Alp, E.; Elmazoglu, Z.; Menevse, S. Treatment with cucurbitacin B alone and in combination with gefitinib induces cell cycle inhibition and apoptosis via EGFR and JAK/STAT pathway in human colorectal cancer cell lines. *Hum. Exp. Toxicol.* **2016**, *35*, 526–543. [CrossRef] [PubMed]
35. Zheng, Q.; Liu, Y.; Liu, W.; Ma, F.; Zhou, Y.; Chen, M.; Chang, J.; Wang, Y.; Yang, G.; He, G. Cucurbitacin B inhibits growth and induces apoptosis through the JAK2/STAT3 and MAPK pathways in SHSY5Y human neuroblastoma cells. *Mol. Med. Rep.* **2014**, *10*, 89–94. [CrossRef] [PubMed]
36. Gupta, P.; Srivastava, S.K. Inhibition of Integrin-HER2 signaling by Cucurbitacin B leads to in vitro and in vivo breast tumor growth suppression. *Oncotarget* **2014**, *5*, 1812–1828. [CrossRef] [PubMed]
37. Zhang, R.; Loganathan, S.; Humphreys, I.; Srivastava, S.K. Benzyl isothiocyanate-induced DNA damage causes G2/M cell cycle arrest and apoptosis in human pancreatic cancer cells. *J. Nutr.* **2006**, *136*, 2728–2734. [CrossRef] [PubMed]
38. Lai, K.C.; Huang, A.C.; Hsu, S.C.; Kuo, C.L.; Yang, J.S.; Wu, S.H.; Chung, J.G. Benzyl isothiocyanate (BITC) inhibits migration and invasion of human colon cancer HT29 cells by inhibiting matrix metalloproteinase-2/-9 and urokinase plasminogen (uPA) through PKC and MAPK signaling pathway. *J. Agric. Food Chem.* **2010**, *58*, 2935–2942. [CrossRef]
39. Boreddy, S.R.; Pramanik, K.C.; Srivastava, S.K. Pancreatic tumor suppression by benzyl isothiocyanate is associated with inhibition of PI3K/AKT/FOXO pathway. *Clin. Cancer Res.* **2011**, *17*, 1784–1795. [CrossRef]
40. Boreddy, S.R.; Sahu, R.P.; Srivastava, S.K. Benzyl isothiocyanate suppresses pancreatic tumor angiogenesis and invasion by inhibiting HIF-alpha/VEGF/Rho-GTPases: Pivotal role of STAT-3. *PLoS ONE* **2011**, *6*, e25799. [CrossRef]
41. Gupta, P.; Srivastava, S.K. Antitumor activity of phenethyl isothiocyanate in HER2-positive breast cancer models. *BMC Med.* **2012**, *10*, 80. [CrossRef] [PubMed]

42. Boyanapalli, S.S.; Li, W.; Fuentes, F.; Guo, Y.; Ramirez, C.N.; Gonzalez, X.P.; Pung, D.; Kong, A.N. Epigenetic reactivation of RASSF1A by phenethyl isothiocyanate (PEITC) and promotion of apoptosis in LNCaP cells. *Pharmacol. Res.* **2016**, *114*, 175–184. [CrossRef]

43. Chen, J.; Duan, Y.; Zhang, X.; Ye, Y.; Ge, B.; Chen, J. Genistein induces apoptosis by the inactivation of the IGF-1R/p-Akt signaling pathway in MCF-7 human breast cancer cells. *Food Funct.* **2015**, *6*, 995–1000. [CrossRef] [PubMed]

44. Sarkar, F.H.; Li, Y. Mechanisms of cancer chemoprevention by soy isoflavone genistein. *Cancer Metastasis Rev.* **2002**, *21*, 265–280. [CrossRef] [PubMed]

45. Wang, F.; Mao, Y.; You, Q.; Hua, D.; Cai, D. Piperlongumine induces apoptosis and autophagy in human lung cancer cells through inhibition of PI3K/Akt/mTOR pathway. *Int. J. Immunopathol. Pharmacol.* **2015**, *28*, 362–373. [CrossRef] [PubMed]

46. Vittorio, O.; Brandl, M.; Cirillo, G.; Kimpton, K.; Hinde, E.; Gaus, K.; Yee, E.; Kumar, N.; Duong, H.; Fleming, C.; et al. Dextran-Catechin: An anticancer chemically-modified natural compound targeting copper that attenuates neuroblastoma growth. *Oncotarget* **2016**, *7*, 47479–47493. [CrossRef] [PubMed]

47. Farhan, M.; Zafar, A.; Chibber, S.; Khan, H.Y.; Arif, H.; Hadi, S.M. Mobilization of copper ions in human peripheral lymphocytes by catechins leading to oxidative DNA breakage: A structure activity study. *Arch. Biochem. Biophys* **2015**, *580*, 31–40. [CrossRef] [PubMed]

48. Chen, H.; Yao, K.; Chang, X.; Shim, J.H.; Kim, H.G.; Malakhova, M.; Kim, D.J.; Bode, A.M.; Dong, Z. Computational and Biochemical Discovery of RSK2 as a Novel Target for Epigallocatechin Gallate (EGCG). *PLoS ONE* **2015**, *10*, e0130049. [CrossRef]

49. Fujiki, H.; Sueoka, E.; Watanabe, T.; Suganuma, M. Synergistic enhancement of anticancer effects on numerous human cancer cell lines treated with the combination of EGCG, other green tea catechins, and anticancer compounds. *J. Cancer Res. Clin. Oncol.* **2015**, *141*, 1511–1522. [CrossRef]

50. Fujiki, H.; Sueoka, E.; Watanabe, T.; Suganuma, M. Primary cancer prevention by green tea, and tertiary cancer prevention by the combination of green tea catechins and anticancer compounds. *J. Cancer Prev.* **2015**, *20*, 1–4. [CrossRef]

51. Filippi, A.; Ciolac, O.A.; Ganea, C.; Mocanu, M.M. ErbB Proteins as Molecular Target of Dietary Phytochemicals in Malignant Diseases. *J. Oncol.* **2017**, *2017*, 1532534. [CrossRef] [PubMed]

52. Pokhriyal, R.; Hariprasad, R.; Kumar, L.; Hariprasad, G. Chemotherapy Resistance in Advanced Ovarian Cancer Patients. *Biomark Cancer* **2019**, *11*, 1179299X19860815. [CrossRef] [PubMed]

53. Oya, Y.; Mondal, A.; Rawangkan, A.; Umsumarng, S.; Iida, K.; Watanabe, T.; Kanno, M.; Suzuki, K.; Li, Z.; Kagechika, H.; et al. Down-regulation of histone deacetylase 4, -5 and -6 as a mechanism of synergistic enhancement of apoptosis in human lung cancer cells treated with the combination of a synthetic retinoid, Am80 and green tea catechin. *J. Nutr. Biochem.* **2017**, *42*, 7–16. [CrossRef] [PubMed]

54. Chen, J.; O'Donoghue, A.; Deng, Y.F.; Zhang, B.; Kent, F.; O'Hare, T. The effect of lycopene on the PI3K/Akt signalling pathway in prostate cancer. *Anticancer Agents Med. Chem.* **2014**, *14*, 800–805. [CrossRef] [PubMed]

55. Gajowik, A.; Dobrzynska, M.M. Lycopene - antioxidant with radioprotective and anticancer properties. A review. *Rocz Panstw Zakl Hig* **2014**, *65*, 263–271. [PubMed]

56. Agarwal, S.; Rao, A.V. Tomato lycopene and its role in human health and chronic diseases. *Can. Med. Assoc. J.* **2000**, *163*, 739–744.

57. Rao, A.V.; Ray, M.R.; Rao, L.G. Lycopene. *Adv. Food Nutr. Res.* **2006**, *51*, 99–164. [CrossRef]

58. Farzaei, M.H.; Bahramsoltani, R.; Rahimi, R. Phytochemicals as Adjunctive with Conventional Anticancer Therapies. *Curr. Pharm. Des.* **2016**, *22*, 4201–4218. [CrossRef]

59. Zu, K.; Mucci, L.; Rosner, B.A.; Clinton, S.K.; Loda, M.; Stampfer, M.J.; Giovannucci, E. Dietary lycopene, angiogenesis, and prostate cancer: A prospective study in the prostate-specific antigen era. *J. Natl. Cancer Inst.* **2014**, *106*, djt430. [CrossRef]

60. Renju, G.L.; Muraleedhara Kurup, G.; Bandugula, V.R. Effect of lycopene isolated from Chlorella marina on proliferation and apoptosis in human prostate cancer cell line PC-3. *Tumour Biol.* **2014**, *35*, 10747–10758. [CrossRef]

61. Soares Nda, C.; Teodoro, A.J.; Oliveira, F.L.; Santos, C.A.; Takiya, C.M.; Junior, O.S.; Bianco, M.; Junior, A.P.; Nasciutti, L.E.; Ferreira, L.B.; et al. Influence of lycopene on cell viability, cell cycle, and apoptosis of human prostate cancer and benign hyperplastic cells. *Nutr. Cancer* **2013**, *65*, 1076–1085. [CrossRef] [PubMed]

62. Assar, E.A.; Vidalle, M.C.; Chopra, M.; Hafizi, S. Lycopene acts through inhibition of IkappaB kinase to suppress NF-kappaB signaling in human prostate and breast cancer cells. *Tumour Biol.* **2016**, *37*, 9375–9385. [CrossRef] [PubMed]

63. Oguz, E.; Kocarslan, S.; Tabur, S.; Sezen, H.; Yilmaz, Z.; Aksoy, N. Effects of Lycopene Alone or Combined with Melatonin on Methotrexate-Induced Nephrotoxicity in Rats. *Asian Pac. J. Cancer Prev.* **2015**, *16*, 6061–6066. [CrossRef] [PubMed]

64. Al-Malki, A.L. Synergestic effect of lycopene and melatonin against the genesis of oxidative stress induced by cyclophosphamide in rats. *Toxicol. Ind. Health* **2014**, *30*, 570–575. [CrossRef]

65. Moselhy, S.S.; Al mslmani, M.A. Chemopreventive effect of lycopene alone or with melatonin against the genesis of oxidative stress and mammary tumors induced by 7,12 dimethyl(a)benzanthracene in sprague dawely female rats. *Mol. Cell Biochem.* **2008**, *319*, 175–180. [CrossRef] [PubMed]

66. Yang, C.M.; Yen, Y.T.; Huang, C.S.; Hu, M.L. Growth inhibitory efficacy of lycopene and beta-carotene against androgen-independent prostate tumor cells xenografted in nude mice. *Mol. Nutr. Food Res.* **2011**, *55*, 606–612. [CrossRef] [PubMed]

67. Schwarz, S.; Obermuller-Jevic, U.C.; Hellmis, E.; Koch, W.; Jacobi, G.; Biesalski, H.K. Lycopene inhibits disease progression in patients with benign prostate hyperplasia. *J. Nutr.* **2008**, *138*, 49–53. [CrossRef] [PubMed]

68. Cai, Y.; Fang, X.; He, C.; Li, P.; Xiao, F.; Wang, Y.; Chen, M. Cucurbitacins: A Systematic Review of the Phytochemistry and Anticancer Activity. *Am. J. Chin. Med.* **2015**, *43*, 1331–1350. [CrossRef] [PubMed]

69. Yang, T.; Liu, J.; Yang, M.; Huang, N.; Zhong, Y.; Zeng, T.; Wei, R.; Wu, Z.; Xiao, C.; Cao, X.; et al. Cucurbitacin B exerts anti-cancer activities in human multiple myeloma cells in vitro and in vivo by modulating multiple cellular pathways. *Oncotarget* **2017**, *8*, 5800–5813. [CrossRef]

70. Zhang, M.; Bian, Z.G.; Zhang, Y.; Wang, J.H.; Kan, L.; Wang, X.; Niu, H.Y.; He, P. Cucurbitacin B inhibits proliferation and induces apoptosis via STAT3 pathway inhibition in A549 lung cancer cells. *Mol. Med. Rep.* **2014**, *10*, 2905–2911. [CrossRef] [PubMed]

71. Ma, W.; Xiang, Y.; Yang, R.; Zhang, T.; Xu, J.; Wu, Y.; Liu, X.; Xiang, K.; Zhao, H.; Liu, Y.; et al. Cucurbitacin B induces inhibitory effects via the CIP2A/PP2A/C-KIT signaling axis in t(8;21) acute myeloid leukemia. *J. Pharmacol. Sci.* **2019**, *139*, 304–310. [CrossRef] [PubMed]

72. Zhang, M.; Sun, C.; Shan, X.; Yang, X.; Li-Ling, J.; Deng, Y. Inhibition of pancreatic cancer cell growth by cucurbitacin B through modulation of signal transducer and activator of transcription 3 signaling. *Pancreas* **2010**, *39*, 923–929. [CrossRef] [PubMed]

73. Sinha, S.; Khan, S.; Shukla, S.; Lakra, A.D.; Kumar, S.; Das, G.; Maurya, R.; Meeran, S.M. Cucurbitacin B inhibits breast cancer metastasis and angiogenesis through VEGF-mediated suppression of FAK/MMP-9 signaling axis. *Int. J. Biochem. Cell Biol.* **2016**, *77*, 41–56. [CrossRef] [PubMed]

74. Shukla, S.; Sinha, S.; Khan, S.; Kumar, S.; Singh, K.; Mitra, K.; Maurya, R.; Meeran, S.M. Cucurbitacin B inhibits the stemness and metastatic abilities of NSCLC via downregulation of canonical Wnt/beta-catenin signaling axis. *Sci. Rep.* **2016**, *6*, 21860. [CrossRef] [PubMed]

75. Zhou, X.; Yang, J.; Wang, Y.; Li, W.; Li-Ling, J.; Deng, Y.; Zhang, M. Cucurbitacin B inhibits 12-O-tetradecanoylphorbol 13-acetate-induced invasion and migration of human hepatoma cells through inactivating mitogen-activated protein kinase and PI3K/Akt signal transduction pathways. *Hepatol. Res.* **2012**, *42*, 401–411. [CrossRef] [PubMed]

76. Thoennissen, N.H.; Iwanski, G.B.; Doan, N.B.; Okamoto, R.; Lin, P.; Abbassi, S.; Song, J.H.; Yin, D.; Toh, M.; Xie, W.D.; et al. Cucurbitacin B induces apoptosis by inhibition of the JAK/STAT pathway and potentiates antiproliferative effects of gemcitabine on pancreatic cancer cells. *Cancer Res.* **2009**, *69*, 5876–5884. [CrossRef]

77. El-Senduny, F.F.; Badria, F.A.; El-Waseef, A.M.; Chauhan, S.C.; Halaweish, F. Approach for chemosensitization of cisplatin-resistant ovarian cancer by cucurbitacin B. *Tumour Biol.* **2016**, *37*, 685–698. [CrossRef] [PubMed]

78. Aribi, A.; Gery, S.; Lee, D.H.; Thoennissen, N.H.; Thoennissen, G.B.; Alvarez, R.; Ho, Q.; Lee, K.; Doan, N.B.; Chan, K.T.; et al. The triterpenoid cucurbitacin B augments the antiproliferative activity of chemotherapy in human breast cancer. *Int. J. Cancer* **2013**, *132*, 2730–2737. [CrossRef] [PubMed]

79. Sun, Y.; Zhang, J.; Zhou, J.; Huang, Z.; Hu, H.; Qiao, M.; Zhao, X.; Chen, D. Synergistic effect of cucurbitacin B in combination with curcumin via enhancing apoptosis induction and reversing multidrug resistance in human hepatoma cells. *Eur. J. Pharmacol.* **2015**, *768*, 28–40. [CrossRef]

80. Hu, H.; Liu, D.; Zhao, X.; Qiao, M.; Chen, D. Preparation, characterization, cellular uptake and evaluation in vivo of solid lipid nanoparticles loaded with cucurbitacin B. *Drug Dev. Ind. Pharm.* **2013**, *39*, 770–779. [CrossRef]
81. Cheng, L.; Xu, P.H.; Shen, B.D.; Shen, G.; Li, J.J.; Qiu, L.; Liu, C.Y.; Yuan, H.L.; Han, J. Improve bile duct-targeted drug delivery and therapeutic efficacy for cholangiocarcinoma by cucurbitacin B loaded phospholipid complex modified with berberine hydrochloride. *Int. J. Pharm.* **2015**, *489*, 148–157. [CrossRef] [PubMed]
82. Wu, X.; Zhou, Q.H.; Xu, K. Are isothiocyanates potential anti-cancer drugs? *Acta Pharmacol. Sin.* **2009**, *30*, 501–512. [CrossRef] [PubMed]
83. Nakamura, Y.; Yoshimoto, M.; Murata, Y.; Shimoishi, Y.; Asai, Y.; Park, E.Y.; Sato, K.; Nakamura, Y. Papaya seed represents a rich source of biologically active isothiocyanate. *J. Agric. Food Chem.* **2007**, *55*, 4407–4413. [CrossRef] [PubMed]
84. Sofrata, A.; Santangelo, E.M.; Azeem, M.; Borg-Karlson, A.K.; Gustafsson, A.; Putsep, K. Benzyl isothiocyanate, a major component from the roots of Salvadora persica is highly active against Gram-negative bacteria. *PLoS ONE* **2011**, *6*, e23045. [CrossRef] [PubMed]
85. Xu, K.; Thornalley, P.J. Studies on the mechanism of the inhibition of human leukaemia cell growth by dietary isothiocyanates and their cysteine adducts in vitro. *Biochem. Pharmacol.* **2000**, *60*, 221–231. [CrossRef]
86. Sehrawat, A.; Kim, S.H.; Vogt, A.; Singh, S.V. Suppression of FOXQ1 in benzyl isothiocyanate-mediated inhibition of epithelial-mesenchymal transition in human breast cancer cells. *Carcinogenesis* **2013**, *34*, 864–873. [CrossRef]
87. Cho, H.J.; Lim, D.Y.; Kwon, G.T.; Kim, J.H.; Huang, Z.; Song, H.; Oh, Y.S.; Kang, Y.H.; Lee, K.W.; Dong, Z.; et al. Benzyl Isothiocyanate Inhibits Prostate Cancer Development in the Transgenic Adenocarcinoma Mouse Prostate (TRAMP) Model, Which Is Associated with the Induction of Cell Cycle G1 Arrest. *Int. J. Mol. Sci.* **2016**, *17*, 264. [CrossRef] [PubMed]
88. Wu, X.; Zhu, Y.; Yan, H.; Liu, B.; Li, Y.; Zhou, Q.; Xu, K. Isothiocyanates induce oxidative stress and suppress the metastasis potential of human non-small cell lung cancer cells. *BMC Cancer* **2010**, *10*, 269. [CrossRef]
89. Sahu, R.P.; Srivastava, S.K. The role of STAT-3 in the induction of apoptosis in pancreatic cancer cells by benzyl isothiocyanate. *J. Natl. Cancer Inst.* **2009**, *101*, 176–193. [CrossRef]
90. Zhu, M.; Li, W.; Dong, X.; Chen, Y.; Lu, Y.; Lin, B.; Guo, J.; Li, M. Benzyl-isothiocyanate Induces Apoptosis and Inhibits Migration and Invasion of Hepatocellular Carcinoma Cells in vitro. *J. Cancer* **2017**, *8*, 240–248. [CrossRef]
91. Xie, B.; Nagalingam, A.; Kuppusamy, P.; Muniraj, N.; Langford, P.; Gyorffy, B.; Saxena, N.K.; Sharma, D. Benzyl Isothiocyanate potentiates p53 signaling and antitumor effects against breast cancer through activation of p53-LKB1 and p73-LKB1 axes. *Sci. Rep.* **2017**, *7*, 40070. [CrossRef] [PubMed]
92. Qhattal, H.S.; Wang, S.; Salihima, T.; Srivastava, S.K.; Liu, X. Nanoemulsions of cancer chemopreventive agent benzyl isothiocyanate display enhanced solubility, dissolution, and permeability. *J. Agric. Food Chem.* **2011**, *59*, 12396–12404. [CrossRef] [PubMed]
93. Wang, L.G.; Chiao, J.W. Prostate cancer chemopreventive activity of phenethyl isothiocyanate through epigenetic regulation (review). *Int. J. Oncol.* **2010**, *37*, 533–539. [CrossRef] [PubMed]
94. Gupta, P.; Adkins, C.; Lockman, P.; Srivastava, S.K. Metastasis of Breast Tumor Cells to Brain Is Suppressed by Phenethyl Isothiocyanate in a Novel In Vivo Metastasis Model. *PLoS ONE* **2013**, *8*, e67278. [CrossRef] [PubMed]
95. Liu, J.; Chen, G.; Pelicano, H.; Liao, J.; Huang, J.; Feng, L.; Keating, M.J.; Huang, P. Targeting p53-deficient chronic lymphocytic leukemia cells in vitro and in vivo by ROS-mediated mechanism. *Oncotarget* **2016**, *7*, 71378–71389. [CrossRef] [PubMed]
96. Cang, S.; Ma, Y.; Chiao, J.W.; Liu, D. Phenethyl isothiocyanate and paclitaxel synergistically enhanced apoptosis and alpha-tubulin hyperacetylation in breast cancer cells. *Exp. Hematol. Oncol.* **2014**, *3*, 5. [CrossRef] [PubMed]
97. Mukherjee, S.; Dey, S.; Bhattacharya, R.K.; Roy, M. Isothiocyanates sensitize the effect of chemotherapeutic drugs via modulation of protein kinase C and telomerase in cervical cancer cells. *Mol. Cell Biochem.* **2009**, *330*, 9–22. [CrossRef] [PubMed]

98. Khor, T.O.; Keum, Y.S.; Lin, W.; Kim, J.H.; Hu, R.; Shen, G.; Xu, C.; Gopalakrishnan, A.; Reddy, B.; Zheng, X.; et al. Combined inhibitory effects of curcumin and phenethyl isothiocyanate on the growth of human PC-3 prostate xenografts in immunodeficient mice. *Cancer Res.* **2006**, *66*, 613–621. [CrossRef]

99. Gupta, P.; Wright, S.E.; Srivastava, S.K. PEITC treatment suppresses myeloid derived tumor suppressor cells to inhibit breast tumor growth. *Oncoimmunology* **2015**, *4*, e981449. [CrossRef]

100. Jiao, D.; Eklind, K.I.; Choi, C.I.; Desai, D.H.; Amin, S.G.; Chung, F.L. Structure-activity relationships of isothiocyanates as mechanism-based inhibitors of 4-(methylnitrosamino)-1-(3-pyridyl)-1-butanone-induced lung tumorigenesis in A/J mice. *Cancer Res.* **1994**, *54*, 4327–4333.

101. Son, H.Y.; Nishikawa, A.; Furukawa, F.; Lee, I.S.; Ikeda, T.; Miyauchi, M.; Nakamura, H.; Hirose, M. Modifying effects of 4-phenylbutyl isothiocyanate on N-nitrosobis(2-oxopropyl)amine-induced tumorigenesis in hamsters. *Cancer Lett.* **2000**, *160*, 141–147. [CrossRef]

102. Ji, Y.; Kuo, Y.; Morris, M.E. Pharmacokinetics of dietary phenethyl isothiocyanate in rats. *Pharm. Res.* **2005**, *22*, 1658–1666. [CrossRef] [PubMed]

103. Konsue, N.; Kirkpatrick, J.; Kuhnert, N.; King, L.J.; Ioannides, C. Repeated oral administration modulates the pharmacokinetic behavior of the chemopreventive agent phenethyl isothiocyanate in rats. *Mol. Nutr. Food Res.* **2010**, *54*, 426–432. [CrossRef]

104. Yuan, J.M.; Stepanov, I.; Murphy, S.E.; Wang, R.; Allen, S.; Jensen, J.; Strayer, L.; Adams-Haduch, J.; Upadhyaya, P.; Le, C.; et al. Clinical Trial of 2-Phenethyl Isothiocyanate as an Inhibitor of Metabolic Activation of a Tobacco-Specific Lung Carcinogen in Cigarette Smokers. *Cancer Prev. Res.* **2016**, *9*, 396–405. [CrossRef] [PubMed]

105. Wang, Q.; Ge, X.; Tian, X.; Zhang, Y.; Zhang, J.; Zhang, P. Soy isoflavone: The multipurpose phytochemical (Review). *Biomed. Rep.* **2013**, *1*, 697–701. [CrossRef] [PubMed]

106. Fletcher, R.J. Food sources of phyto-oestrogens and their precursors in Europe. *Br. J. Nutr.* **2003**, *89*, S39–S43. [CrossRef] [PubMed]

107. Sarkar, F.H.; Li, Y. The role of isoflavones in cancer chemoprevention. *Front. Biosci.* **2004**, *9*, 2714–2724. [CrossRef] [PubMed]

108. Davis, J.N.; Singh, B.; Bhuiyan, M.; Sarkar, F.H. Genistein-induced upregulation of p21WAF1, downregulation of cyclin B, and induction of apoptosis in prostate cancer cells. *Nutr. Cancer* **1998**, *32*, 123–131. [CrossRef]

109. Li, Y.; Upadhyay, S.; Bhuiyan, M.; Sarkar, F.H. Induction of apoptosis in breast cancer cells MDA-MB-231 by genistein. *Oncogene* **1999**, *18*, 3166–3172. [CrossRef]

110. Lian, F.; Bhuiyan, M.; Li, Y.W.; Wall, N.; Kraut, M.; Sarkar, F.H. Genistein-induced G2-M arrest, p21WAF1 upregulation, and apoptosis in a non-small-cell lung cancer cell line. *Nutr. Cancer* **1998**, *31*, 184–191. [CrossRef]

111. Alhasan, S.A.; Pietraszkiwicz, H.; Alonso, M.D.; Ensley, J.; Sarkar, F.H. Genistein-induced cell cycle arrest and apoptosis in a head and neck squamous cell carcinoma cell line. *Nutr. Cancer* **1999**, *34*, 12–19. [CrossRef]

112. Liu, H.; Lee, G.; Lee, J.I.; Ahn, T.G.; Kim, S.A. Effects of genistein on anti-tumor activity of cisplatin in human cervical cancer cell lines. *Obstet. Gynecol. Sci.* **2019**, *62*, 322–328. [CrossRef] [PubMed]

113. Wang, Y.; Li, W.; Wang, Z.; Ren, H.; Li, Y.; Zhang, Y.; Yang, P.; Pan, S. Genistein upregulates cyclin D1 and CDK4 expression and promotes the proliferation of ovarian cancer OVCAR-5 cells. *Clin. Chim. Acta* **2019**. [CrossRef] [PubMed]

114. Li, E.; Zhang, T.; Sun, X.; Li, Y.; Geng, H.; Yu, D.; Zhong, C. Sonic hedgehog pathway mediates genistein inhibition of renal cancer stem cells. *Oncol. Lett.* **2019**, *18*, 3081–3091. [CrossRef]

115. Park, C.; Cha, H.J.; Lee, H.; Hwang-Bo, H.; Ji, S.Y.; Kim, M.Y.; Hong, S.H.; Jeong, J.W.; Han, M.H.; Choi, S.H.; et al. Induction of G2/M Cell Cycle Arrest and Apoptosis by Genistein in Human Bladder Cancer T24 Cells through Inhibition of the ROS-Dependent PI3k/Akt Signal Transduction Pathway. *Antioxidants* **2019**, *8*, 327. [CrossRef] [PubMed]

116. Zhang, Q.; Bao, J.; Yang, J. Genistein-triggered anticancer activity against liver cancer cell line HepG2 involves ROS generation, mitochondrial apoptosis, G2/M cell cycle arrest and inhibition of cell migration. *Arch. Med. Sci.* **2019**, *15*, 1001–1009. [CrossRef]

117. Hillman, G.G.; Singh-Gupta, V. Soy isoflavones sensitize cancer cells to radiotherapy. *Free Radic Biol Med.* **2011**, *51*, 289–298. [CrossRef] [PubMed]

118. Singh-Gupta, V.; Joiner, M.C.; Runyan, L.; Yunker, C.K.; Sarkar, F.H.; Miller, S.; Gadgeel, S.M.; Konski, A.A.; Hillman, G.G. Soy isoflavones augment radiation effect by inhibiting APE1/Ref-1 DNA repair activity in non-small cell lung cancer. *J. Thorac. Oncol.* **2011**, *6*, 688–698. [CrossRef]

119. Rajaei, S.; Alihemmati Ph, D.A.; Abedelahi Ph, D.A. Antioxidant effect of genistein on ovarian tissue morphology, oxidant and antioxidant activity in rats with induced polycystic ovary syndrome. *Int. J. Reprod. Biomed.* **2019**, *17*. [CrossRef] [PubMed]

120. Susanikova, I.; Puchl'ova, M.; Lachova, V.; Svajdlenka, E.; Mucaji, P.; Smetana, K., Jr.; Gal, P. Genistein and Selected Phytoestrogen-Containing Extracts Differently Modulate Antioxidant Properties and Cell Differentiation: An in Vitro Study in NIH-3T3, HaCaT and MCF-7 Cells. *Folia. Biol.* **2019**, *65*, 24–35.

121. Busby, M.G.; Jeffcoat, A.R.; Bloedon, L.T.; Koch, M.A.; Black, T.; Dix, K.J.; Heizer, W.D.; Thomas, B.F.; Hill, J.M.; Crowell, J.A.; et al. Clinical characteristics and pharmacokinetics of purified soy isoflavones: Single-dose administration to healthy men. *Am. J. Clin. Nutr.* **2002**, *75*, 126–136. [CrossRef]

122. Bezerra, D.P.; Pessoa, C.; de Moraes, M.O.; Saker-Neto, N.; Silveira, E.R.; Costa-Lotufo, L.V. Overview of the therapeutic potential of piplartine (piperlongumine). *Eur J. Pharm. Sci.* **2013**, *48*, 453–463. [CrossRef] [PubMed]

123. Prasad, S.; Tyagi, A.K. Historical Spice as a Future Drug: Therapeutic Potential of Piperlongumine. *Curr. Pharm. Des.* **2016**, *22*, 4151–4159. [CrossRef]

124. Yao, Y.; Sun, Y.; Shi, M.; Xia, D.; Zhao, K.; Zeng, L.; Yao, R.; Zhang, Y.; Li, Z.; Niu, M.; et al. Piperlongumine induces apoptosis and reduces bortezomib resistance by inhibiting STAT3 in multiple myeloma cells. *Oncotarget* **2016**, *7*, 73497–73508. [CrossRef]

125. Fofaria, N.M.; Srivastava, S.K. Critical role of STAT3 in melanoma metastasis through anoikis resistance. *Oncotarget* **2014**, *5*, 7051–7064. [CrossRef] [PubMed]

126. Dhillon, H.; Chikara, S.; Reindl, K.M. Piperlongumine induces pancreatic cancer cell death by enhancing reactive oxygen species and DNA damage. *Toxicol. Rep.* **2014**, *1*, 309–318. [CrossRef] [PubMed]

127. Han, J.G.; Gupta, S.C.; Prasad, S.; Aggarwal, B.B. Piperlongumine chemosensitizes tumor cells through interaction with cysteine 179 of IkappaBalpha kinase, leading to suppression of NF-kappaB-regulated gene products. *Mol. Cancer Ther.* **2014**, *13*, 2422–2435. [CrossRef]

128. Randhawa, H.; Kibble, K.; Zeng, H.; Moyer, M.P.; Reindl, K.M. Activation of ERK signaling and induction of colon cancer cell death by piperlongumine. *Toxicol In Vitro* **2013**, *27*, 1626–1633. [CrossRef]

129. Chen, S.Y.; Liu, G.H.; Chao, W.Y.; Shi, C.S.; Lin, C.Y.; Lim, Y.P.; Lu, C.H.; Lai, P.Y.; Chen, H.R.; Lee, Y.R. Piperlongumine Suppresses Proliferation of Human Oral Squamous Cell Carcinoma through Cell Cycle Arrest, Apoptosis and Senescence. *Int. J. Mol. Sci.* **2016**, *17*, 616. [CrossRef]

130. Li, Q.; Chen, L.; Dong, Z.; Zhao, Y.; Deng, H.; Wu, J.; Wu, X.; Li, W. Piperlongumine analogue L50377 induces pyroptosis via ROS mediated NF-kappaB suppression in non-small-cell lung cancer. *Chem. Biol. Interact.* **2019**, *313*, 108820. [CrossRef]

131. Zhang, P.; Shi, L.; Zhang, T.; Hong, L.; He, W.; Cao, P.; Shen, X.; Zheng, P.; Xia, Y.; Zou, P. Piperlongumine potentiates the antitumor efficacy of oxaliplatin through ROS induction in gastric cancer cells. *Cell. Oncol.* **2019**, 1–14. [CrossRef] [PubMed]

132. Chen, S.Y.; Huang, H.Y.; Lin, H.P.; Fang, C.Y. Piperlongumine induces autophagy in biliary cancer cells via reactive oxygen species-activated Erk signaling pathway. *Int. J. Mol. Med.* **2019**, *44*, 1687–1696. [CrossRef] [PubMed]

133. Kong, E.H.; Kim, Y.J.; Kim, Y.J.; Cho, H.J.; Yu, S.N.; Kim, K.Y.; Chang, J.H.; Ahn, S.C. Piplartine induces caspase-mediated apoptosis in PC-3 human prostate cancer cells. *Oncol. Rep.* **2008**, *20*, 785–792. [PubMed]

134. Fofaria, N.M.; Srivastava, S.K. STAT3 induces anoikis resistance, promotes cell invasion and metastatic potential in pancreatic cancer cells. *Carcinogenesis* **2015**, *36*, 142–150. [CrossRef] [PubMed]

135. Gong, L.H.; Chen, X.X.; Wang, H.; Jiang, Q.W.; Pan, S.S.; Qiu, J.G.; Mei, X.L.; Xue, Y.Q.; Qin, W.M.; Zheng, F.Y.; et al. Piperlongumine induces apoptosis and synergizes with cisplatin or paclitaxel in human ovarian cancer cells. *Oxid Med. Cell Longev.* **2014**, *2014*, 906804. [CrossRef] [PubMed]

136. Fofaria, N.M.; Qhattal, H.S.; Liu, X.; Srivastava, S.K. Nanoemulsion formulations for anti-cancer agent piplartine–Characterization, toxicological, pharmacokinetics and efficacy studies. *Int. J. Pharm.* **2016**, *498*, 12–22. [CrossRef] [PubMed]

137. Glade, M.J. Food, nutrition, and the prevention of cancer: A global perspective. American Institute for Cancer Research/World Cancer Research Fund, American Institute for Cancer Research, 1997. *Nutrition* **1999**, *15*, 523–526. [CrossRef]

138. Amin, A.R.; Kucuk, O.; Khuri, F.R.; Shin, D.M. Perspectives for cancer prevention with natural compounds. *J. Clin. Oncol.* **2009**, *27*, 2712–2725. [CrossRef]

Review

Cellular Stress-Modulating Drugs Can Potentially Be Identified by in Silico Screening with Connectivity Map (CMap)

Yurong Gao [1,†], Sungwoo Kim [1,†], Yun-Il Lee [2,*] and Jaemin Lee [1,*]

[1] Department of New Biology, Daegu Gyeongbuk Institute of Science and Technology (DGIST), Daegu 42988, Korea; gaoyuri212@dgist.ac.kr (Y.G.); sungwookim@dgist.ac.kr (S.K.)
[2] Well Aging Research Center, Daegu Gyeongbuk Institute of Science and Technology (DGIST), Daegu 42988, Korea
* Correspondence: ylee56@dgist.ac.kr (Y.-I.L.); jaeminlee@dgist.ac.kr (J.L.)
† These authors contributed equally to this work.

Received: 1 October 2019; Accepted: 6 November 2019; Published: 9 November 2019

Abstract: Accompanied by increased life span, aging-associated diseases, such as metabolic diseases and cancers, have become serious health threats. Recent studies have documented that aging-associated diseases are caused by prolonged cellular stresses such as endoplasmic reticulum (ER) stress, mitochondrial stress, and oxidative stress. Thus, ameliorating cellular stresses could be an effective approach to treat aging-associated diseases and, more importantly, to prevent such diseases from happening. However, cellular stresses and their molecular responses within the cell are typically mediated by a variety of factors encompassing different signaling pathways. Therefore, a target-based drug discovery method currently being used widely (reverse pharmacology) may not be adequate to uncover novel drugs targeting cellular stresses and related diseases. The connectivity map (CMap) is an online pharmacogenomic database cataloging gene expression data from cultured cells treated individually with various chemicals, including a variety of phytochemicals. Moreover, by querying through CMap, researchers may screen registered chemicals in silico and obtain the likelihood of drugs showing a similar gene expression profile with desired and chemopreventive conditions. Thus, CMap is an effective genome-based tool to discover novel chemopreventive drugs.

Keywords: cellular stress; endoplasmic reticulum stress; ER stress; mitochondrial stress; oxidative stress; hypoxia; connectivity map; CMap; drug discovery

---

1. Introduction

Recent progresses in public health, the health care system, and medicine have greatly helped to extend our life span [1]. However, extended life span inevitably increases the risk of aging-associated diseases including cardiovascular diseases and cancers. Furthermore, a surplus of food consumption and lack of physical activity from a sedentary lifestyle has led to the drastic increase of obesity and its associated metabolic disorders such as type 2 diabetes [2,3]. Recent studies have demonstrated that aging-associated diseases, metabolic disorders, and cancers are caused by prolonged exposure to cellular stresses such as endoplasmic reticulum (ER) stress, mitochondrial stress, heat shock stress, and oxidative stress [4,5]. For example, the development of leptin resistance and insulin resistance leads to obesity and type 2 diabetes, respectively, and chronic inflammation and cellular stresses, including ER stress, oxidative stress, and mitochondrial stress have been reported to contribute to leptin and insulin resistance [4–7]. Furthermore, metabolic and cellular stresses also play a crucial role in the development of cancer and its pathophysiology [4,8,9]. Chronic exposure of cells to cellular stresses such as oxidative stress may lead to tumorigenesis; however, elevated cellular stresses such as hypoxia and ER stress may kill cancer cells [4,8,9]. Indeed, cancer cells have been shown to actively employ stress responses (e.g., unfolded protein response (UPR) against ER stress) to survive from excess cellular stresses [4,8,9]. Therefore, alleviating certain cellular stresses may prevent the development of cancer, whereas suppressing adaptive responses and escalating stresses can be useful in removing existing cancer cells [4,8,9].

Therefore, developing chemopreventive ways to target appropriate cellular stresses could be an effective prevention and therapeutic treatment toward various aging-associated disorders [10]. However, cellular stresses and related molecular responses are mediated by a myriad of molecules encompassing multiple signaling pathways [4,5]. In addition, categorized cellular stresses do not take place solely inside of cells; instead, several stresses appear altogether [4,5]. For this reason, a target-based drug discovery process (reverse pharmacology) may not be adequate to discover novel chemicals that can address cellular stresses and associated disorders, although this is currently being used widely in academia and pharmaceutical companies (Figure 1A).

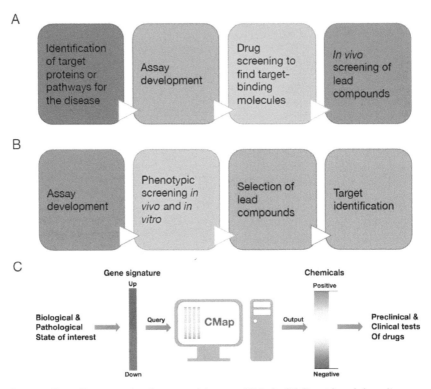

Figure 1. Drug discovery using the connectivity map (CMap). (**A**) Target-based drug discovery. (**B**) Phenotypic drug discovery. (**C**) CMap-based drug discovery. Gene signature of the biological or pathological state of interest can be used as a query to search through CMap. CMap provides the search result as a list of small molecules scored to predict their probability to mimic or reverse gene expression profiles of the state of interest. Candidate chemicals can be further tested in in vitro cell culture and in vivo animal experiments before proceeding with clinical trials to human subjects.

Phenotypic drug discovery (forward pharmacology) started to regain interest recently due to its potential usefulness in finding novel drugs to target complex diseases wherein the mechanism needs to be understood further, thanks to recent technological advances in cell-based phenotypic screening and analysis of vast genomic data (Figure 1B) [11]. The connectivity map (CMap) is an online genome-based database established by Todd R. Golub's group at the Broad Institute (Boston, MA, USA), and catalogs transcriptome data from cultured cells treated individually with small molecules (Figure 1C) [12,13]. By searching on CMap, researchers can screen registered chemicals in silico and obtain the list of drugs displaying a similar gene expression profile with the desired biological or pathological conditions as a rank. Numerous studies have successfully demonstrated CMap's potential as an effective pharmacogenomic drug discovery tool. In this article, we review the current understanding of cellular stresses and signaling responses, and discuss CMap as a potentially useful in silico drug screening tool to unearth novel drugs and phytochemicals to address cellular stresses and their related disorders.

2. Cellular Stresses

2.1. Heat Shock Stress and Heat Shock Response

Newly synthesized proteins form their native tertiary structure primarily based on their thermodynamic stability [14]. However, certain environmental conditions (e.g., heat, over-nutrition) and mutations within proteins often disturb proper protein folding and lead them to form aggregates [14]. Studies have shown that accumulated misfolded proteins and their aggregates cause many debilitating diseases, notably neurodegenerative diseases such as Alzheimer's disease, Huntington's disease, and Parkinson's disease [15]. In order to facilitate appropriate protein folding and to prevent misfolded protein from forming aggregates, cells produce chaperone proteins such as cytoplasmic heat shock proteins (HSPs) and ER chaperones [15–18].

Heat shock response was initially reported from the observation in which active transcription (chromosomal puffs) was induced by heat treatment in the saliva gland of a fruit fly, *Drosophila busckii* [19]. Many of these loci have been identified to encode HSPs which are categorized and named based on their molecular weights—small HSPs, HSP40, HSP60, HSP70, HSP90, and HSP110 [20]. Although the specific role and mechanism of each HSP still needs to be investigated, HSPs generally function cytoprotectively [21–23]. One of the widely studied roles of HSPs is to function as molecular chaperones. They bind to misfolded and unfolded proteins, thus helping in folding and preventing them from forming aggregates [21–23]. Additionally, HSPs have been shown to modulate protein localization inside of cells and to promote antigen presentation [24].

Heat shock response including HSP expression is induced not only by heat but also by other cellular stresses such as oxidative stress, osmotic stress, and exposure to heavy metals [21–23]. Subsequently, these stresses activate heat shock transcription factors (HSFs), a major transcription factor family mediating heat shock response. However, it is not understood clearly how HSFs sense cellular stresses. There are several isomers of HSFs (6 isoforms were identified in human—HSF1, HSF2, HSF4, HSF5, HSFX, and HSFY), and HSF1 is the most extensively studied among HSF isomers [22,25]. HSF1 exists as an inactive monomer in cytosol under normal conditions. In response to various stressors, HSF1 becomes an active transcription factor by forming a homotrimer and translocates to the nucleus [26–28]. Although the details of how the structure and activity of HSF1 are regulated are still under investigation, it has been suggested that physical interaction between HSPs and HSF1 leads to HSF1's monomerization and cytosol localization under unstressed state, and in turn inhibits HSF1's activity [29,30]. Under heat shock stress, HSPs are released from HSF1 probably by recruiting to unfolded or misfolded proteins, which subsequently allows HSF1 to form a homotrimer, to translocate to the nucleus, and to transcribe its target genes with unique HSF1 binding promoter (heat shock element) (Figure 2A) [22,25–30]. The changes in HSF1's intrinsic structure itself during environmental stress, especially heat, have been shown to promote HSF1's homotrimerization and nuclear translocation (Figure 2A) [31]. Furthermore, various post-translational modifications such as acetylation and phosphorylation have been shown to modulate HSF1's activity [22,25].

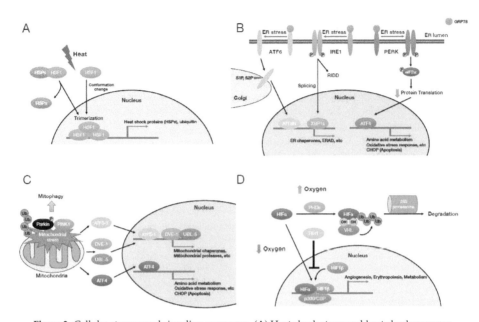

Figure 2. Cellular stresses and signaling responses. (**A**) Heat shock stress and heat shock response. The stressors such as heat lead to releasing of heat shock proteins (HSPs) from heat shock factor 1 (HSF1) or directly changing the conformation of HSF1 resulting in its trimerization, nuclear translocation, and target gene transcription. (**B**) Endoplasmic reticulum (ER) stress and unfolded protein response (UPR). The accumulation of unfolded or misfolded proteins activates three ER transmembrane proteins—activating transcription factor-6 (ATF6), inositol requiring protein-1 (IRE1), and protein kinase RNA-like ER kinase (PERK). ATF6 and IRE1 generate the functional transcription factors, ATF6N and spliced form of X-box binding protein 1 (XBP1s), which translocate to the nucleus and transcribe their target genes, whereas PERK suppresses protein translation and thus reduces protein load into the ER. (**C**) Mitochondrial stress and mitochondrial unfolded protein response (UPR^{mt}). Mitochondrial stress activates several transcription factors, activating transcription factor associated with stress-1 (ATFS-1) and defective proventriculus (Drosophila) homolog-1/ubiquitin-like 5 (DVE-1/UBL-5) (*Caenorhabditis elegans*) and ATF4 (mammals), which promote their target gene expression to restore mitochondrial homeostasis. Mitochondrial stress also triggers autophagy (mitophagy) via Parkin and Pink1. (**D**) Hypoxia and hypoxia-induced factor. Under normoxia, hypoxia-inducible factor α (HIFα) is hydroxylated on proline by prolyl hydroxylase domain enzymes (PHDs) or on asparagine by factor inhibiting HIF1 (FIH1), and the activity of HIFα is suppressed by its von Hippel–Lindau (VHL)-mediated ubiquitylation and degradation or its loss of the interaction with p300/CREB-binding protein (CBP).

Several studies have documented the role of heat shock response in aging, decreased and impaired function of HSF1 and other protein quality control machinery during aging have been reported, and further HSF1 activation was shown to increase the life span in a worm, *Caenorhabditis elegans* [22,32,33]. In addition, increased expression of HSF1 and HSP70 helps to ameliorate pathologies of neurodegenerative diseases such as Huntington's disease, Parkinson's disease, and amyotrophic lateral sclerosis (ALS) in mouse and fly models [34–37]. Moreover, mice deficient of HSF1 are resistant to form tumors under oncogenic conditions, suggesting that heat shock response protects tumor cells from cellular stresses and promotes their survival and proliferation [38].

2.2. Endoplasmic Reticulum (ER) Stress and Unfolded Protein Response (UPR)

The ER is an intracellular organelle that can be found in all eukaryotic cells. The ER bound with ribosomes (rough endoplasmic reticulum (RER)) is the major place to synthesize secretory and membrane proteins. The ER also produces lipids and stores intracellular calcium [5,39]. Newly translated proteins are moved into the ER lumen where they are folded into their native structure and also modified post-translationally by disulfide bond formation and glycosylation. Within the ER lumen, the quality control machinery such as ER chaperones helps to ensure proper protein folding [16]. However, when the ER fails to secure proper folding of ER proteins, protein homeostasis (proteostasis) is perturbed, and such a condition is referred to as ER stress [5,40]. Although the accumulation of unfolded or misfolded proteins beyond ER's folding capacity is a primary cause of ER stress, metabolic stress, over-nutritional condition, and other cellular stresses also induce ER stress [5,40]. Under ER stress, cells employ an adaptive mechanism, UPR, to reestablish the ER homeostasis. The initial goal of the UPR signaling is to restore the ER proteostasis by increasing the expression of genes which promote protein folding and attenuating general protein translation which reduces additional protein load into the ER [5,40]. In addition, terminally misfolded proteins in the ER are translocated to the cytoplasm and degraded by the 26S proteasome, which is known as ER-associated degradation (ERAD) [41]. However, when ER proteostasis is not restored after these initial responses, UPR signaling launches cell death pathways [5,40].

The UPR signaling is initiated by three ER-located transmembrane proteins in metazoans, namely, inositol requiring protein-1 (IRE1), protein kinase RNA-like ER kinase (PERK), and activating transcription factor-6 (ATF6) (Figure 2B). IRE1 (yeast) or IRE1α (mammal) is a type I transmembrane protein residing in the ER and consists of an ER-lumenal domain and a cytoplasmic region with serine/threonine kinase domain and a ribonuclease (RNase) domain [42,43]. Under normal conditions, IRE1/IRE1α exists as a monomer by physical association of its ER-lumenal domain with an ER chaperone, glucose-regulated protein 78 kDa (GRP78). However, under ER stress which demands more ER chaperones to help the folding of unfolded or misfolded proteins, GRP78 is released from IRE1/IRE1α, which then triggers the dimerization/oligomerization of IRE1/IRE1α. Dimerization/oligomerization in turn leads to auto-transphosphorylation of IRE1/IRE1α at multiple sites including Ser724 of mammalian IRE1α [44,45], which ultimately activates the RNase domain of IRE1/IRE1α [46]. The RNase domain of IRE1/IRE1α selectively excises a 252-base intron of *HAC1* mRNA by IRE1 (yeast) and a 26-base fragment from *XBP1* (X-box binding protein 1) mRNA (*XBP1u*) by IRE1α (mammal) [47–49]. Spliced *HAC1* and *XBP1* (*XBP1s*) mRNA generate functional transcription factors, Hac1p and XBP1s protein, which translocate to the nucleus and transcribe their target genes which are generally involved in protein folding, ER biogenesis, and ERAD to restore ER proteostasis (Figure 2B) [47–49]. In addition to the splicing of HAC1 and XBP1 mRNA, IRE1/IRE1α cleaves and downregulates miRNAs, mRNAs, and other ER-associated RNAs, which is referred to as regulated IRE1-dependent decay (RIDD) [50–53]. XBP1s protein also shows various crosstalks with other signaling molecules including p38 MAPK, IKKβ, p85α/β, BRD7, PGC-1α, and FOXO1, which regulate XBP1s activity and its intracellular localization, and also modulate systemic glucose and lipid metabolism [54–59].

PERK is an ER-residing type I transmembrane protein composed of an ER-lumenal domain and a cytoplasmic serine/threonine kinase domain. The ER-lumenal domain of PERK is structurally homologous with the one of IRE1α, thus the dissociation of GRP78 from PERK monomer upon ER stress prompts homodimerization, auto-transphosphorylation, and activation of the kinase domain of PERK (Figure 2B) [60]. The activated PERK subsequently phosphorylates eukaryotic translation initiation factor 2 subunit alpha (eIF2α) at Ser51, resulting in the suppression of the assembly of ribosomal complex and global protein translation [61]. Despite the suppressed protein translation by eIF2α phosphorylation, certain transcription factors such as ATF4 and ATF5 can be actively translated due to multiple upstream open reading frames (uORFs) in their mRNA [62]. ATF4 then induces the expression of the proapoptotic transcription factor, C/EBP homologous protein (CHOP), which has been proposed as a major mediator of ER stress-induced apoptosis (Figure 2B) [63,64].

ATF6 is a type II ER transmembrane protein consisting with an ER-lumenal domain sensing the ER stress and a cytoplasmic domain that is a bZIP transcription factor [65]. The transcriptional activity of ATF6 remains inhibited without ER stress due to its retention in the ER via its physical association with GRP78. The dissociation of GRP78 from ATF6 under ER stress allows ATF6 to translocate to the Golgi where it is cleaved by site-1 protease (S1P) and S2P (Figure 2B) [66]. After cleavage, the cytoplasmic domain of ATF6 (N-terminal ATF6, ATF6N), an active transcription factor, translocates to the nucleus and transcribes its target genes in order to restore ER proteostasis (Figure 2B) [65].

ER stress and UPR signaling play a critical role in metabolic regulation and diseases [5]. Increased ER stress has been reported in several metabolically important tissues such as the liver, hypothalamus, and white adipose tissues of obese animal models [67,68]. Furthermore, the treatment of chemical chaperones alleviating ER stress, such as 4-phenylbutyric acid (4-PBA), and tauroursodeoxycholic acid (TUDCA) reduces ER stress and restores insulin and leptin sensitivity in animal models and human subjects, which suggests that modulating ER stress and its associated signaling pathways can be a useful therapeutic treatment to various metabolic diseases [67,69–71]. Additionally, several recent efforts have identified numerous novel chemicals as specific modulators of the individual UPR factors such as IRE1α, PERK, and ATF6 [72–74].

Cancer cells are constantly exposed to elevated ER stress and thus employ UPR and other signaling responses to ensure their survival from ER stress. Increased expression of UPR signaling factors such as XBP1s correlates with poor prognosis of several cancers such as glioblastoma, breast cancer and leukemia, and pharmacological or genetic inhibition of UPR responses demonstrates varying degrees of tumor-suppressing effects [75,76]. In addition, one of the mechanisms of Food and Drug Administration (FDA)-approved bortezomib, a proteasome inhibitor against multiple myeloma and mantle cell lymphoma, is to trigger ER stress-induced cell death in these cancer cells [77].

2.3. Mitochondrial Stress

Mitochondria are organelles derived from alphaproteobacteria that were engulfed by a eukaryotic progenitor before evolving as endosymbionts between 1 to 2 billion years ago [78,79]. Mitochondria form a highly dynamic network and continually undergo fusion and fission [80]. Mitochondria primarily function as a powerhouse of eukaryotic cells with oxidative phosphorylation protein complexes that are involved in electron transport and ATP synthesis. Mitochondria also perform crucial functions in many essential metabolisms and signaling pathways including iron–sulfur cluster synthesis, calcium buffering, and stress responses such as autophagy and apoptosis [7,81–83]. It is therefore not surprising that their dysfunction has been associated with a variety of diseases such as neurodegeneration, metabolic disease, heart failure, and cancer [7,81–83].

Eukaryotic cells have evolved multiple stress responses and adaptations to recognize and resolve mitochondrial dysfunctions. Protease-mediated mitochondrial protein quality control has been known for many years as the first line of defense against mitochondrial damage through the degradation of non-assembled proteins and misfolded proteins. The main ATP-dependent proteases performing protein surveillance are the Lon protease homologue (LONP), Clp protease proteolytic subunit (CLPP), intermembrane AAA protease (Yme1), and matrix AAA protease (AFG3L2/SPG7). Two ATP-independent proteases participate as well in mitochondrial protein quality control—mitochondrial inner membrane protease Atp23 homologue (ATP23) and intermembrane Ser protease (HTRA2) [84].

A recent series of studies has revealed that mitochondrial unfolded protein response (UPR^{mt}) counteracts mitochondrial damage. Mitochondrial proteotoxic stress activates the UPR^{mt}, which results in increased transcription of mitochondrial chaperones to help mitochondrial protein folding and proteases to degrade misfolded proteins. The mechanistic understanding of how the UPR^{mt} regulates the transcription has been extensively studied in *C. elegans*, in which the matrix protease CLPP digests unfolded or unassembled mitochondrial proteins into peptides. These peptides are transported to the cytoplasm and induce a transcriptional response in the nucleus via activating transcription factor associated with stress-1 (ATFS-1). ATFS-1 is normally imported into mitochondria where it is degraded by the LONP. However, in response to mitochondrial stress, ATFS-1 accumulates in the cytosol and subsequently traffics to the nucleus (Figure 2C) [85]. In addition to ATFS-1, mitochondrial stress also induces ubiquitin-like 5 (UBL-5) expression and UBL-5 protein forms a complex with defective proventriculus (Drosophila) homolog-1 (DVE-1), a transcription factor, which translocates into the nucleus (Figure 2C) [86]. In the nucleus, ATFS-1 and DVE-1-UBL-5 induce the transcription of mitochondrial chaperones and proteases [85,86]. However, in mammals, the understanding of UPR^{mt} is not clear. It has been reported that the transcription factor ATF5 regulates a mammalian UPR^{mt} and appears to function as mammalian orthologs of ATFS-1 [87]. Another study found that mammalian UPR^{mt} altered the expression of nuclear genes including mitochondrial chaperonins that is involved in protein folding, concurrently with reduced protein synthesis in the matrix via rapid but reversible translational inhibition. Functional studies also revealed that transcriptional repression and LON protease-mediated degradation of mitochondrial pre-RNA processing nuclease MRPP3 lead to defects in pre-RNA processing within the mitochondria, which in turn suppresses the translation of mtDNA-encoded proteins, thereby reducing protein folding load in the mitochondrial matrix [88]. Another study demonstrated that ATF4 is a main player in the mitochondrial stress response in mammals, which acts downstream of the integrated stress response (Figure 2C). ATF4 promotes the expression of various cytoprotective genes, some of which reprogram cellular metabolism toward the synthesis of key metabolites, especially serine. Newly produced serine may promote lipid and phospholipid synthesis which have been known to be critical in mitochondrial stress [89]. Moreover, UPR^{mt} attenuates mitochondrial translation by decreasing the levels of mitochondrial ribosomal proteins independently of ATF4 [89].

Mitophagy is selective autophagy which degrades damaged mitochondria, thereby maintaining a healthy mitochondrial population. Mitophagy requires PINK1, a kinase that is imported into mitochondria under normal conditions and subsequently degraded by proteolysis. When mitochondria are depolarized and dysfunctional, PINK1 is stabilized on the outer mitochondrial membrane, and recruits Parkin, a ubiquitin ligase, on the damaged mitochondria. The outer membrane on the mitochondria is then ubiquitylated by Parkin. Consequently, the poly-ubiquitinated mitochondria are selectively recognized and bound by autophagy machinery, triggering the selected degradation of mitochondria (Figure 2C) [90,91].

Aging accompanies the accumulation of dysfunctional mitochondria and mutations in genes involved in mitochondrial function, which affect life span [92,93]. In addition, mitochondrial dysfunction is linked to various metabolic diseases such as obesity, type 2 diabetes, hypertension, and non-alcoholic fatty liver disease [83,94,95]. Moreover, as exemplified by Parkinson's disease, impaired mitophagy and mitochondrial dysfunction have been suggested to cause various neurodegenerative diseases [96,97]. Mutations in PINK1, PARK2 (Parkin), ATP13A2, and DJ-1 impair mitophagy and elicit mitochondrial dysfunction, in turn leading to autosomal recessive Parkinson's disease [98,99]. Additionally, mitochondrial dysfunction is observed in Alzheimer's disease, Huntington's disease, ALS, and other neuropathies, but its causal role in these neurodegenerative diseases has not yet been established [96,100]. Since Otto Warburg discovered that cancer cells mainly utilize aerobic glycolysis to produce lactate from glucose in the presence of oxygen (Warburg effect), the defects of oxidative phosphorylation in mitochondria was believed to produce this Warburg effect in cancer cells [101]. However, recent studies document that cancers alter the mitochondrial function instead of inactivating it to produce metabolite needed by cancer cells [101,102]. Mutations in tricarboxylic acid (TCA) cycle enzymes such as isocitrate dehydrogenase 2 (IDH2), succinate dehydrogenase, and fumarate hydratase are frequently found in human cancers [101,102], and the inhibitor of mutant IDH2, enasidenib, was approved by the FDA to treat acute myeloid leukemia [103,104].

2.4. Hypoxia

Molecular oxygen (O_2) is a critical substrate for mitochondrial ATP production, signaling, and numerous cellular metabolisms. The maintenance of O_2 homeostasis is, therefore, essential for the development of multicellular animal life. O_2 deprivation (hypoxia) is the condition in which cellular O_2 delivery does not meet the demand. Hypoxia is one of defining features of solid tumors associated with increased therapeutic resistance [105–107]. The central mediators of cellular adaptation to hypoxia are hypoxia-inducible factors (HIFs), a family of heterodimeric basic helix-loop-helix transcription factors composed of an oxygen-sensitive HIFα subunit and a constitutively expressed HIF1β subunit. Three HIFα subunits are identified in mammals—HIF1α, HIF2α, and HIF3α. In the presence of oxygen, HIFα subunits are rapidly hydroxylated on proline residues by a group of prolyl hydroxylase domain (PHD) enzymes. Once hydroxylated, HIFα binds to the von Hippel–Lindau (VHL) protein, an E3 ubiquitin ligase targeting HIFα for proteasomal degradation (Figure 2D). In another mode of HIFα regulation, HIFα undergoes asparaginyl hydroxylation by factor inhibiting HIF1 (FIH1), which inactivates HIFα transcriptional activity by preventing its interaction with the transcriptional co-activator CREB-binding protein (CBP) and histone acetyltransferase p300 (Figure 2D). Thus, PHDs and FIH1 function as O_2-dependent oxygenases to post-translationally modify HIFs to suppress their transcriptional activity [108]. Conversely, during hypoxia, PHD and FIH activity is suppressed, resulting in HIFα stabilization and dimerization with HIF1β. Subsequently, the HIF dimer translocates to the nucleus and transcribes its target genes with hypoxia-responsive elements (HREs), HIF-binding promoters (Figure 2D) [109–111]. HIF target genes generally stimulate vascularization (VEGF), raise the blood's oxygen carrying capacity (erythropoietin), and modulate mitochondrial metabolism.

The largest group of genes regulated by HIF1 are associated with glucose metabolism. HIF1 can increase the rate of glucose uptake through the upregulation of the glucose transporters, GLUT1 and GLUT3. Furthermore, HIF1 stimulates enzymes responsible for the glycolytic breakdown of intracellular glucose to pyruvate. HIF1 also upregulates lactate dehydrogenase A (LDHA) which converts pyruvate to lactate. The lactate can then be transported out of the cell through the action of the HIF-inducible cell surface monocarboxylate transporter 4 (MCT4) [112,113]. Thus, HIF1 activation leads to an increase in glycolysis.

Mitochondria and O_2 are inextricably intertwined. There are several mechanisms by which HIF signaling can affect mitochondrial function. HIF1 induces the expression of pyruvate dehydrogenase kinase 1 (PDK1), which phosphorylates and inactivates the mitochondrial pyruvate dehydrogenase (PDH) and blocks the conversion of pyruvate to acetyl-CoA, thereby suppressing the TCA cycle and attenuating oxidative phosphorylation and excessive toxic reactive oxygen species (ROS) production [114]. HIF1 also modulates mitochondrial metabolism by replacing the cytochrome c oxidase subunit COX4-1 with COX4-2, in which HIF1 increases the transcription of COX4-2 while downregulating COX4-1 protein levels by augmenting the expression of Lon protease. COX4-2 is more efficient at facilitating the electron transfer to O_2, and thereby lowers ROS levels [115]. In addition, HIF1 upregulates BNIP3 and BNIP3L, which promote mitophagy [105]. In another report, the researchers suggest chronic hypoxia could be used as an unexpected treatment for defects in the mitochondrial respiratory chain [116].

Regulation of hypoxic responses via the HIFs is well established, but growing evidence also indicates that HIF-independent mechanisms are also involved. In one study, hypoxic response depends on the accumulation of lactate which binds to the NDRG3 protein and stabilizes it. NDRG3 is an oxygen-regulated protein and also a substrate of the PHD2/VHL system. The stabilized NDRG3 mediates hypoxia-induced activation of the Raf-ERK pathway and promotes angiogenesis and cell growth [110]. In another study, hypoxia promotes survival of in vitro and in vivo models of Friedreich's ataxia by restoring the steady-state levels of Fe–S clusters independently of HIF. Mitochondrial protein frataxin (FXN) participates in the biosynthesis of Fe–S clusters, and FXN-deficient yeast, human cells, and *C. elegans*, which cannot survive under normoxia, were able to grow continuously in ambient 1%

O_2, a hypoxic condition. This indicates that hypoxia somehow could directly promote Fe–S synthesis bypassing the requirement of FXN [117].

Cancer cells are constantly exposed to the hypoxic condition, thus cancer cells frequently employ various responses ameliorating hypoxic stress. Increased expression of HIF1α and HIF2α correlates with negative outcome of human tumors, and HIFs in cancer cells promote glucose metabolism and angiogenesis to help tumor proliferation and survival [118]. In addition to cancer metabolism, hypoxia signaling contributes to systemic glucose and lipid metabolism; depletion of HIF1α in pancreas β-cells causes glucose intolerance due to impaired insulin secretion [119]. Additionally, genetic and pharmacological suppression of HIF2α activity in the intestine alleviates hepatic steatosis of obese mice, whereas activation of HIF2α in the liver improves glucose metabolism and ameliorates type 2 diabetes [120–122].

2.5. Oxidative Stress

Oxidation–reduction (redox) homeostasis is crucial to maintaining nearly all principal cellular processes. During the redox reaction, various oxidants and antioxidants are generated endogenously, and when oxidants are produced or obtained beyond the balancing redox capacity of cells, it leads to oxidative stress. ROS, which causes oxidative stress, includes not only narrowly defined ROS but also various other kinds of chemicals such as reactive nitrogen species, reactive chlorine/bromine species, reactive sulfur species, reactive carbonyl species, and reactive selenium species [123,124]. ROS is continuously generated during metabolism, which has been considered to facilitate accumulated DNA damages and ultimately lead to the development of cancers and cellular aging. ROS and accompanying oxidative stress also have been demonstrated to contribute to the pathophysiologies of various chronic diseases such as cardiovascular diseases, obesity, diabetes, and neurodegenerative diseases [125]. However, recent studies also show that ROS plays a beneficial role in many cellular functions. For example, ROS generated from phagocytes constitutes a pathogen-killing mechanism during phagocytosis. Furthermore, some ROS such as hydrogen peroxide (H_2O_2) and nitric oxide (NO) play a role in cellular signaling and in post-translational modifications of proteins such as sulfenylation and S-nitrosylation [126–130]. The majority of ROS is produced from the electron transport chain of mitochondria as a superoxide anion radical, $O_2\bullet^-$, and most of $O_2\bullet^-$ is converted to H_2O_2 by manganese superoxide dismutase (MnSOD) [131–133]. Additionally, NADPH oxidases, which are activated by growth factors, also generate H_2O_2 [134], whereas NO synthases produce NO [135].

Because oxidative stress can be produced at every cellular metabolic process, a myriad of signaling responses even in other stress responses are employed to curb oxidative stresses, which include NRF2-KEAP1, p53, MAPKs (JNK, p38 MAPK, ERK), PI3K/Akt, NF-κB, heat shock response, and UPR [125,136]. In general, the majority of these pathways exercise pro-survival responses, whereas some responses from JNK, p38, p53, and UPR pathways (e.g., CHOP) exert cell death [5,125]. Among these oxidative stress responses, NRF2-KEAP1 is regarded as one of the main regulators of the cellular antioxidant responses. NRF2 is a transcription factor and its protein levels are maintained at low under unstressed conditions by three E3 ubiquitin ligase complexes—KEAP1-CUL3-RBX1, β-TrCP-SKP1-CUL1-RBX1, and HRD1 [137]. However, KEAP1-CUL3-RBX1 is considered as a principal negative regulator responding to the changes of redox condition [136,137]. KEAP1 is a substrate adaptor protein of the CUL3-RBX1 E3 ligase complex and binds to NRF2 to prompt NRF2 ubiquitylation and its subsequent degradation during unstressed conditions. Under oxidative stress condition, excessive ROS reacts with cysteines (especially Cys151) at the N-terminal part of KEAP1, leading to its conformational changes and subsequent loss of affinity to NRF2. In turn, NRF2 translocates to the nucleus, forms a heterodimer with sMAF, and then transcribes its target genes with antioxidant response element, many of which contribute to antioxidant responses (e.g., glucose 6-phosphate dehydrogenase, 6-phosphogluconate dehydrogenase, malic enzyme 1, and isocitrate dehydrogenase 1, which are involved in NADPH production) [136,137].

Many studies have suggested that ROS and oxidative stress contribute to cellular senescence, aging, and aging-associated diseases [125]. During the progression of type 2 diabetes, pancreatic β-cell dysfunction is caused by increased ER stress, mitochondrial stress, and oxidative stress [138]. Moreover, ROS-induced DNA damage, in addition to the chemical modifications of macromolecules such as lipids and proteins, is considered to lead to the development of cancer, whereas many chemotherapy and radiation therapy treatments induce excessive oxidative stress to kill cancer cells [139,140]. Furthermore, genes in the KEAP1-NRF2 pathway are frequently mutated in certain cancers such as squamous cell carcinoma and lung adenocarcinoma showing the strong resistance to chemotherapy and radiation therapy [141,142].

3. Connectivity Map (CMap)

As we explained above, cellular stresses and their related signaling responses are mediated by various environmental factors (e.g., heat, oxidants, osmotic stress, and over-nutrition) and a plethora of signaling molecules. Therefore, finding chemopreventive and even therapeutic chemicals targeting cellular stresses and their associated diseases is challenging and has proven to be difficult with target-based drug discovery. Because of its potential advantage to address complex diseases that require more understanding of their mechanisms, and also recent advances in screening methods for phenotypic drug discovery such as cell-based phenotypic screening and pharmacogenomic analysis, phenotypic drug discovery has started to regain its interest and usage in drug screening.

Recently, the connectivity map (CMap) and the upgraded CMap (L1000) have been demonstrated as useful in silico drug screening tools to target cellular stresses and their related disorders [12,13,143,144]. The CMap (https://portals.broadinstitute.org/cmap/) is a gene expression compendium archiving gene expression data from cultured cells, treated with individual chemical perturbagens and whose ≈22,000 gene expression levels were analyzed with microarray (CMap Build 2 stores results from over 1300 chemical treatments that include a variety of phytochemicals).

Importantly, researchers can query the CMap with their gene expression signatures that consist of a list of genes upregulated and downregulated in the biological or pathological states of interest (Figure 1C). In order to compare the query signature to the entire microarray data in the CMap, which were generated from different cell lines and batches as well as with various doses and treatment time, CMap uses a nonparametric, rank-based pattern-matching analysis. In the end, CMap presents its query result as a list of drugs with a "connectivity score" ranging from +1 (positive connectivity) to -1 (negative connectivity) (Figure 1C). Drugs with a positive connectivity score may generate similar gene expression outcomes with the state of interest (query state), whereas ones with a negative score produce reverse gene expression patterns with the query. Additionally, drugs with a near zero score are unlikely to induce any related responses with the query state. Therefore, the CMap potentially provides a list of candidate chemicals which may mimic or reverse the biological or pathological state of interest [12,13].

Recently, increasing numbers of studies have used CMap to uncover promising small molecules to address various diseases. For example, searching on CMap with gene expression data from tissues (liver and hypothalamus) showing diminished ER stress and improved leptin/insulin receptor signaling as query signatures successfully identified celastrol as an effective leptin sensitizer and chemical chaperone ameliorating obesity in the leptin-resistant mouse model [145]. Celastrol is a phytochemical originally extracted from the root of the thunder god vine, *Tripterygium wilfordii*, which has been used as a medicinal plant in China and other East Asian countries as a treatment of inflammatory diseases such as rheumatoid arthritis [145,146]. Furthermore, using the gene expression signature of celastrol as a query on CMap uncovered that withaferin A is also a chemical chaperone and a leptin sensitizer, and significantly ameliorates obesity [147]. Similar to celastrol, withaferin A is also a phytochemical originally extracted from leaves, berries, and roots of *Withania somnifera*, a winter cherry (also called Ashwagandha in India), which has been used as a medicinal plant in India as a treatment of various disorders including inflammation, autoimmune diseases, tumors, stress, anxiety, and aging [148–150]. Besides the discovery of celastrol and withaferin A as chemical chaperones and anti-obesity drugs, CMap has been successfully utilized to uncover numerous chemicals with potentials to treat various other diseases, for example, COX2- and ADRA2A-targeting chemicals to treat type 1 and type 2 diabetes [151], tomatidine (a phytochemical from tomato plants) for skeletal muscle atrophy [152], anisomycin for spinal muscle atrophy [153], topiramate for inflammatory bowel disease [154], kaempferol (a phytochemical) for cigarette smoke-induced inflammation [155], pyrvinium for obesity [156], cannabidiol (a phytochemical from *Cannabis sativa*, marijuana plant) for diabetic cardiomyopathy [157], piperazine for central nervous system injury [158], and many other chemicals for cancers such as medulloblastoma [159], breast cancers [160,161], lung cancers [162,163], glioblastoma [164], ovarian cancer [165], prostate cancers [166], myeloma [167], atypical meningioma [168], leukemia [169–172], and many others [173–175].

Despite CMap's promising potential as a genome-based and phenotypic drug discovery tool, CMap has limitations. First, constructing and expanding reference profiles of CMap database are time consuming and expensive because CMap is built upon full transcriptome analysis. Second, CMap is still built on data from limited numbers of small molecules and cell lines. In addition, gene expression data from cultured cells may not be appropriate to address the diseases happening in our body or in specific organs. Third, CMap results may not provide enough information about direct drug targets because CMap is a phenotypic drug discovery tool. To overcome these shortcomings, the same team at the Broad Institute who created the original CMap has developed the "next generation connectivity map" or L1000 (https://clue.io/) as part of the National Institutes of Health (NIH) Library of Integrated Network-Based Cellular Signatures (LINCS) initiative [144]. The current L1000 expands the original CMap by using nearly 28,000 perturbagens including over 19,000 small molecules and ≈7000 genetic modulations using knockdown with shRNAs and over-expression with cDNAs. L1000 also includes more cell lines (nine core cell lines) to test perturbagens or uses 3 to 77 variable cell lines for chemicals without characterized mode of action. Moreover, in order to build the new CMap through high-throughput screening at lower costs, L1000 uses only 1000 landmark transcripts as references instead of the full transcriptome, which the authors claim addresses ≈80% of the information in the entire transcriptome [144]. Collectively, L1000 alongside with the original CMap provide powerful in silico pharmacogenomic ways for researchers to discover novel small molecules targeting various diseases that currently do not have effective therapeutics due to their complicated pathophysiologies.

4. Conclusions and Future Perspectives

As our modern society enters the state of population aging, aging-associated diseases such as cardiovascular diseases, obesity, diabetes, neurodegenerative diseases, and cancers have become a major health threat as well as a serious economic and social burden. Even though tremendous efforts have expanded our understanding of the pathophysiologies of these disorders and have also developed numerous medications against them, such efforts still fell short to alleviate significantly chronic and aging-associated disorders. This is partly due to their compounding nature in which a myriad of genetic and environmental factors are interwoven with each other. Recently, a growing number of studies have documented that cellular stresses caused by the disruption of homeostasis within the cell contribute to the development of aging-associated diseases and have suggested that ameliorating these cellular stresses could be an effective prevention and therapeutic treatment. There are several uniquely categorized cellular stresses such as heat shock stress, ER stress, mitochondrial stress, oxidative stress, and hypoxia. However, it should be noted that cellular stresses do not occur individually but frequently happen together. Due to these complexities, developing chemopreventive and therapeutic treatments against cellular stresses and their associated diseases has not yet achieved any significant progress. However, recent technological and genomic advances bring new opportunities to tackle many debilitating chronic disorders. Among them, CMap and its upgraded L1000 are potentially powerful genome-based in silico drug discovery methods based on phenotypic drug discovery, and many studies have successfully used CMap to uncover novel chemicals to alleviate cellular stresses and aging-associated diseases. Furthermore, there are still many possibilities to expand CMap and L1000 in the future in order to be more effective as follows. (1) The numbers of perturbagens (small chemicals and genetic modulations) in CMap/L1000 could increase further, including numerous phytochemicals available currently, and CRISPR/cas9 could be also utilized as genetic perturbation. (2) CMap/L1000 could include more cell types, especially induced pluripotent stem cells (iPSC) and tissue-specific organoids. Additionally, (3) future CMap/L1000 or other pharmacogenomic tools could include more phenotypic information, including proteomic and epigenetic data and also high-content imaging profiles. Furthermore, (4) recent advances in machine learning could empower future genome-based in silico drug discovery tools by potentially providing the information about probable modes of action and target proteins of small molecules.

Historically, phytochemicals have provided huge medical benefits to humankind, as famously shown by salicin (from the willow tree and modified to aspirin®), morphine (from the opium poppy), cocaine (from coca leaves), guanidine (from the French lilac and modified to metformin), and many other examples. However, many phytochemicals' potential medical benefits are still unknown. However, with recent phenotypic drug discovery tools such as CMap, we can finally be in the position to uncover novel functions of phytochemicals which could be both chemopreventive and therapeutic toward many chronic diseases caused by cellular stresses.

Author Contributions: All authors contributed to researching the literature and writing the article.

Funding: This work was supported by DGIST R&D and the Basic Science Research Program through the National Research Foundation of Korea (NRF) funded by the Ministry of Science and ICT (MSIT) or the Ministry of Education of the Republic of Korea to S.K. (2018R1A6A3A01013000), Y.-I.L. (18-LC-01, 19-BT-01), and J.L. (18-LC-01, 2017R1A2B4006200). J.L. also received funding from the Korea Institute of Oriental Medicine (KIOM) provided by the MSIT (KSN1812160).

Conflicts of Interest: The authors declare no conflict of interest.

Abbreviations

β-TrCP	Beta-transducin repeat containing E3 ubiquitin protein ligase
AAA	ATPases associated with diverse cellular activities
AFG3L2	AFG3-like protein 2
ALS	Amyotrophic lateral sclerosis
AMPK	AMP-activated protein kinase
BNIP3L	BCL2 interacting protein 3 like
BRD7	Bromodomain-containing protein 7
CLPP	Clp protease proteolytic subunit
CUL1	Cullin 1
CUL3	Cullin 3
ERK	Extracellular signal-regulated kinase
FDA	Food and Drug Administration, USA
HRD1	HMG-CoA reductase degradation 1 homolog
IDH2	Isocitrate dehydrogenase 2
IKKβ	Inhibitor of nuclear factor kappa-B kinase subunit beta
JNK	c-Jun N-terminal kinase
KEAP1	Kelch-like ECH-associated protein 1
MAPK	Mitogen-activated protein kinase
NADPH	Nicotinamide adenine dinucleotide phosphate, reduced form
NF-κB	Nuclear factor kappa-light-chain-enhancer of activated B cells
NRF2	Nuclear factor erythroid 2-related factor 2
PGC-1α	Peroxisome proliferator-activated receptor gamma coactivator-1 alpha
PI3K	Phosphoinositide 3-kinase
PINK1	PTEN-induced kinase 1
RBX1	Ring box 1
SKP1	S-phase kinase-associated protein 1

sMAF	Small musculoaponeurotic fibrosarcoma
SPG7	Spastic paraplegia 7
TCA	Tricarboxylic acid
VEGF-B	Vascular endothelial growth factor B

References

1. Vijg, J.; Le Bourg, E. Aging and the Inevitable Limit to Human Life Span. *Gerontology* **2017**, *63*, 432–434. [CrossRef] [PubMed]
2. Campisi, J.; Kapahi, P.; Lithgow, G.J.; Melov, S.; Newman, J.C.; Verdin, E. From discoveries in ageing research to therapeutics for healthy ageing. *Nature* **2019**, *571*, 183–192. [CrossRef] [PubMed]
3. Franceschi, C.; Garagnani, P.; Parini, P.; Giuliani, C.; Santoro, A. Inflammaging: A new immune-metabolic viewpoint for age-related diseases. *Nat. Rev. Endocrinol.* **2018**, *14*, 576–590. [CrossRef] [PubMed]
4. Galluzzi, L.; Yamazaki, T.; Kroemer, G. Linking cellular stress responses to systemic homeostasis. *Nat. Rev. Mol. Cell Biol.* **2018**, *19*, 731–745. [CrossRef]
5. Lee, J.; Ozcan, U. Unfolded protein response signaling and metabolic diseases. *J. Biol. Chem.* **2014**, *289*, 1203–1211. [CrossRef]
6. Jovaisaite, V.; Mouchiroud, L.; Auwerx, J. The mitochondrial unfolded protein response, a conserved stress response pathway with implications in health and disease. *J. Exp. Biol.* **2014**, *217*, 137–143. [CrossRef]
7. Andreux, P.A.; Houtkooper, R.H.; Auwerx, J. Pharmacological approaches to restore mitochondrial function. *Nat. Rev. Drug Discov.* **2013**, *12*, 465–483. [CrossRef]
8. Joshi, S.; Wang, T.; Araujo, T.L.S.; Sharma, S.; Brodsky, J.L.; Chiosis, G. Adapting to stress—Chaperome networks in cancer. *Nat. Rev. Cancer* **2018**, *18*, 562–575. [CrossRef]
9. Buono, R.; Longo, V.D. Starvation, Stress Resistance, and Cancer. *Trends Endocrinol. Metab.* **2018**, *29*, 271–280. [CrossRef]
10. Steward, W.P.; Brown, K. Cancer chemoprevention: A rapidly evolving field. *Br. J. Cancer* **2013**, *109*, 1–7. [CrossRef]
11. Moffat, J.G.; Vincent, F.; Lee, J.A.; Eder, J.; Prunotto, M. Opportunities and challenges in phenotypic drug discovery: An industry perspective. *Nat. Rev. Drug Discov.* **2017**, *16*, 531–543. [CrossRef]
12. Lamb, J. The Connectivity Map: A new tool for biomedical research. *Nat. Rev. Cancer* **2007**, *7*, 54–60. [CrossRef] [PubMed]
13. Lamb, J.; Crawford, E.D.; Peck, D.; Modell, J.W.; Blat, I.C.; Wrobel, M.J.; Lerner, J.; Brunet, J.P.; Subramanian, A.; Ross, K.N.; et al. The Connectivity Map: Using gene-expression signatures to connect small molecules, genes, and disease. *Science* **2006**, *313*, 1929–1935. [CrossRef] [PubMed]
14. Moran Luengo, T.; Mayer, M.P.; Rudiger, S.G.D. The Hsp70-Hsp90 Chaperone Cascade in Protein Folding. *Trends Cell Biol.* **2019**, *29*, 164–177. [CrossRef] [PubMed]
15. Hipp, M.S.; Park, S.H.; Hartl, F.U. Proteostasis impairment in protein-misfolding and -aggregation diseases. *Trends Cell Biol.* **2014**, *24*, 506–514. [CrossRef] [PubMed]
16. Sun, Z.; Brodsky, J.L. Protein quality control in the secretory pathway. *J. Cell Biol.* **2019**, *218*, 3171–3187. [CrossRef]
17. Kaushik, S.; Cuervo, A.M. Proteostasis and aging. *Nat. Med.* **2015**, *21*, 1406–1415. [CrossRef]
18. Hipp, M.S.; Kasturi, P.; Hartl, F.U. The proteostasis network and its decline in ageing. *Nat. Rev. Mol. Cell Biol.* **2019**, *20*, 421–435. [CrossRef]
19. Ritossa, F. A new puffing pattern induced by temperature shock and DNP in drosophila. *Experientia* **1962**, *18*, 571–573. [CrossRef]
20. Kregel, K.C. Heat shock proteins: Modifying factors in physiological stress responses and acquired thermotolerance. *J. Appl. Physiol. 1985* **2002**, *92*, 2177–2186. [CrossRef]
21. Chatterjee, S.; Burns, T.F. Targeting Heat Shock Proteins in Cancer: A Promising Therapeutic Approach. *Int. J. Mol. Sci.* **2017**, *18*, 1978. [CrossRef] [PubMed]
22. Gomez-Pastor, R.; Burchfiel, E.T.; Thiele, D.J. Regulation of heat shock transcription factors and their roles in physiology and disease. *Nat. Rev. Mol. Cell Biol.* **2018**, *19*, 4–19. [CrossRef] [PubMed]
23. Wu, J.; Liu, T.; Rios, Z.; Mei, Q.; Lin, X.; Cao, S. Heat Shock Proteins and Cancer. *Trends Pharmacol. Sci.* **2017**, *38*, 226–256. [CrossRef] [PubMed]

24. Javid, B.; MacAry, P.A.; Lehner, P.J. Structure and function: Heat shock proteins and adaptive immunity. *J. Immunol.* **2007**, *179*, 2035–2040. [CrossRef] [PubMed]
25. Akerfelt, M.; Morimoto, R.I.; Sistonen, L. Heat shock factors: Integrators of cell stress, development and lifespan. *Nat. Rev. Mol. Cell Biol.* **2010**, *11*, 545–555. [CrossRef] [PubMed]
26. Mercier, P.A.; Winegarden, N.A.; Westwood, J.T. Human heat shock factor 1 is predominantly a nuclear protein before and after heat stress. *J. Cell Sci.* **1999**, *112*, 2765–2774. [PubMed]
27. Baler, R.; Dahl, G.; Voellmy, R. Activation of human heat shock genes is accompanied by oligomerization, modification, and rapid translocation of heat shock transcription factor HSF1. *Mol. Cell. Biol.* **1993**, *13*, 2486–2496. [CrossRef]
28. Sarge, K.D.; Murphy, S.P.; Morimoto, R.I. Activation of heat shock gene transcription by heat shock factor 1 involves oligomerization, acquisition of DNA-binding activity, and nuclear localization and can occur in the absence of stress. *Mol. Cell. Biol.* **1993**, *13*, 1392–1407. [CrossRef]
29. Ali, A.; Bharadwaj, S.; O'Carroll, R.; Ovsenek, N. HSP90 interacts with and regulates the activity of heat shock factor 1 in Xenopus oocytes. *Mol. Cell. Biol.* **1998**, *18*, 4949–4960. [CrossRef]
30. Zou, J.; Guo, Y.; Guettouche, T.; Smith, D.F.; Voellmy, R. Repression of heat shock transcription factor HSF1 activation by HSP90 (HSP90 complex) that forms a stress-sensitive complex with HSF1. *Cell* **1998**, *94*, 471–480. [CrossRef]
31. Hentze, N.; Le Breton, L.; Wiesner, J.; Kempf, G.; Mayer, M.P. Molecular mechanism of thermosensory function of human heat shock transcription factor Hsf1. *Elife* **2016**, *5*, e11576. [CrossRef] [PubMed]
32. Morley, J.F.; Morimoto, R.I. Regulation of longevity in Caenorhabditis elegans by heat shock factor and molecular chaperones. *Mol. Biol. Cell* **2004**, *15*, 657–664. [CrossRef] [PubMed]
33. Hsu, A.L.; Murphy, C.T.; Kenyon, C. Regulation of aging and age-related disease by DAF-16 and heat-shock factor. *Science* **2003**, *300*, 1142–1145. [CrossRef] [PubMed]
34. Fujimoto, M.; Takaki, E.; Hayashi, T.; Kitaura, Y.; Tanaka, Y.; Inouye, S.; Nakai, A. Active HSF1 significantly suppresses polyglutamine aggregate formation in cellular and mouse models. *J. Biol. Chem.* **2005**, *280*, 34908–34916. [CrossRef] [PubMed]
35. Hayashida, N.; Fujimoto, M.; Tan, K.; Prakasam, R.; Shinkawa, T.; Li, L.; Ichikawa, H.; Takii, R.; Nakai, A. Heat shock factor 1 ameliorates proteotoxicity in cooperation with the transcription factor NFAT. *EMBO J.* **2010**, *29*, 3459–3469. [CrossRef] [PubMed]
36. Chen, H.J.; Mitchell, J.C.; Novoselov, S.; Miller, J.; Nishimura, A.L.; Scotter, E.L.; Vance, C.A.; Cheetham, M.E.; Shaw, C.E. The heat shock response plays an important role in TDP-43 clearance: Evidence for dysfunction in amyotrophic lateral sclerosis. *Brain* **2016**, *139*, 1417–1432. [CrossRef] [PubMed]
37. Auluck, P.K.; Chan, H.Y.; Trojanowski, J.Q.; Lee, V.M.; Bonini, N.M. Chaperone suppression of alpha-synuclein toxicity in a Drosophila model for Parkinson's disease. *Science* **2002**, *295*, 865–868. [CrossRef]
38. Dai, C.; Whitesell, L.; Rogers, A.B.; Lindquist, S. Heat shock factor 1 is a powerful multifaceted modifier of carcinogenesis. *Cell* **2007**, *130*, 1005–1018. [CrossRef]
39. Voeltz, G.K.; Rolls, M.M.; Rapoport, T.A. Structural organization of the endoplasmic reticulum. *EMBO Rep.* **2002**, *3*, 944–950. [CrossRef]
40. Hetz, C.; Papa, F.R. The Unfolded Protein Response and Cell Fate Control. *Mol. Cell* **2018**, *69*, 169–181. [CrossRef]
41. Qi, L.; Tsai, B.; Arvan, P. New Insights into the Physiological Role of Endoplasmic Reticulum-Associated Degradation. *Trends Cell Biol.* **2017**, *27*, 430–440. [CrossRef] [PubMed]
42. Cox, J.S.; Shamu, C.E.; Walter, P. Transcriptional induction of genes encoding endoplasmic reticulum resident proteins requires a transmembrane protein kinase. *Cell* **1993**, *73*, 1197–1206. [CrossRef]
43. Mori, K.; Ma, W.; Gething, M.J.; Sambrook, J. A transmembrane protein with a cdc2+/CDC28-related kinase activity is required for signaling from the ER to the nucleus. *Cell* **1993**, *74*, 743–756. [PubMed]
44. Ali, M.M.; Bagratuni, T.; Davenport, E.L.; Nowak, P.R.; Silva-Santisteban, M.C.; Hardcastle, A.; McAndrews, C.; Rowlands, M.G.; Morgan, G.J.; Aherne, W.; et al. Structure of the Ire1 autophosphorylation complex and implications for the unfolded protein response. *EMBO J.* **2011**, *30*, 894–905. [CrossRef] [PubMed]
45. Lee, K.P.; Dey, M.; Neculai, D.; Cao, C.; Dever, T.E.; Sicheri, F. Structure of the dual enzyme Ire1 reveals the basis for catalysis and regulation in nonconventional RNA splicing. *Cell* **2008**, *132*, 89–100. [CrossRef] [PubMed]

46. Cox, J.S.; Walter, P. A novel mechanism for regulating activity of a transcription factor that controls the unfolded protein response. *Cell* **1996**, *87*, 391–404. [CrossRef]
47. Yoshida, H.; Matsui, T.; Yamamoto, A.; Okada, T.; Mori, K. XBP1 mRNA is induced by ATF6 and spliced by IRE1 in response to ER stress to produce a highly active transcription factor. *Cell* **2001**, *107*, 881–891. [CrossRef]
48. Chapman, R.E.; Walter, P. Translational attenuation mediated by an mRNA intron. *Curr. Biol.* **1997**, *7*, 850–859. [CrossRef]
49. Kawahara, T.; Yanagi, H.; Yura, T.; Mori, K. Endoplasmic reticulum stress-induced mRNA splicing permits synthesis of transcription factor Hac1p/Ern4p that activates the unfolded protein response. *Mol. Biol. Cell* **1997**, *8*, 1845–1862. [CrossRef]
50. Hollien, J.; Lin, J.H.; Li, H.; Stevens, N.; Walter, P.; Weissman, J.S. Regulated Ire1-dependent decay of messenger RNAs in mammalian cells. *J. Cell Biol.* **2009**, *186*, 323–331. [CrossRef]
51. Han, D.; Lerner, A.G.; Vande Walle, L.; Upton, J.P.; Xu, W.; Hagen, A.; Backes, B.J.; Oakes, S.A.; Papa, F.R. IRE1alpha kinase activation modes control alternate endoribonuclease outputs to determine divergent cell fates. *Cell* **2009**, *138*, 562–575. [CrossRef] [PubMed]
52. Upton, J.P.; Wang, L.; Han, D.; Wang, E.S.; Huskey, N.E.; Lim, L.; Truitt, M.; McManus, M.T.; Ruggero, D.; Goga, A.; et al. IRE1alpha cleaves select microRNAs during ER stress to derepress translation of proapoptotic Caspase-2. *Science* **2012**, *338*, 818–822. [CrossRef] [PubMed]
53. Maurel, M.; Chevet, E.; Tavernier, J.; Gerlo, S. Getting RIDD of RNA: IRE1 in cell fate regulation. *Trends Biochem. Sci.* **2014**, *39*, 245–254. [CrossRef] [PubMed]
54. Lee, J.; Salazar Hernandez, M.A.; Auen, T.; Mucka, P.; Lee, J.; Ozcan, U. PGC-1alpha functions as a co-suppressor of XBP1s to regulate glucose metabolism. *Mol. Metab.* **2018**, *7*, 119–131. [CrossRef] [PubMed]
55. Lee, J.; Sun, C.; Zhou, Y.; Gokalp, D.; Herrema, H.; Park, S.W.; Davis, R.J.; Ozcan, U. p38 MAPK-mediated regulation of Xbp1s is crucial for glucose homeostasis. *Nat. Med.* **2011**, *17*, 1251–1260. [CrossRef]
56. Park, S.W.; Herrema, H.; Salazar, M.; Cakir, I.; Cabi, S.; Basibuyuk Sahin, F.; Chiu, Y.H.; Cantley, L.C.; Ozcan, U. BRD7 regulates XBP1s' activity and glucose homeostasis through its interaction with the regulatory subunits of PI3K. *Cell Metab.* **2014**, *20*, 73–84. [CrossRef]
57. Park, S.W.; Zhou, Y.; Lee, J.; Lu, A.; Sun, C.; Chung, J.; Ueki, K.; Ozcan, U. The regulatory subunits of PI3K, p85alpha and p85beta, interact with XBP-1 and increase its nuclear translocation. *Nat. Med.* **2010**, *16*, 429–437. [CrossRef]
58. Zhou, Y.; Lee, J.; Reno, C.M.; Sun, C.; Park, S.W.; Chung, J.; Fisher, S.J.; White, M.F.; Biddinger, S.B.; Ozcan, U. Regulation of glucose homeostasis through a XBP-1-FoxO1 interaction. *Nat. Med.* **2011**, *17*, 356–365. [CrossRef]
59. Liu, J.; Ibi, D.; Taniguchi, K.; Lee, J.; Herrema, H.; Akosman, B.; Mucka, P.; Salazar Hernandez, M.A.; Uyar, M.F.; Park, S.W.; et al. Inflammation Improves Glucose Homeostasis through IKKbeta-XBP1s Interaction. *Cell* **2016**, *167*, 1052–1066. [CrossRef]
60. Harding, H.P.; Zhang, Y.; Ron, D. Protein translation and folding are coupled by an endoplasmic-reticulum-resident kinase. *Nature* **1999**, *397*, 271–274. [CrossRef]
61. Ma, K.; Vattem, K.M.; Wek, R.C. Dimerization and release of molecular chaperone inhibition facilitate activation of eukaryotic initiation factor-2 kinase in response to endoplasmic reticulum stress. *J. Biol. Chem.* **2002**, *277*, 18728–18735. [CrossRef] [PubMed]
62. Wek, R.C.; Cavener, D.R. Translational control and the unfolded protein response. *Antioxid. Redox Signal.* **2007**, *9*, 2357–2371. [CrossRef] [PubMed]
63. Zinszner, H.; Kuroda, M.; Wang, X.; Batchvarova, N.; Lightfoot, R.T.; Remotti, H.; Stevens, J.L.; Ron, D. CHOP is implicated in programmed cell death in response to impaired function of the endoplasmic reticulum. *Genes Dev.* **1998**, *12*, 982–995. [CrossRef] [PubMed]
64. Harding, H.P.; Novoa, I.; Zhang, Y.; Zeng, H.; Wek, R.; Schapira, M.; Ron, D. Regulated translation initiation controls stress-induced gene expression in mammalian cells. *Mol. Cell* **2000**, *6*, 1099–1108. [CrossRef]
65. Haze, K.; Yoshida, H.; Yanagi, H.; Yura, T.; Mori, K. Mammalian transcription factor ATF6 is synthesized as a transmembrane protein and activated by proteolysis in response to endoplasmic reticulum stress. *Mol. Biol. Cell* **1999**, *10*, 3787–3799. [CrossRef]

66. Shen, J.; Chen, X.; Hendershot, L.; Prywes, R. ER stress regulation of ATF6 localization by dissociation of BiP/GRP78 binding and unmasking of Golgi localization signals. *Dev. Cell* **2002**, *3*, 99–111. [CrossRef]
67. Ozcan, L.; Ergin, A.S.; Lu, A.; Chung, J.; Sarkar, S.; Nie, D.; Myers, M.G., Jr.; Ozcan, U. Endoplasmic reticulum stress plays a central role in development of leptin resistance. *Cell Metab.* **2009**, *9*, 35–51. [CrossRef]
68. Ozcan, U.; Cao, Q.; Yilmaz, E.; Lee, A.H.; Iwakoshi, N.N.; Ozdelen, E.; Tuncman, G.; Gorgun, C.; Glimcher, L.H.; Hotamisligil, G.S. Endoplasmic reticulum stress links obesity, insulin action, and type 2 diabetes. *Science* **2004**, *306*, 457–461. [CrossRef]
69. Kars, M.; Yang, L.; Gregor, M.F.; Mohammed, B.S.; Pietka, T.A.; Finck, B.N.; Patterson, B.W.; Horton, J.D.; Mittendorfer, B.; Hotamisligil, G.S.; et al. Tauroursodeoxycholic Acid may improve liver and muscle but not adipose tissue insulin sensitivity in obese men and women. *Diabetes* **2010**, *59*, 1899–1905. [CrossRef]
70. Ozcan, U.; Yilmaz, E.; Ozcan, L.; Furuhashi, M.; Vaillancourt, E.; Smith, R.O.; Gorgun, C.Z.; Hotamisligil, G.S. Chemical chaperones reduce ER stress and restore glucose homeostasis in a mouse model of type 2 diabetes. *Science* **2006**, *313*, 1137–1140. [CrossRef]
71. Xiao, C.; Giacca, A.; Lewis, G.F. Sodium phenylbutyrate, a drug with known capacity to reduce endoplasmic reticulum stress, partially alleviates lipid-induced insulin resistance and beta-cell dysfunction in humans. *Diabetes* **2011**, *60*, 918–924. [CrossRef] [PubMed]
72. Gonzalez-Teuber, V.; Albert-Gasco, H.; Auyeung, V.C.; Papa, F.R.; Mallucci, G.R.; Hetz, C. Small Molecules to Improve ER Proteostasis in Disease. *Trends Pharmacol. Sci.* **2019**, *40*, 684–695. [CrossRef] [PubMed]
73. Hetz, C.; Axten, J.M.; Patterson, J.B. Pharmacological targeting of the unfolded protein response for disease intervention. *Nat. Chem. Biol.* **2019**, *15*, 764–775. [CrossRef] [PubMed]
74. Hetz, C.; Chevet, E.; Harding, H.P. Targeting the unfolded protein response in disease. *Nat. Rev. Drug Discov.* **2013**, *12*, 703–719. [CrossRef] [PubMed]
75. Urra, H.; Dufey, E.; Avril, T.; Chevet, E.; Hetz, C. Endoplasmic Reticulum Stress and the Hallmarks of Cancer. *Trends Cancer* **2016**, *2*, 252–262. [CrossRef] [PubMed]
76. Cubillos-Ruiz, J.R.; Bettigole, S.E.; Glimcher, L.H. Tumorigenic and Immunosuppressive Effects of Endoplasmic Reticulum Stress in Cancer. *Cell* **2017**, *168*, 692–706. [CrossRef]
77. Nikesitch, N.; Lee, J.M.; Ling, S.; Roberts, T.L. Endoplasmic reticulum stress in the development of multiple myeloma and drug resistance. *Clin. Transl. Immunol.* **2018**, *7*, e1007. [CrossRef]
78. Lane, N.; Martin, W. The energetics of genome complexity. *Nature* **2010**, *467*, 929–934. [CrossRef]
79. Youle, R.J. Mitochondria-Striking a balance between host and endosymbiont. *Science* **2019**, *365*, eaaw9855. [CrossRef]
80. Van der Bliek, A.M.; Shen, Q.; Kawajiri, S. Mechanisms of mitochondrial fission and fusion. *Cold Spring Harb. Perspect. Biol.* **2013**, *5*, a011072. [CrossRef]
81. Pfanner, N.; Warscheid, B.; Wiedemann, N. Mitochondrial proteins: From biogenesis to functional networks. *Nat. Rev. Mol. Cell Biol.* **2019**, *20*, 267–284. [CrossRef] [PubMed]
82. Nunnari, J.; Suomalainen, A. Mitochondria: In sickness and in health. *Cell* **2012**, *148*, 1145–1159. [CrossRef] [PubMed]
83. Murphy, M.P.; Hartley, R.C. Mitochondria as a therapeutic target for common pathologies. *Nat. Rev. Drug Discov.* **2018**, *17*, 865–886. [CrossRef] [PubMed]
84. Quiros, P.M.; Langer, T.; Lopez-Otin, C. New roles for mitochondrial proteases in health, ageing and disease. *Nat. Rev. Mol. Cell Biol.* **2015**, *16*, 345–359. [CrossRef] [PubMed]
85. Nargund, A.M.; Pellegrino, M.W.; Fiorese, C.J.; Baker, B.M.; Haynes, C.M. Mitochondrial import efficiency of ATFS-1 regulates mitochondrial UPR activation. *Science* **2012**, *337*, 587–590. [CrossRef] [PubMed]
86. Benedetti, C.; Haynes, C.M.; Yang, Y.; Harding, H.P.; Ron, D. Ubiquitin-like protein 5 positively regulates chaperone gene expression in the mitochondrial unfolded protein response. *Genetics* **2006**, *174*, 229–239. [CrossRef] [PubMed]
87. Fiorese, C.J.; Schulz, A.M.; Lin, Y.F.; Rosin, N.; Pellegrino, M.W.; Haynes, C.M. The Transcription Factor ATF5 Mediates a Mammalian Mitochondrial UPR. *Curr. Biol.* **2016**, *26*, 2037–2043. [CrossRef]
88. Munch, C.; Harper, J.W. Mitochondrial unfolded protein response controls matrix pre-RNA processing and translation. *Nature* **2016**, *534*, 710–713. [CrossRef]
89. Quiros, P.M.; Prado, M.A.; Zamboni, N.; D'Amico, D.; Williams, R.W.; Finley, D.; Gygi, S.P.; Auwerx, J. Multi-omics analysis identifies ATF4 as a key regulator of the mitochondrial stress response in mammals. *J. Cell Biol.* **2017**, *216*, 2027–2045. [CrossRef]

90. Jin, S.M.; Youle, R.J. The accumulation of misfolded proteins in the mitochondrial matrix is sensed by PINK1 to induce PARK2/Parkin-mediated mitophagy of polarized mitochondria. *Autophagy* **2013**, *9*, 1750–1757. [CrossRef]

91. Youle, R.J.; Narendra, D.P. Mechanisms of mitophagy. *Nat. Rev. Mol. Cell Biol.* **2011**, *12*, 9–14. [CrossRef] [PubMed]

92. Wang, Y.; Hekimi, S. Mitochondrial dysfunction and longevity in animals: Untangling the knot. *Science* **2015**, *350*, 1204–1207. [CrossRef] [PubMed]

93. Lee, S.S.; Lee, R.Y.; Fraser, A.G.; Kamath, R.S.; Ahringer, J.; Ruvkun, G. A systematic RNAi screen identifies a critical role for mitochondria in C. elegans longevity. *Nat. Genet.* **2003**, *33*, 40–48. [CrossRef] [PubMed]

94. Nassir, F.; Ibdah, J.A. Role of mitochondria in nonalcoholic fatty liver disease. *Int. J. Mol. Sci.* **2014**, *15*, 8713–8742. [CrossRef]

95. Szendroedi, J.; Phielix, E.; Roden, M. The role of mitochondria in insulin resistance and type 2 diabetes mellitus. *Nat. Rev. Endocrinol.* **2011**, *8*, 92–103. [CrossRef]

96. Hudson, G. The Ageing Brain, Mitochondria and Neurodegeneration. In *Mitochondrial Dysfunction in Neurodegenerative Disorders*; Reeve, A.K., Simcox, E.M., Duchen, M.R., Turnbull, D.M., Eds.; Springer International Publishing: Cham, Switzerland, 2016; pp. 59–80.

97. Cho, B.; Kim, T.; Huh, Y.J.; Lee, J.; Lee, Y.I. Amelioration of Mitochondrial Quality Control and Proteostasis by Natural Compounds in Parkinson's Disease Models. *Int. J. Mol. Sci.* **2019**, *20*, 5208. [CrossRef]

98. Blesa, J.; Trigo-Damas, I.; Quiroga-Varela, A.; del Rey, N.L.-G. Parkinson's Disease-Associated Mutations Affect Mitochondrial Function. In *Mitochondrial Mechanisms of Degeneration and Repair in Parkinson's Disease*; Buhlman, L.M., Ed.; Springer International Publishing: Cham, Switzerland, 2016; pp. 139–158.

99. Chen, C.; Turnbull, D.M.; Reeve, A.K. Mitochondrial Dysfunction in Parkinson's Disease-Cause or Consequence? *Biology* **2019**, *8*, 38. [CrossRef]

100. Wu, Y.; Chen, M.; Jiang, J. Mitochondrial dysfunction in neurodegenerative diseases and drug targets via apoptotic signaling. *Mitochondrion* **2019**, *49*, 35–45. [CrossRef]

101. Zong, W.X.; Rabinowitz, J.D.; White, E. Mitochondria and Cancer. *Mol. Cell* **2016**, *61*, 667–676. [CrossRef]

102. Vyas, S.; Zaganjor, E.; Haigis, M.C. Mitochondria and Cancer. *Cell* **2016**, *166*, 555–566. [CrossRef]

103. Mullard, A. FDA approves first-in-class cancer metabolism drug. *Nat. Rev. Drug Discov.* **2017**, *16*, 593. [CrossRef] [PubMed]

104. Pollyea, D.A.; Tallman, M.S.; de Botton, S.; Kantarjian, H.M.; Collins, R.; Stein, A.S.; Frattini, M.G.; Xu, Q.; Tosolini, A.; See, W.L.; et al. Enasidenib, an inhibitor of mutant IDH2 proteins, induces durable remissions in older patients with newly diagnosed acute myeloid leukemia. *Leukemia* **2019**, *33*, 2575–2584. [CrossRef] [PubMed]

105. Nakazawa, M.S.; Keith, B.; Simon, M.C. Oxygen availability and metabolic adaptations. *Nat. Rev. Cancer* **2016**, *16*, 663–673. [CrossRef] [PubMed]

106. Nobre, A.R.; Entenberg, D.; Wang, Y.; Condeelis, J.; Aguirre-Ghiso, J.A. The Different Routes to Metastasis via Hypoxia-Regulated Programs. *Trends Cell Biol.* **2018**, *28*, 941–956. [CrossRef] [PubMed]

107. Xie, H.; Simon, M.C. Oxygen availability and metabolic reprogramming in cancer. *J. Biol. Chem.* **2017**, *292*, 16825–16832. [CrossRef]

108. Hewitson, K.S.; McNeill, L.A.; Elkins, J.M.; Schofield, C.J. The role of iron and 2-oxoglutarate oxygenases in signalling. *Biochem. Soc. Trans.* **2003**, *31*, 510–515. [CrossRef] [PubMed]

109. Gonzalez, F.J.; Xie, C.; Jiang, C. The role of hypoxia-inducible factors in metabolic diseases. *Nat. Rev. Endocrinol.* **2018**, *15*, 21–32. [CrossRef]

110. Lee, K.E.; Simon, M.C. SnapShot: Hypoxia-Inducible Factors. *Cell* **2015**, *163*, 1288. [CrossRef]

111. Thompson, C.B. Into Thin Air: How We Sense and Respond to Hypoxia. *Cell* **2016**, *167*, 9–11. [CrossRef]

112. Denko, N.C. Hypoxia, HIF1 and glucose metabolism in the solid tumour. *Nat. Rev. Cancer* **2008**, *8*, 705–713. [CrossRef]

113. Ullah, M.S.; Davies, A.J.; Halestrap, A.P. The plasma membrane lactate transporter MCT4, but not MCT1, is up-regulated by hypoxia through a HIF-1alpha-dependent mechanism. *J. Biol. Chem.* **2006**, *281*, 9030–9037. [CrossRef] [PubMed]

114. Kim, J.W.; Tchernyshyov, I.; Semenza, G.L.; Dang, C.V. HIF-1-mediated expression of pyruvate dehydrogenase kinase: A metabolic switch required for cellular adaptation to hypoxia. *Cell Metab.* **2006**, *3*, 177–185. [CrossRef] [PubMed]

115. Fukuda, R.; Zhang, H.; Kim, J.W.; Shimoda, L.; Dang, C.V.; Semenza, G.L. HIF-1 regulates cytochrome oxidase subunits to optimize efficiency of respiration in hypoxic cells. *Cell* **2007**, *129*, 111–122. [CrossRef] [PubMed]
116. Jain, I.H.; Zazzeron, L.; Goli, R.; Alexa, K.; Schatzman-Bone, S.; Dhillon, H.; Goldberger, O.; Peng, J.; Shalem, O.; Sanjana, N.E.; et al. Hypoxia as a therapy for mitochondrial disease. *Science* **2016**, *352*, 54–61. [CrossRef]
117. Ast, T.; Meisel, J.D.; Patra, S.; Wang, H.; Grange, R.M.H.; Kim, S.H.; Calvo, S.E.; Orefice, L.L.; Nagashima, F.; Ichinose, F.; et al. Hypoxia Rescues Frataxin Loss by Restoring Iron Sulfur Cluster Biogenesis. *Cell* **2019**, *177*, 1507–1521. [CrossRef]
118. Semenza, G.L. Oxygen sensing, hypoxia-inducible factors, and disease pathophysiology. *Annu. Rev. Pathol.* **2014**, *9*, 47–71. [CrossRef]
119. Cheng, K.; Ho, K.; Stokes, R.; Scott, C.; Lau, S.M.; Hawthorne, W.J.; O'Connell, P.J.; Loudovaris, T.; Kay, T.W.; Kulkarni, R.N.; et al. Hypoxia-inducible factor-1alpha regulates beta cell function in mouse and human islets. *J. Clin. Investig.* **2010**, *120*, 2171–2183. [CrossRef]
120. Taniguchi, C.M.; Finger, E.C.; Krieg, A.J.; Wu, C.; Diep, A.N.; LaGory, E.L.; Wei, K.; McGinnis, L.M.; Yuan, J.; Kuo, C.J.; et al. Cross-talk between hypoxia and insulin signaling through Phd3 regulates hepatic glucose and lipid metabolism and ameliorates diabetes. *Nat. Med.* **2013**, *19*, 1325–1330. [CrossRef]
121. Wei, K.; Piecewicz, S.M.; McGinnis, L.M.; Taniguchi, C.M.; Wiegand, S.J.; Anderson, K.; Chan, C.W.; Mulligan, K.X.; Kuo, D.; Yuan, J.; et al. A liver Hif-2alpha-Irs2 pathway sensitizes hepatic insulin signaling and is modulated by Vegf inhibition. *Nat. Med.* **2013**, *19*, 1331–1337. [CrossRef]
122. Xie, C.; Yagai, T.; Luo, Y.; Liang, X.; Chen, T.; Wang, Q.; Sun, D.; Zhao, J.; Ramakrishnan, S.K.; Sun, L.; et al. Activation of intestinal hypoxia-inducible factor 2alpha during obesity contributes to hepatic steatosis. *Nat. Med.* **2017**, *23*, 1298–1308. [CrossRef]
123. Sies, H.; Berndt, C.; Jones, D.P. Oxidative Stress. *Annu. Rev. Biochem.* **2017**, *86*, 715–748. [CrossRef] [PubMed]
124. Luo, H.; Chiang, H.H.; Louw, M.; Susanto, A.; Chen, D. Nutrient Sensing and the Oxidative Stress Response. *Trends Endocrinol. Metab.* **2017**, *28*, 449–460. [CrossRef] [PubMed]
125. Finkel, T.; Holbrook, N.J. Oxidants, oxidative stress and the biology of ageing. *Nature* **2000**, *408*, 239–247. [CrossRef] [PubMed]
126. Collins, Y.; Chouchani, E.T.; James, A.M.; Menger, K.E.; Cocheme, H.M.; Murphy, M.P. Mitochondrial redox signalling at a glance. *J. Cell Sci.* **2012**, *125*, 801–806. [CrossRef] [PubMed]
127. Chouchani, E.T.; Kazak, L.; Jedrychowski, M.P.; Lu, G.Z.; Erickson, B.K.; Szpyt, J.; Pierce, K.A.; Laznik-Bogoslavski, D.; Vetrivelan, R.; Clish, C.B.; et al. Mitochondrial ROS regulate thermogenic energy expenditure and sulfenylation of UCP1. *Nature* **2016**, *532*, 112–116. [CrossRef] [PubMed]
128. Dupre-Crochet, S.; Erard, M.; Nubetae, O. ROS production in phagocytes: Why, when, and where? *J. Leukoc. Biol.* **2013**, *94*, 657–670. [CrossRef]
129. Mullebner, A.; Dorighello, G.G.; Kozlov, A.V.; Duvigneau, J.C. Interaction between Mitochondrial Reactive Oxygen Species, Heme Oxygenase, and Nitric Oxide Synthase Stimulates Phagocytosis in Macrophages. *Front. Med.* **2017**, *4*, 252. [CrossRef]
130. Iovine, N.M.; Pursnani, S.; Voldman, A.; Wasserman, G.; Blaser, M.J.; Weinrauch, Y. Reactive nitrogen species contribute to innate host defense against Campylobacter jejuni. *Infect. Immun.* **2008**, *76*, 986–993. [CrossRef]
131. Murphy, M.P. How mitochondria produce reactive oxygen species. *Biochem. J.* **2009**, *417*, 1–13. [CrossRef]
132. Powers, S.K.; Ji, L.L.; Kavazis, A.N.; Jackson, M.J. Reactive oxygen species: Impact on skeletal muscle. *Compr. Physiol.* **2011**, *1*, 941–969.
133. Finkel, T. Signal transduction by mitochondrial oxidants. *J. Biol. Chem.* **2012**, *287*, 4434–4440. [CrossRef] [PubMed]
134. Meitzler, J.L.; Antony, S.; Wu, Y.; Juhasz, A.; Liu, H.; Jiang, G.; Lu, J.; Roy, K.; Doroshow, J.H. NADPH oxidases: A perspective on reactive oxygen species production in tumor biology. *Antioxid. Redox Signal.* **2014**, *20*, 2873–2889. [CrossRef] [PubMed]
135. Nisoli, E.; Carruba, M.O. Nitric oxide and mitochondrial biogenesis. *J. Cell Sci.* **2006**, *119*, 2855–2862. [CrossRef] [PubMed]
136. Cuadrado, A.; Rojo, A.I.; Wells, G.; Hayes, J.D.; Cousin, S.P.; Rumsey, W.L.; Attucks, O.C.; Franklin, S.; Levonen, A.L.; Kensler, T.W.; et al. Therapeutic targeting of the NRF2 and KEAP1 partnership in chronic diseases. *Nat. Rev. Drug Discov.* **2019**, *18*, 295–317. [CrossRef] [PubMed]

137. Rojo de la Vega, M.; Chapman, E.; Zhang, D.D. NRF2 and the Hallmarks of Cancer. *Cancer Cell* **2018**, *34*, 21–43. [CrossRef]

138. Prentki, M.; Nolan, C.J. Islet beta cell failure in type 2 diabetes. *J. Clin. Investig.* **2006**, *116*, 1802–1812. [CrossRef]

139. Campbell, A.; Solaimani, P. Oxidative and Inflammatory Pathways in Age-Related Chronic Disease Processes. In *Inflammation, Aging, and Oxidative Stress*; Bondy, S.C., Campbell, A., Eds.; Springer International Publishing: Cham, Switzerland, 2016; pp. 95–106.

140. Dasgupta, A.; Klein, K. *Antioxidants in Food, Vitamins and Supplements*; Elsevier: San Diego, CA, USA, 2014; pp. 129–150.

141. Jeong, Y.; Hellyer, J.A.; Stehr, H.; Hoang, N.T.; Niu, X.; Das, M.; Padda, S.K.; Ramchandran, K.; Neal, J.W.; Wakelee, H.A.; et al. Role of KEAP1/NFE2L2 mutations in the chemotherapeutic response of non-small cell lung cancer patients. *Clin. Cancer Res.* **2019**. [CrossRef]

142. Jeong, Y.; Hoang, N.T.; Lovejoy, A.; Stehr, H.; Newman, A.M.; Gentles, A.J.; Kong, W.; Truong, D.; Martin, S.; Chaudhuri, A.; et al. Role of KEAP1/NRF2 and TP53 Mutations in Lung Squamous Cell Carcinoma Development and Radiation Resistance. *Cancer Discov.* **2017**, *7*, 86–101. [CrossRef]

143. Musa, A.; Ghoraie, L.S.; Zhang, S.D.; Glazko, G.; Yli-Harja, O.; Dehmer, M.; Haibe-Kains, B.; Emmert-Streib, F. A review of connectivity map and computational approaches in pharmacogenomics. *Brief. Bioinform.* **2018**, *19*, 506–523.

144. Subramanian, A.; Narayan, R.; Corsello, S.M.; Peck, D.D.; Natoli, T.E.; Lu, X.; Gould, J.; Davis, J.F.; Tubelli, A.A.; Asiedu, J.K.; et al. A Next Generation Connectivity Map: L1000 Platform and the First 1,000,000 Profiles. *Cell* **2017**, *171*, 1437–1452. [CrossRef]

145. Liu, J.; Lee, J.; Salazar Hernandez, M.A.; Mazitschek, R.; Ozcan, U. Treatment of obesity with celastrol. *Cell* **2015**, *161*, 999–1011. [CrossRef] [PubMed]

146. Zhang, C.; Sun, P.P.; Guo, H.T.; Liu, Y.; Li, J.; He, X.J.; Lu, A.P. Safety Profiles of Tripterygium wilfordii Hook F: A Systematic Review and Meta-Analysis. *Front. Pharmacol.* **2016**, *7*, 402. [CrossRef] [PubMed]

147. Lee, J.; Liu, J.; Feng, X.; Salazar Hernandez, M.A.; Mucka, P.; Ibi, D.; Choi, J.W.; Ozcan, U. Withaferin A is a leptin sensitizer with strong antidiabetic properties in mice. *Nat. Med.* **2016**, *22*, 1023–1032. [CrossRef] [PubMed]

148. Mirjalili, M.H.; Moyano, E.; Bonfill, M.; Cusido, R.M.; Palazon, J. Steroidal lactones from Withania somnifera, an ancient plant for novel medicine. *Molecules* **2009**, *14*, 2373–2393. [CrossRef] [PubMed]

149. Winters, M. Ancient medicine, modern use: Withania somnifera and its potential role in integrative oncology. *Altern. Med. Rev.* **2006**, *11*, 269–277. [PubMed]

150. Mishra, L.C.; Singh, B.B.; Dagenais, S. Scientific basis for the therapeutic use of Withania somnifera (ashwagandha): A review. *Altern. Med. Rev.* **2000**, *5*, 334–346. [PubMed]

151. Zhang, M.; Luo, H.; Xi, Z.; Rogaeva, E. Drug repositioning for diabetes based on 'omics' data mining. *PLoS ONE* **2015**, *10*, e0126082. [CrossRef]

152. Dyle, M.C.; Ebert, S.M.; Cook, D.P.; Kunkel, S.D.; Fox, D.K.; Bongers, K.S.; Bullard, S.A.; Dierdorff, J.M.; Adams, C.M. Systems-based discovery of tomatidine as a natural small molecule inhibitor of skeletal muscle atrophy. *J. Biol. Chem.* **2014**, *289*, 14913–14924. [CrossRef]

153. Farooq, F.; Balabanian, S.; Liu, X.; Holcik, M.; MacKenzie, A. p38 Mitogen-activated protein kinase stabilizes SMN mRNA through RNA binding protein HuR. *Hum. Mol. Genet.* **2009**, *18*, 4035–4045. [CrossRef]

154. Dudley, J.T.; Sirota, M.; Shenoy, M.; Pai, R.K.; Roedder, S.; Chiang, A.P.; Morgan, A.A.; Sarwal, M.M.; Pasricha, P.J.; Butte, A.J. Computational repositioning of the anticonvulsant topiramate for inflammatory bowel disease. *Sci. Transl. Med.* **2011**, *3*, 96ra76. [CrossRef]

155. Vanderstocken, G.; Dvorkin-Gheva, A.; Shen, P.; Brandsma, C.A.; Obeidat, M.; Bosse, Y.; Hassell, J.A.; Stampfli, M.R. Identification of Drug Candidates to Suppress Cigarette Smoke-induced Inflammation via Connectivity Map Analyses. *Am. J. Respir. Cell Mol. Biol.* **2018**, *58*, 727–735. [CrossRef] [PubMed]

156. Wang, Z.; Dai, Z.; Luo, Z.; Zuo, C. Identification of Pyrvinium, an Anthelmintic Drug, as a Novel Anti-Adipogenic Compound Based on the Gene Expression Microarray and Connectivity Map. *Molecules* **2019**, *24*, 2391. [CrossRef] [PubMed]

157. Rajesh, M.; Mukhopadhyay, P.; Batkai, S.; Patel, V.; Saito, K.; Matsumoto, S.; Kashiwaya, Y.; Horvath, B.; Mukhopadhyay, B.; Becker, L.; et al. Cannabidiol attenuates cardiac dysfunction, oxidative stress, fibrosis, and inflammatory and cell death signaling pathways in diabetic cardiomyopathy. *J. Am. Coll. Cardiol.* **2010**, *56*, 2115–2125. [CrossRef] [PubMed]

158. Johnstone, A.L.; Reierson, G.W.; Smith, R.P.; Goldberg, J.L.; Lemmon, V.P.; Bixby, J.L. A chemical genetic approach identifies piperazine antipsychotics as promoters of CNS neurite growth on inhibitory substrates. *Mol. Cell. Neurosci.* **2012**, *50*, 125–135. [CrossRef] [PubMed]

159. Singh, A.R.; Joshi, S.; Zulcic, M.; Alcaraz, M.; Garlich, J.R.; Morales, G.A.; Cho, Y.J.; Bao, L.; Levy, M.L.; Newbury, R.; et al. PI-3K Inhibitors Preferentially Target CD15+ Cancer Stem Cell Population in SHH Driven Medulloblastoma. *PLoS ONE* **2016**, *11*, e0150836. [CrossRef] [PubMed]

160. Muthuswami, M.; Ramesh, V.; Banerjee, S.; Viveka Thangaraj, S.; Periasamy, J.; Bhaskar Rao, D.; Barnabas, G.D.; Raghavan, S.; Ganesan, K. Breast tumors with elevated expression of 1q candidate genes confer poor clinical outcome and sensitivity to Ras/PI3K inhibition. *PLoS ONE* **2013**, *8*, e77553. [CrossRef] [PubMed]

161. Wang, S.E.; Xiang, B.; Guix, M.; Olivares, M.G.; Parker, J.; Chung, C.H.; Pandiella, A.; Arteaga, C.L. Transforming growth factor beta engages TACE and ErbB3 to activate phosphatidylinositol-3 kinase/Akt in ErbB2-overexpressing breast cancer and desensitizes cells to trastuzumab. *Mol. Cell. Biol.* **2008**, *28*, 5605–5620. [CrossRef]

162. Wang, G.; Ye, Y.; Yang, X.; Liao, H.; Zhao, C.; Liang, S. Expression-based in silico screening of candidate therapeutic compounds for lung adenocarcinoma. *PLoS ONE* **2011**, *6*, e14573. [CrossRef]

163. Fortney, K.; Griesman, J.; Kotlyar, M.; Pastrello, C.; Angeli, M.; Sound-Tsao, M.; Jurisica, I. Prioritizing therapeutics for lung cancer: An integrative meta-analysis of cancer gene signatures and chemogenomic data. *PLoS Comput. Biol.* **2015**, *11*, e1004068. [CrossRef]

164. Cheng, H.W.; Liang, Y.H.; Kuo, Y.L.; Chuu, C.P.; Lin, C.Y.; Lee, M.H.; Wu, A.T.; Yeh, C.T.; Chen, E.I.; Whang-Peng, J.; et al. Identification of thioridazine, an antipsychotic drug, as an antiglioblastoma and anticancer stem cell agent using public gene expression data. *Cell Death Dis.* **2015**, *6*, e1753. [CrossRef]

165. Rho, S.B.; Kim, B.R.; Kang, S. A gene signature-based approach identifies thioridazine as an inhibitor of phosphatidylinositol-3′-kinase (PI3K)/AKT pathway in ovarian cancer cells. *Gynecol. Oncol.* **2011**, *120*, 121–127. [CrossRef] [PubMed]

166. Hieronymus, H.; Lamb, J.; Ross, K.N.; Peng, X.P.; Clement, C.; Rodina, A.; Nieto, M.; Du, J.; Stegmaier, K.; Raj, S.M.; et al. Gene expression signature-based chemical genomic prediction identifies a novel class of HSP90 pathway modulators. *Cancer Cell* **2006**, *10*, 321–330. [CrossRef] [PubMed]

167. Tiedemann, R.E.; Schmidt, J.; Keats, J.J.; Shi, C.X.; Zhu, Y.X.; Palmer, S.E.; Mao, X.; Schimmer, A.D.; Stewart, A.K. Identification of a potent natural triterpenoid inhibitor of proteosome chymotrypsin-like activity and NF-kappaB with antimyeloma activity in vitro and in vivo. *Blood* **2009**, *113*, 4027–4037. [CrossRef] [PubMed]

168. Zador, Z.; King, A.T.; Geifman, N. New drug candidates for treatment of atypical meningiomas: An integrated approach using gene expression signatures for drug repurposing. *PLoS ONE* **2018**, *13*, e0194701. [CrossRef] [PubMed]

169. Sanda, T.; Li, X.; Gutierrez, A.; Ahn, Y.; Neuberg, D.S.; O'Neil, J.; Strack, P.R.; Winter, C.G.; Winter, S.S.; Larson, R.S.; et al. Interconnecting molecular pathways in the pathogenesis and drug sensitivity of T-cell acute lymphoblastic leukemia. *Blood* **2010**, *115*, 1735–1745. [CrossRef] [PubMed]

170. Hassane, D.C.; Guzman, M.L.; Corbett, C.; Li, X.; Abboud, R.; Young, F.; Liesveld, J.L.; Carroll, M.; Jordan, C.T. Discovery of agents that eradicate leukemia stem cells using an in silico screen of public gene expression data. *Blood* **2008**, *111*, 5654–5662. [CrossRef] [PubMed]

171. Schnell, S.A.; Ambesi-Impiombato, A.; Sanchez-Martin, M.; Belver, L.; Xu, L.; Qin, Y.; Kageyama, R.; Ferrando, A.A. Therapeutic targeting of HES1 transcriptional programs in T-ALL. *Blood* **2015**, *125*, 2806–2814. [CrossRef]

172. Churchman, M.L.; Low, J.; Qu, C.; Paietta, E.M.; Kasper, L.H.; Chang, Y.; Payne-Turner, D.; Althoff, M.J.; Song, G.; Chen, S.C.; et al. Efficacy of Retinoids in IKZF1-Mutated BCR-ABL1 Acute Lymphoblastic Leukemia. *Cancer Cell* **2015**, *28*, 343–356. [CrossRef]

173. Rosenbluth, J.M.; Mays, D.J.; Pino, M.F.; Tang, L.J.; Pietenpol, J.A. A gene signature-based approach identifies mTOR as a regulator of p73. *Mol. Cell. Biol.* **2008**, *28*, 5951–5964. [CrossRef]

174. Saito, S.; Furuno, A.; Sakurai, J.; Sakamoto, A.; Park, H.R.; Shin-Ya, K.; Tsuruo, T.; Tomida, A. Chemical genomics identifies the unfolded protein response as a target for selective cancer cell killing during glucose deprivation. *Cancer Res.* **2009**, *69*, 4225–4234. [CrossRef]

175. Stockwell, S.R.; Platt, G.; Barrie, S.E.; Zoumpoulidou, G.; Te Poele, R.H.; Aherne, G.W.; Wilson, S.C.; Sheldrake, P.; McDonald, E.; Venet, M.; et al. Mechanism-based screen for G1/S checkpoint activators identifies a selective activator of EIF2AK3/PERK signalling. *PLoS ONE* **2012**, *7*, e28568. [CrossRef] [PubMed]

International Journal of
Molecular Sciences

Review

Potential Implications of Quercetin and its Derivatives in Cardioprotection

Kristina Ferenczyova [1,†], Barbora Kalocayova [1,†] and Monika Bartekova [1,2,*]

1   Institute for Heart Research, Centre of Experimental Medicine, Slovak Academy of Sciences, 84104 Bratislava, Slovakia; kristina.ferenczyova@savba.sk (K.F.); barbora.kalocayova@savba.sk (B.K.)
2   Institute of Physiology, Comenius University in Bratislava, 81372 Bratislava, Slovakia
*   Correspondence: monika.bartekova@savba.sk; Tel.: +421-2-3229-5427
†   These authors contributed equally to the paper.

Received: 7 February 2020; Accepted: 25 February 2020; Published: 26 February 2020

Abstract: Quercetin (QCT) is a natural polyphenolic compound enriched in human food, mainly in vegetables, fruits and berries. QCT and its main derivatives, such as rhamnetin, rutin, hyperoside, etc., have been documented to possess many beneficial effects in the human body including their positive effects in the cardiovascular system. However, clinical implications of QCT and its derivatives are still rare. In the current paper we provide a complex picture of the most recent knowledge on the effects of QCT and its derivatives in different types of cardiac injury, mainly in ischemia-reperfusion (I/R) injury of the heart, but also in other pathologies such as anthracycline-induced cardiotoxicity or oxidative stress-induced cardiac injury, documented in in vitro and ex vivo, as well as in in vivo experimental models of cardiac injury. Moreover, we focus on cardiac effects of QCT in presence of metabolic comorbidities in addition to cardiovascular disease (CVD). Finally, we provide a short summary of clinical studies focused on cardiac effects of QCT. In general, it seems that QCT and its metabolites exert strong cardioprotective effects in a wide range of experimental models of cardiac injury, likely via their antioxidant, anti-inflammatory and molecular pathways-modulating properties; however, ageing and presence of lifestyle-related comorbidities may confound their beneficial effects in heart disease. On the other hand, due to very limited number of clinical trials focused on cardiac effects of QCT and its derivatives, clinical data are inconclusive. Thus, additional well-designed human studies including a high enough number of patients testing different concentrations of QCT are needed to reveal real therapeutic potential of QCT in CVD. Finally, several negative or controversial effects of QCT in the heart have been reported, and this should be also taken into consideration in QCT-based approaches aimed to treat CVD in humans.

Keywords: quercetin (QCT); QCT derivatives; cardioprotection

---

1. Introduction

During the last decades, constantly growing interest of the effects of flavonoids and other polyphenols on human health has been noticed. Flavonoids are a group of polyphenolic compounds present in the diet representing a promising therapeutic and/or preventive agents for a variety of diseases including cardiovascular disease, diabetes mellitus, hypertension and cancer [1–4].

Quercetin (QCT) is a common flavonoid highly enriched in frequently consumed fruits, vegetables and berries. Major natural sources of QCT and its derivatives are onions, peppers, plums, mangos and various types of berries. Extensive research is focused on exploring the beneficial effects of QCT for human health at all body systems including cardiovascular, nervous, gastrointestinal and others, as well as on uncovering molecular mechanisms involved in QCT action in the body. By its antioxidant, anti-inflammatory, anti-thrombotic, anti-apoptotic and other effects [5], QCT possesses a wide range of multiple activities influencing many different signaling pathways. Thus, QCT affects a number of physiological processes, and is believed to be beneficial in various human diseases including cancer, obesity and diabetes, gastrointestinal and renal diseases [6–8].

In cardiovascular system, QCT and certain QCT-containing food have been shown to exert strong anti-hypertensive effects in both experimental animals and humans through numerous mechanisms such as attenuation of oxidative stress, affecting intracellular protein kinase cascades, as well as via remodeling of extracellular matrix in the vasculature [9–12].

In addition to its vascular effects, QCT has been shown to exert robust heart-protective effects in different kinds of cardiac injury, including ischemia-reperfusion (I/R) injury, doxorubicin-induced cardiotoxicity, diabetic cardiomyopathy and others [13–17]. Cardioprotective effects of QCT are associated with affecting many different signaling pathways and proteins, including inhibition of apoptosis and decreasing oxidative stress, as well as affecting inflammatory proteins in the heart [14–16,18].

In line with increasing evidence of beneficial effects of QCT in different types of heart disease, the aim of the present review is to summarize current knowledge on potential cardioprotective effects of QCT and its derivatives in different types of cardiac injury. The paper focus mainly on the recent experimental studies exploring effects of this flavonoid in in vitro as well as in vivo models of cardiac injury, and provide detailed information about proposed mechanisms involved in cardiac effects of QCT and its derivatives. Finally, potential difficulties of QCT use in humans are outlined in the paper, including potential confounding factors that may affect QCT efficiency in preventing cardiac injury.

2. QCT and its Derivatives: Structure, Sources, Metabolism, Bioavailability

QCT (2-(3,4-dihydroxyphenyl)-3,5,7-trihydroxy-chromen-4-one) (IUPAC name) is one of the major representatives of the flavonol family, a subgroup of flavonoids, compounds characterized by 3-hydroxyflavone backbone (Figure 1A). QCT is considered a strong antioxidant possessing the ability to scavenge free radicals and to bind transition metal ions [19]. The catechol and the OH groups at position C3 give QCT the optimal configuration for free radical scavenging. All these properties are primarily attributed to the presence of two antioxidant pharmacophores within the molecule. Despite its attractive molecule shape and preferences, some limitations complicate the use of QCT as a drug. In fact, bioavailability of QCT aglycone defined as the portion of an initially administered dose that reaches the systemic circulation unchanged after a single oral dose was estimated at 4%, which is very low, mostly due to its fast and extensive metabolism. The factors that most influence and usually improve bioavailability of quercetin are the properties of attached sugar moieties and its solubility in water or fats [20]. In addition to its low bioavailability, QCT has low water solubility (0.01 mg/mL (25 C)) [21], high chemical instability and short biological half-life (the average terminal half-life of QCT is 3.5 h [22]), which could reduce its efficacy when it is used in the food and pharmaceuticals [23].

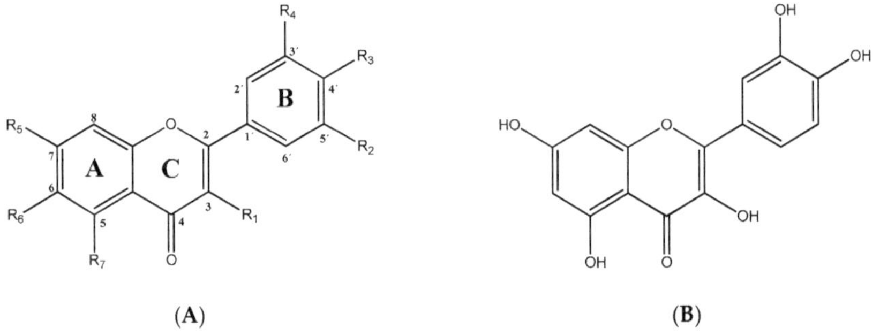

Figure 1. Chemical structures of: (**A**) flavone backbone with potential substituent sites; (**B**) QCT.

2.1. Chemistry of QCT and its Derivatives

QCT molecule is formed of a 15-carbon skeleton consisting of two phenyl rings (A and B) typical for flavonols, attached by an oxygen-containing heterocyclic ring (C). Common feature of flavonols is the hydroxyl group on C-3 carbon [24]. QCT molecule itself occurs as an aglycone with five hydroxyl groups on the flavone backbone (Figure 1B). Hydroxyl groups determine reactivity and biological activity of QCT, and limit its ability to create derivatives. Despite the presence of hydroxyl groups, QCT molecule has lipophilic character, while its derivatives may become more hydrophilic [25].

In contrast to other food supplements, QCT is mostly bound to a saccharide in nature. This conjugate is known as a QCT glycoside. While glycosylation of at least one hydroxyl group increases hydrophilicity of QCT derivatives, binding of alkoxyl groups or alkylation maintains the lipophilic character of the molecule [26,27]. In plants, changing the profile of a QCT molecule from lipophilic to hydrophilic is aimed to increase its solubility in the cytosol of cells. Consequently, soluble molecules are more easily transported to different parts of plant, thus increasing the possibility of their storage in vacuoles [28,29].

There is a clear correlation between the structure of a QCT molecule and its antioxidant activity. Higher occupancy of hydroxyl groups by saccharides leads to lower antioxidant activity of QCT derivative. Therefore, QCT is the most effective antioxidant among all QCT derivatives since no hydroxyl group are occupied in a QCT molecule [19,30]. QCT, as well as its derivatives, are usually found in the form of yellow-colored powder or small crystals, and cannot be synthetized in the human body [31]. Molecules derived from QCT are classified as: (1) O-glycosides, (2) C-glycosides, (3) ethers, (4) derivatives containing alkyl substituents (prenyls) (Table 1).

Table 1. Overview of QCT derivatives, chemical structures and natural sources.

Chemical Structure	Common Name/ Systematic Name	Food Sources	References
QCT-3-O-glycosides			
	Hyperoside/ QCT-3-O-galactoside	Mango Cranberries Blueberries Chokeberries	[32] [33]
	Quercitrin/ QCT-3-O-rhamnoside	Mango Spinach	[32] [34]
	Isoquercitrin/ QCT-3-O-glucoside	Beans Plums Onions Mango	[35] [36] [37] [32]

Table 1. *Cont.*

Chemical Structure	Common Name/ Systematic Name	Food Sources	References
	Rutin/ QCT-3-O- rutinoside	Plums Cherries Tomatoes Buckwheat	[36] [38] [39] [40]
	QCT-3-O-sophoroside	Broccoli	[41]
QCT-7-O-glycosides			
	QCT- 7-O-glucoside	Beans	[35]
	QCT- 3-O-rhamnoside- 7-O-glucoside	Pepper	[42]
Acyl and sulfate QCT glycosides			
	QCT- 3-O-(2″-acetylgalactoside)	*Hypericum perforatum*	[43]
	QCT-3-O-glucoside-5′-sulfate	Cornflower	[44]
QCT-C-glycosides			

Table 1. *Cont.*

Chemical Structure	Common Name/ Systematic Name	Food Sources	References
	QCT-6-C-glucoside	*Ageratina calophylla*	[25]
QCT ethers	Rhamnetin	*Rhamnus petiolaris*	[45]
	Isorhamnetin	Onions Honey	[46] [47]
QCT prenyls	8-prenyl-QCT	*Desmodium caudatum*	[48]

2.1.1. QCT-O-Glycosides

In nature, QCT is widely distributed in O-glycoside form with one or more hydroxyl groups replaced by different saccharides. QCT-3-O-glycosides are largely present in fruits, vegetables and the anatomical parts of plants. In these derivatives, the hydroxyl group on C-3 carbon is glycosylated by monosaccharides such as glucose, galactose, xylose or rhamnose [29]. Significant quantities of hyperoside (QCT 3-O-galactoside) were found in mango [32] and small fruits, especially cranberries, blueberries and chokeberries [33]. Quercitrin (QCT-3-O-rhamnoside) was detected in mango [32] and spinach [34]; isoquercitrin (QCT-3-O-glucoside) was found in beans [35], plums [36], onions [37] and mango [32]. QCT derivatives with more complex saccharides bound to C-3 hydroxyl group can also be found in plant foods, namely rutin with terminal sugar rutinose (disaccharide), which is found in abundance in plums [36], cherries [38], tomatoes [39] and buckwheat [40], and QCT-3-O-sophoroside (disaccharide sugar moiety), which is found in broccoli [41].

Hydroxyl group on C-7 carbon of QCT molecule can be also O-glycosylated, as in the case of QCT 7-O-glucosid found in beans [35]. 7-O-glycosylation is often accompanied by methylationon C-3 carbon, for instance in QCT-3-O-rhamnoside-7-O-glucoside found in pepper fruit [42]. In nature, however, a number of glycosides derived from QCT can be found, since sugar moieties can form additional bonds and bind substituents such as acyls (links with aliphatic acids, e.g., malonic, acetic, aromatic acids including caffeic or benzoic acids) or sulfates (SO_4^{2-}) [25]. An example of acyl derivative is QCT-3-O-(2'-acetylgalactoside) [43]. QCT-3-O-glucoside-5'-sulfate identified in the cornflower [44] is one of the few representatives of QCT sulfates that are only rarely found in nature.

2.1.2. QCT-C-Glycosides

Another group of QCT derivatives are C-glycosides, which are very rare in nature. Glycosylation usually occurs on C-6 carbon. An example of such a derivative is QCT-6-C-glucoside, which was originally found in plant *Ageratina calophylla* [25].

2.1.3. QCT Ethers

In the third group of QCT derivatives, a bond is formed between the alcohol molecule and any hydroxyl group of the QCT molecule, most often methanol. Representatives of this group can be found in food, such as isorhamnetin (3-O-methylQCT) enriched in onions and honey [46,47], and rhamnetin (7-O-methyl QCT) enriched in berries *Rhamnus petiolaris* [45].

2.1.4. Alkyl-Containing QCT Derivatives (Prenyls)

The last group of QCT derivatives is only very rarely described in the literature, and its representatives have not been tested for their cardiovascular effects thus far. Thus, this group has minor importance in our overview. An example of a QCT derivative of this group is 8-prenyl-QCT, present in *Desmodium caudatum* [48].

2.2. Metabolization of QCT in the Body

Depending on the substituent on the QCT backbone, absorption of QCT derivatives occurs in different parts of the gastrointestinal tract. It has been shown that QCT in the form of aglycone, in contrast to its glycoside forms absorbed primarily in the intestine, is absorbed already in the stomach. However, the mechanism of absorption in the stomach still remains unknown [49]. Investigations performed in human-derived Caco-2 cells, a model of epithelial cells of intestinal absorption, revealed higher permeability of QCT aglycone as compared to QCT glycosides via cell monolayer by simple passive diffusion in the small intestine [50]. This observation correlates with the fact that QCT is more lipophilic than its hydrophilic derivatives [51]. Hydrolysis of the glycosidic bond of QCT monosaccharide derivatives (such as isoquercitrin) occurs in the lumen of the small intestine by the activity of lactase-phlorizin hydrolase (LPH), a β-glucosidase located at the apical membrane of enterocytes. This results in formation of QCT aglycone which enters the enterocyte by simple diffusion [52].

Studies have shown that glucose-linked QCT derivatives are transported by another mode of transport from the small intestinal lumen to the enterocyte cytosol, by a sodium-dependent glucose cotransporter-1 (SGLT-1) [53]. When glucose-linked QCT derivatives enter into the enterocyte, their molecules are degraded to QCT aglycone and glucose by cytolosic β-glucosidase. QCT oligosaccharides and polysaccharides as well as monosaccharide derivatives, which have not been absorbed or processed yet are deglycosylated in more distal intestinal parts—the large intestine (colon) by microbiota-derived β-glucosidase back to QCT aglycone [54], which is subsequently absorbed or degraded to phenolic acids [55]. Enterobacteria responsible for QCT metabolization in the colon belong to different strains, for instance, *Clostridium orbiscindens* [56]. As followed, hydrolysis of QCT glycosides to QCT aglycone is essential for their efficient absorption, either in enterocytes or by enterobacteria. QCT aglycone from both small and large intestine in enterocytes/colonocytes. Moreover, QCT aglycone in enterocytes presents a subject to enzymes of phase II metabolism catalyzing conjugation reactions (glucuronidation and/or sulfate conjugation) by UGT (UDP-glucuronosyltransferase) [57], SULT (sulfotransferase) [58] and modification reactions (O-methylation) by COMT (catechol-O-methyltransferase) [59], mostly before entering the portal vein via ATP-binding cassette (ABC) transporters [60]. This was investigated by studies where the presence of residues of unmetabolized QCT algycone was confirmed, but mostly QCT methylated and/or unmethylated QCT metabolites (glucuronides and sulphates) were found in human plasma [61], lymph [62] and in portal vein [63]. The most commonly present methylated phase II QCT metabolites include isorhamnetin and tamarixetin [64] or unmethylated

QCT 3-O-β-D-glucuronide [65]. QCT metabolites, which enter the liver by passive diffusion or by organic anion transporters (OATs), are extensively exposed to further reactions catalyzed by phase II metabolism enzymes. Subsequently, they are excreted into the bloodstream for further action in the body or directed to the bile [5,63].

The elimination phase III of metabolism begins in liver by excretion of QCT metabolites to bile continuing to duodenum and also in the small intestine itself, where the metabolites are transported back to the intestinal lumen by MRP-2 protein (multidrug resistance-associated protein 2) [66]. Thus, in large intestine, in addition to deglycosylation by microbiota-derived β-glucosidase [67], there occurs a final degradation of unabsorbed QCT derivatives as well as QCT metabolites, which were transported back to intestine via bile. Degradation involves deconjugation and deglycosylation of QCT metabolites to QCT aglycone with the aim of fission of the A and B-rings of the QCT backbone, leading to the formation of low molecular weight phenolic acids. This is also confirmed by the presence of microbiota-derived β-glucuronidase in large intestine microflora, which, after deglucuronidation, provides QCT aglycone for further degradation [55]. The most common degradation products, such as 3,4-hydroxyphenylacetic acid, hippuric acid but also QCT aglycone itself, are either re-absorbed into the bloodstream circulation or excreted by feces from the body [68]. An overall picture of QCT metabolization is outlined in Figure 2.

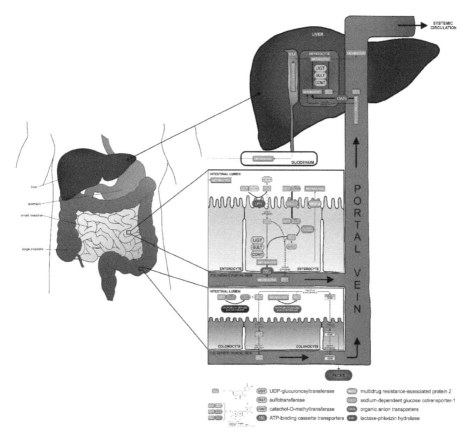

Figure 2. Overview of QCT metabolization in the body. QCT and its monosaccharide* derivatives (including QCT glucoside**) are metabolized in small intestine. After a chain of reactions catalyzed by enzymes UGT, SULT or COMT causing glucoronidation, sulfation or methylation, respectively, QCT metabolites are either transported by ABC transporters to the portal vein and then to liver or re-uptake and transport back to the intestinal lumen by MRP-2, continuing to the large intestine. QCT aglycone as a possible product of QCT glycosides and QCT glucosides is transferred by passive diffusion through enterocytes to hepatic portal vein and consequently to the liver. In the large intestine, mainly QCT oligosaccharides and polysaccharides (QCT glycosides***) are enzymatically deglycosylated to QCT aglycone, which is transported from intestinal lumen to portal vein by passive diffusion through colonocytes. Degradation of QCT metabolites, which were transported from the small intestine to the large intestine, occurs in the large intestinal lumen, where they are degraded to phenolic acids. In the liver, further metabolization of thus far created QCT metabolites or QCT aglycone occurs by their conjugation (by UGT or SULT) or modification (by COMT). Finally, QCT metabolites are transported from liver to either systemic circulation or back to duodenum (small intestine) via bile, possibly heading to large intestinal final degradation. For more details, see Chapter 2.2.

3. QCT and its Derivatives as Cardioprotective Agents

One of the major therapeutic goals of modern cardiology is to design strategies aimed at saving myocardium from the negative effects of ischemia-reperfusion (I/R) injury associated with such pathological states as ischemic heart disease and acute myocardial infarction, the major types of cardiovascular disease (CVD) and top causes of death worldwide. QCT, as well as several other natural polyphenols, has been documented to exert beneficial effects in CVD, including cardiac I/R injury.

The cardioprotective activity of QCT and its derivatives in patients suffering from ischemic heart disease (IHD) is enforced, and was repeatedly confirmed in experimental studies performed in both cellular and animal models of cardiac I/R injury. A potential mechanism of QCT action in the heart has also been extensively studied. In addition, there is an urgent need to develop therapeutic strategies against non-ischemic cardiac pathologies, such as various cardiomyopathies of different origin. In line with this need, cardioprotective potential of QCT has also been explored in experimental models of non-ischemic cardiac diseases. In this section cardioprotective effects of QCT documented in various experimental models of cardiac damage are reviewed.

3.1. In Vitro and Ex Vivo Cardioprotection Afforded by QCT and QCT-Rich Plants

Cardioprotective effects of QCT have been documented in numerous models of in vitro cardiomyocyte injury. In the model of 4-hydroxynonenal-induced toxicity in H9c2 cardiac-derived cell line (4-hydroxy-2-nonenal is a secondary product of lipoperoxidation, and can form protein adducts and modifies cell signaling), QCT pretreatment (0.1–10 μM for 24 h) decreased ROS production, p-SAPK/JNK levels, p-Hsp27 levels, caspase-3 expression and improved cell viability, thus ameliorating in vitro oxidative damage to rat cardiomyocytes [69]. A study of Chen et al. [70] demonstrated that 4-h pretreatment with QCT in different concentrations (50–200 μM) reduced cardiotoxicity in cancer chemotherapy-induced cell damage in H9c2 cells during 24 h exposure to 0.45 μM doxorubicin. Moreover, application of its methanol extract alligator weed (*Alternanthera philoxeroides*), a plant rich in QCT (10–160 mg/mL, for 24) prevented cardiomyocyte apoptosis induced by doxorubicin in H9c2 cells [71]. Naturally occurring QCT is also present in *Syzygium cumini* seeds. One-day lasting incubation of H9c2 cells with extract from this plant (1–500 μg) protected cells against tertiary butyl hydrogen peroxide (TBHP)-induced oxidative stress [72]. QCT pretreatment (10–16 μM) proved its cardioprotective effects in H9c2 cells subjected to hypoxia/reoxygenation (H/R) (4 h/6 h) by inhibition of JNK (c-Jun N-terminal Kinase) and p38 mitogen-activated protein kinase signaling pathways and modulated the expression of Bcl-2 (B-cell lymphoma 2) and Bax (Bcl-2-associated X) proteins [73]. Pretreatment (24, 48 and 72 h) of neonatal rat primary cardiomyocytes with QCT (10–80 μM) before anoxia/reoxygenation (4 h/2 h) improved cell survival rate, decreased ROS generation, avoided collapse of the mitochondria membrane potential, inhibited the opening of mitochondrial permeability transition pores (mPTP) and alleviated subsequent apoptosis in injury. The authors of this study also hypothesized that cardioprotective effects of QCT may be mediated via enhancing protein expression of PKCε and ameliorating the activity of downstream mediators of its pathway [74]. Furthermore, addition of QCT (20 μM) to culture medium increased the cell viability of H9c2 cells with LPS induced inflammation [75].

It is known that QCT, like other antioxidants, is very rapidly metabolized in the organism, thus, the application form of QCT might play an important role in its effects. It was documented that 24-h pretreatment with encapsulated QCT into poly(lactic-co-glycolic) acid (PLGA) nanoparticles had a cardioprotective effect in H9c2 cells exposed to H/R injury (3 h/1.5 h). Encapsulated PLGA-QCT (5 μM) protected cells more effectively than free QCT (5 μM), likely due to lower oxidized thiols, maintaining the mitochondrial oxygen consumption rate and membrane potential, which sustain superior ATP production that leads to the preservation of mitochondrial function and ATP synthesis [76]. Combined treatment with QCT and resveratrol encapsulated in Pluronic® F-127 micelles (mRQ) (RES:QCT in 1:1 molar ratio, capable of retaining 1.1 mg/mL of resveratrol and 1.42 mg/mL of QCT, respectively) showed new possible strategy to eliminate acute doxorubicin-induced cardiotoxicity in vitro in H9c2 cells via scavenging of ROS and decreasing caspase 3/7 activity [77].

In addition to cell culture models in cardiac-derived cells, in vitro effects of QCT have been examined in isolated heart models of I/R injury (ex vivo models). We have documented that acute administration of QCT (15 mmol/L infusion for 15 min before the onset of ischemia or during whole reperfusion, respectively) improved recovery of cardiac function after global I/R (25 min/2 h) in Langendorff-perfused rat hearts and reduced infarct size in these hearts [13]. Administration of QCT (1 mg/kg) into Krebs-Henseleit buffer during reperfusion period improved function of Langendorff-perfused rat hearts after I/R injury (30 min/30 min) through inhibition of the HMGB1 (High mobility group box-1) pathway [78].

3.2. In Vitro Cardioprotection Afforded by QCT Derivatives

In addition to QCT alone, QCT derivatives were documented to exert cardioprotection in different experimental settings simulating cardiac injury. Pretreatment of neonatal rat cardiomyocytes (NRCMs) with isorhamnetin (3′-O-methyl-QCT; 10–40 mM) 24 h before anoxia/reoxygenation (3 h/2 h) increased cell viability and expression of SIRT1, reduced the generation of ROS, inhibited opening of mPTPs, reduced the loss of $\Delta\psi$m and decreased the activation of caspase-3 and release of cytochrome c thus reducing apoptosis, and finally, reduced the the release of lactate dehydrogenase and creatine phosphokinase from cardiomyocytes [79]. 12-h pretreatment with dihydro-QCT (2.5–80 μM) protected H9c2cells against H/R injury (H-6 h/R-16 h) by inhibiting oxidative stress- and endoplasmic reticulum stress-induced apoptosis via activation of the PI3K/Akt pathway [80]. Another QCT derivate, ZYZ-772 (QCT-3-O-(6″-O-α-l-rhamnopyransoyl) -β-d-glucopyranoside-7-O-β-d-glucopyranoside; 1–50 μM for 2 h) protected H9c2 cells against $CoCl_2$-induced H/R (12 h/4 h) injury. It is suggested that ZYZ-772 protected cells by suppression of Nox4/MAPK/P53 axis in conditions of $CoCl_2$-induced hypoxia injury [81]. Hypoxia-induced apoptosis of NRCMs was attenuated by pretreatment with hyperoside (QCT-3-O-galactoside; 0.5–50 μM for 12, 24, 36 h) in an in vitro model of cardiac H/R (8 h/2 h) injury, likely through suppression of the Bnip3 expression [82]. Perfusion of isolated hearts with dihydro-QCT (5–20 μM) added into the Krebs–Henseleit solution for 20 min prior to I/R (45 min/50 min) protected hearts by inhibiting oxidative stress- and endoplasmic reticulum stress-induced apoptosis via the PI3K/Akt pathway [80]. It was documented that 24-h lasting supplementation with isoquercetin (isoquercitrin, isoQCT; 20–80 μg/mL) increased cell viability of H9c2 cells after I/R (6 h/12 h) injury by protection of mitochondrial function and prevention of cytochrome c release [83]. In the study of Daubney et al. [84], the effects of 24 h pretreatment of H9c2 cells with QCT and two of its major metabolites QCT-3-glucuronide and 3′-O-methyl-QCT prior to 2-h exposure to 600 μM H_2O_2 were monitored. As a result, QCT triggered cardioprotection against oxidative stress-induced cell death via attenuation of H_2O_2-induced activation of ERK1/2, PKB, p38 MAPK and JNK. On the other hand, inhibitors of these kinases did not modulate QCT-induced protection against H_2O_2-induced cell death. Interestingly, cardioprotection was observed with QCT and 3′-O-methyl-QCT, but not with QCT-3-glucuronide.

3.3. In Vivo Cardioprotection Afforded by QCT and QCT-Rich Plants

Cardioprotective potential of QCT has been widely documented in different in vivo animal models of cardiac injury. It was suggested that phytochemical QCT may play a key role in cardioprotection and help in remodeling of the heart during isoproterenol-induced cardiac ischemia and fibrosis [85]. Two weeks of QCT pretreatment (50 mg/kg) of rats with isoproterenol-induced myocardial infarction induced cardioprotective effects manifested by significantly attenuated oxidative stress, inflammation, as well as protected heart architecture. These effects of QCT were associated with downregulation of the expression of calpain [86]. QCT was shown beneficial also in Duchenne muscular dystrophy, a juvenile musculoskeletal genetic disease associated with progressive cardiac pathology. In an animal model of muscular dystrophy, long-term dietary QCT enrichment (0.2%) improved cardiac function in aged Mdx/Utrn$^{+/-}$ mice (lack of dystrophin and heterozygous knockout for utrophin; aged Mdx/Utrn$^{+/-}$ mice exhibit accelerated declines in cardiac health and dystrophic pathology) and increased mitochondrial protein content and dystrophin glycoprotein complex formation [87]. Treatment of Lewis rats with QCT (10 mg/kg) protected against progression of experimental autoimmune myocarditis by suppression of oxidative and endoplasmic reticulum stress via endothelin-1/MAPK signaling. In the study, myocardial dimensions and cardiac function were preserved significantly in the QCT-treated rats in comparison with the rats treated with vehicle [88]. QCT pretreatment (4 weeks in a dose 25 mg/kg, once-daily gavage) also significantly reduced cardiac mitochondrial H_2O_2 production, total content of Ca^{2+} in cardiac tissue and collagen volume fraction in a model of cardiac injury induced by chronic aldosterone/salt treatment in male Sprague-Dawley rats, which is typically accompanied with adverse structural remodeling of myocardium [89].

In addition to effects of QCT supplementation in pure form, 60-days treatment with *Phyllanthus amarus* (plant reach in QCT) showed protection of the heart from high fructose-diet induced damage. The *Phyllanthus amarus* treatment protected male Wistar rats from high fructose-diet-induced increase in stress markers and a decrease in non-enzymatic and enzymatic antioxidants in the heart and aorta [90]. An interesting form of QCT administration was used in study Cote et al. [77], where a combination of QCT with Resveratrol in Pluronic® F-127 micelles (mRQ) (RES:QCTin 1:1 molar ratio, capable of retaining 1.1 mg/mL of Resveratrol and 1.42 mg/mL of QCT, respectively) was prepared for application. In vivo treatment of mice with mRQ conferred full cardioprotection in doxorubicin-induced cardiotoxicity [77]. To elucidate molecular signaling pathways involved in QCT-induced cardioprotection male Wistar albino rats with sodium nitrite-induced hypoxia were used. Pretreatment of hypoxic rats with QCT (200 mg/kg, i.p.) was accompanied with down-regulation of mRNA expression of nuclear factor kappa-B (NF-κB), Bax, and flt-1 and suppressed DNA damage. Thus, QCT effectively declined the cardiotoxic effects of sodium nitrite and ameliorated cardiac injury in these rats [91].

It is well known that homeostasis of the endoplasmic reticulum and its correct function is disrupted in various types of cardiac disease. Interestingly, QCT is a substance capable to activate IRE1 (Inositol-requiring transmembrane kinase/endoribonuclease 1), an important transmembrane protein of endoplasmic reticulum [92,93], thus, potentially influencing the function of endoplasmic reticulum under stress conditions. It was documented that the p21-activated kinase 2 (Pak2)-cardiac deleted mice (Pak2-CKO) exhibited impaired function of endoplasmic reticulum, dysfunction of the heart and serious cell death due to tunicamycin treatment-induced stress or pressure overload. Administration of QCT (10 mg/kg/day, daily gavage) for 2 weeks alleviated malfunction of endoplasmic reticulum in Pak2-CKO hearts the second day after transverse aortic constriction [94].

In addition to the above mentioned types of cardiac injury, cardioprotective effects of QCT have been widely documented in several in vivo models of myocardial ischemic injury. In an in vivo rat model of cardiac I/R injury (30 min/4 h), orally given QCT (250 mg/kg for 10 days) decreased oxidative stress, repressed inflammatory cascade, inhibited apoptosis and activated the PI3K/Akt pathway (involved in the anti-apoptotic effect) in the heart tissue [16]. With the same dose, QCT administration for 10 days suppressed the NF-κB pathway via up-regulating PPARγ expression in mice exposed to simulated I/R (30 min/24 h) [95]. Treatment of rats with QCT (1 mg/kg/day) induced a significant reduction of infarct size and improved hemodynamic abnormalities in hearts subjected to 30 min ischemia by left coronary artery occlusion followed by 12 h reperfusion. QCT treatment also decreased expression of both tumor necrosis factor-alpha (TNF-α) and interleukin-10 (IL-10) and lowered serum levels of inflammatory cytokines, suggesting anti-inflammatory effects of QCT in preventing cardiac I/R injury [96]. One-week treatment of female Sprague Dawley rats with QCT (25–100 mg/kg, gavage, daily) protected rats against coronary artery ligature-induced I/R (30 min/2 h) injury via an increased SIRT1/PGC-1a pathway and Bcl-2/Bax ratio [97].

In our studies, we have also documented several anti-ischemic effects of chronic in vivo QCT administration. 4-weeks lasting in vivo oral treatment with QCT (20 mg/kg/day) improved post-ischemic (25 min/40 min) recovery of heart function of isolated rat hearts from juvenile but not from adult Wistar rats [13]. We have also shown that prolonged in vivo QCT treatment (20 mg/kg/day for 6 weeks) significantly improved post-ischemic recovery of heart function of isolated hearts from both healthy and doxorubicin-treated rats [14]. Importantly, QCT not only protected hearts against I/R injury, but also reversed doxorubicin-induced detrimental changes in the heart tissue including ultrastructural changes, matrix metalloproteinase-2 activation and apoptosis induction [14].

3.4. In Vivo Cardioprotection Afforded by QCT Derivatives

Regarding in vivo effects of QCT derivatives in cardiac injury, it was documented that two weeks lasting treatment with isoQCT (80 mg/kg/day by gavage) protected male Sprague-Dawley rat hearts against acute myocardial infarction *in vivo*. IsoQCT protected myocardium through anti-inflammatory and anti-apoptotic effects, and via regulation of the TLR4-NF-κB signaling pathway [98]. Pretreatment of male Wistar rats with another QCT derivative troxerutin ((3′,4′,7-Tris[O-(2-hydroxyethyl)]rutin; 150 mg/kg for one month) protected myocardium against I/R injury (30 min/45 min) maintained by ligation of the left anterior descending artery. Rats treated with troxerutin exhibited significantly reduced myocardial infarct size, improved cardiac function likely via the modulated PI3K/Akt pathway [99]. Concordantly, treatment of male Wistar rats with troxerutin (150 mg/kg daily for one month) protected isolated hearts against I/R (30 min/45 min) injury via the inhibition of myocardial inflammatory cytokines TNF-α and IL-1β and inhibited activation of leukocyte-endothelial cell interaction molecule (ICAM-1) after I/R insult [100]. Plants such as stonebreaker (*Phyllanthus amarus*) and bitter gourd (*Momordica charantia*) represent good sources of antioxidants and QCT, as well as its derivatives quercitrin, isoquercitrin and rutin. Supplementation of extracts from these plants (each 200 and 400 mg/kg for 2 weeks by gavage) protected male Wistar albino rats against doxorubicin-induced cardiotoxicity by reversing redox imbalance and by modulating biomolecules associated with worsened cardiac function altered by doxorubicin, such as angiotensin-converting enzyme, arginase, acetylcholinesterase and adenosine deaminase [101].

Proposed cardioprotective effects of QCT and its derivatives documented in experimental studies are summarized in the Table 2.

Table 2. Summary of potential cardioprotective effects of QCT and its derivatives.

Derivative	Dose	Exp. Model	Type of Injury	Effect	Mechanism	Reference
Quercetin (QCT)	1–250 mg/kg	Rodents (mice/rats)	I/R	↓oxidative stress ↓inflammation ↓infarct size ↑heart function	↓ROS, ↓HMGB1, ↓NF-kB, ↓TNF-α, ↓apoptosis ↑PI3K/Akt, ↑SIRT1/PGC-1α	[14,16,78,91, 95–97,102]
	20 mg/kg	Rats	Isoproterenol-induced MI	↓oxidative stress ↓inflammation	↓ROS, ↓calpain	[86]
	0.2% in food	Mdx/Utrn$^{+/-}$ mice	Duchenne muscular dystrophy	↑mitochondrial function	↓NF-kB, ↓TGF-β1, ↓F4/80	[87]
	10 mg/kg	Rats	Autoimmune myocarditis	↓oxidative stress	↓ROS, ↓ER stress, ↑endothelin-1/MAPK	[88]
	10–50 mg/kg	Rats	Diabetic cardiomyopathy	↓oxidative stress ↓cardiac injury ↓inflammation ↓apoptosis	↓troponin C, ↓CK-MB, ↓LDH, ↓ROS ↓ Bax, ↓caspases-3,-9	[103]
	10–80 µM	Cell cultures (H9c2, NRCM)	I/R	↑cell viability ↓oxidative stress ↑mitochondrial function	↓ROS, ↓JNK, ↓p38, ↓MAPK, ↑Bcl-2/Bax, ↑PKCε	[73,74]
	0.1–10 µM	H9c2	4-hydroxynonenal – induced toxicity	↓oxidative stress ↑cell viability	↓ROS, ↓p-SAPK/JNK, ↓p-HSP27, ↓caspase 3	[69]
	500–200 µM	H9c2	Doxorubicin – induced toxicity	↑cell viability ↓ inflammation	↑Src kinase activity, ↓ROS, ↓STAT3	[70]
	100µM	H9c2	H$_2$O$_2$ – induced toxicity	↓oxidative stress ↑cell viability	↓ROS, ↓P38, ↓MAPK, ↓JNK	[84]
Troxerutin	150 mg/kg	Rats	I/R	↓infarct size ↑cardiac function ↓arrhythmias ↓inflammation	↑PI3K/Akt, ↓TNF-α, ↓IL-1b, ↓ICAM-1	[90,100,104]
Hyperoside	0.5–50 µM	NRCMs	I/R	↑cell viability	↓Bnip3	[82]
IsoQCT	20–80 µM/ml	H9c2	I/R	↑cell viability ↓cell apoptosis mitochondrial protection	↓ROS generation ↓cytochrome c release	[83]
	80 mg/kg	Rats	AMI	↓inflammation ↓apoptosis	↓TLR4-NF-kB	[98]

Table 2. *Cont.*

Derivative	Dose	Exp. Model	Type of Injury	Effect	Mechanism	Reference
Isorhamnetin	10–40μM	NRCMs	I/R	↓oxidative stress mitochondrial protection	↓ mPTP opening, ↓caspase-3 activity, ↓cytochrome c release, ↓ROS	[79]
DihydroQCT	2,5–80 μM	H9c2	I/R	↓oxidative stress ↓apoptosis	↓ROS, ↓ER stress, ↑PI3K/Akt	[80]
	5–20 μM in K-H	Rats	I/R	↓oxidative stress ↓ apoptosis	↓ROS, ↓ER stress, ↑PI3K/Akt	[80]
ZYZ-772	1–50 μM	H9c2	CoCl$_2$ – induced H/R	↑cell viability ↓oxidative stress ↓ apoptosis	↓ROS, ↓Nox4/MAPK/p53	[81]

Abbreviations: I/R—ischemia/reperfusion; H/R—hypoxia/reoxygenation, MI—myocardial infarction; AMI—acute myocardial infarction; NRCM—neonatal rat cardiac myocytes; K-H—Krebs-Henseleit buffer, ROS—reactive oxygen species, ER – endoplasmic reticulum, LDH—lactate dehydrogenase, JNK—c-Jun-N-terminal kinase, PI3K—phosphoinositide 3-kinase, Akt—protein kinase B, Bcl-2 – B-cell lymphoma 2; Bax—Bcl-2-associated X protein, MAPK—mitogen-activated protein kinase, ICAM-1—intercellular adhesion molecule 1, TLR4—toll-like receptor 4, mPTP—mitochondrial permeability transition pore, TNF-α—tumor necrosis factor α, Bnip3—Bcl-2 nineteen-kD interacting protein 3, Nox4—NADPH oxidase 4, SIRT1—Silent information regulator 1, PGC-1α—peroxisome proliferator initiated receptor gamma and coactivator 1 alpha.

4. Role of Comorbidities in Cardioprotection by QCT and its Derivatives

In the previous parts of this review, QCT was tested for its cardioprotective effects more or less exclusively in healthy animals or standard cell cultures. However, the presence of different comorbidities in individuals suffering from heart disease might influence the efficacy or even reverse effects of treatments aimed to prevent cardiac injury, including cardioprotective effects of QCT. Moreover, treatment may influence comorbidity itself and thus evoke different mechanisms and effects than those afforded in the absence of comorbidities. In line with this view, we provide a short overview of cardiac effects of QCT in presence of comorbidities documented thus far. In addition, potential influence of QCT on the progression of comorbidity itself, e.g., diabetes, will be discussed as well. One of the major complications of *Diabetes mellitus* is diabetic cardiomyopathy [105]. Bioactive compounds such as QCT have been shown to exert beneficial effects in ameliorating the pathogenesis of diabetic cardiomyopathy. The 28 days lasting administration of QCT (10–50 mg/kg) to Sprague Dawley male rats with streptozotocin (STZ)-induced diabetes caused significant decrease of cardiac injury markers levels, particularly troponin-C, creatine kinase-isoenzyme (CK-MB) and lactate dehydrogenase (LDH). In addition, ameliorated histopathological changes, oxidative stress, inflammation and apoptosis levels were observed [103]. In the study of Soman et al. [106], it was found that pure QCT (50 mg/kg) as well as extract from *Psidium guajava* (a plant highly enriched with QCT) showed beneficial effects on the diabetic heart. After the induction of diabetes by STZ (55 mg/kg) in female Sprague Dawley rats, QCT or *Psidium guajava* extract, respectively, was administered for 60 days. Both treatments were accompanied with decreased levels of AGEs (advanced glycation end products) in the diabetic heart suggesting beneficial cardiac effects of QCT in diabetic subjects [106]. Moreover, cardioprotective effects of QCT and rutin (QCT derivative) were documented in I/R-induced myocardial infarction in both normal and diabetic rats. Albino Wistar rats with STZ-induced diabetes (45 mg/kg) were treated with QCT or rutin (5–10 mg/kg, i.p.) 10 min before the onset of reperfusion. After I/R (30 min/4 h) induced by coronary artery occlusion it was documented that the heart of rats treated with QCT or rutin, respectively, exhibited significantly lower infarct sizes in both normal and diabetic animals in a similar approach [102]. Finally, hearts from STZ-diabetic Male Wistar rats treated with troxerutin (150 mg/kg, daily gavage) for 4 weeks were exposed to I/R injury on Langendorff aparatus (30 min/60 min). Troxerutin pretreatment improved myocardial function after I/R injury in both healthy and diabetic rat hearts likely through anti-arrhythmic and anti-inflammatory effects [104].

Hypercholesterolemia is another major risk factor for the development of myocardial damage. It is suggested that QCT could be effective modulator of plasma cholesterol and may have protective effect in cardiac remodeling in hypercholesterolemia. In the study of Ulasova et al. [107], 6 weeks lasting oral administration of QCT (0.1µmol/kg) markedly reduced total cholesterol and very low density lipoprotein (VLDL) levels in plasma of Apo[-/-] hypercholesterolemic mice, a model with typically developed left ventricular hypertrophy. After QCT treatment, the hypertrophy was reduced followed by deceased left ventricle posterior wall thickness and left ventricle mass [107]. *Crataegus pinnatifida* is fruit rich in polyphenols, among others also rutin and isoquercitrin. It was documented that high-fat diet fed atherosclerotic rats supplemented with extract from the *Crataegus pinnatifida* (72 and 288 mg/kg) via the intragastric route for 4 weeks had lower plasma levels of lipids (total cholesterol, total triglycerides, LDL-cholesterol, HDL-cholesterol), decreased inflammatory response and inhibited pathological changes in the arteries of atherosclerotic rats suggesting potential of the *Crataegus pinnatifida* to reduce the development of cardiovascular diseases [108]. On the other hand, our recent study [109] documented different effects of QCT on vasculature and the heart in *Diabetes mellitus* type 2. In the study, 6-month and 1-year-old male Zucker diabetic fatty rats (ZDF) were daily treated with QCT (20 mg/kg) for 6 weeks. QCT exerted age-dependent beneficial effects on vascular function and blood pressure but was inefficient in preventing myocardial I/R (30 min/2 h) injury in ZDF rats [109].

5. Cardiovascular Effects of QCT in Human Studies and Clinical Trials

Up to now (February 19, 2020), 70 QCT clinical trials have been registered at ClinicalTrials.gov, a database of privately and publicly funded clinical studies conducted worldwide (available online: https://clinicaltrials.gov/ct2/results?term=quercetin). However, only few of them were aimed to reveal the cardiovascular effects of QCT; moreover, not all of them examined effects of QCT alone; some effects of different QCT-containing mixtures have been used as well.

Despite reports that increased risk of coronary heart disease (CHD) in some populations is associated with very low dietary supply of flavonoids (among others also QCT) [110], only a very limited number of human studies were focused directly on cardiac effects of QCT. Among them, it was documented that QCT possesses anti-ischemic and anti-arrhythmic effects, and exerts a regulating influence on vegetative homeostasis in patients with a chronic form of IHD with metabolic syndrome [111]. In patients with stable coronary heart disease (CHD), QCT (120 mg/day for 2 months, p.o.) significantly improved the left ventricular (LV) systolic function in terms of ejection fraction and improved LV diastolic function in terms of the ratio of the phases of the transmitral flow. Moreover, 24-h Holter electrocardiographic (ECG) monitoring showed decreased total time and number of episodes of ST segment depression in QCT-treated patients, altogether suggesting cardioprotective properties of QCT in CHD [112].

In addition to their cardiac effects, clinical studies focused on vascular effects of QCT and its derivatives have been performed. It was documented that 2-week QCT supplementation (500 mg/day) in 72 adult women with *Diabetes mellitus* type 2 significantly lowered systolic blood pressure; however, this had no effect on other cardiovascular risk factors and inflammatory biomarkers [113]. On the other hand, 4-week treatment with encapsulated QCT-3-glucoside (160 mg/day) in 37 healthy participants of both genders resulted in no changes in flow-mediated arterial dilation, insulin resistance or other cardiovascular risk factors [114]. A recent meta-analysis of clinical data documented that QCT supplementation (possibly limited to, or greater with dosages of >500 mg/day) significantly reduced blood pressure [115]. Finally, one-year supplementation with QCT in patients with gout, a disease associated with increased risk of cardiovascular diseases including heart failure, also suffered from essential hypertension treated with standard therapy (antihypertensive and urate-lowering regimens) improved left ventricular diastolic function, purine metabolism, renal function and normalized blood pressure [116].

6. Controversial Findings and Potential Cardiotoxic Effects of QCT and its Derivatives

As mentioned already, QCT exerts many biological beneficial effects including those in the cardiovascular system. However, controversial data and even cardiotoxic effects of QCT have been documented as well, and should be mentioned in this review to create an overall picture of cardiac effects of QCT.

It is known that the beneficial effects of certain cardioprotective interventions, e.g., acute as well as late phase of cardioprotection induced by ischemic preconditioning, are eliminated in hyperlipidemic hearts. In line with this, the effects of QCT and glycogen synthase kinase-3β (GSK-3β) inhibitors were tested in isolated hearts from hyperlipidemic rats (induced by 6-week lasting high-fat diet) subjected to I/R injury (30 min/2 h). GSK-3β inhibitors SB216763 (SB) and indirubin-3-monoxime (IND) were administered 24 h before, and QCT (4 mg/kg, i.p.) was given 25 h before the isolation of hearts. GSK-3β inhibitors were found to exert cardioprotective effects in I/R injury, and these effects were attenuated by QCT, manifested by increased myocardial infarct size and release of lactate dehydrogenase and creatine kinase-MB. In this study, QCT was uncommonly used as an inhibitor of HSP72 (heat shock protein 72), not as a cardioprotective compound [117]. Yao et al. [118] reported that pretreatment of rats with lipopolysaccharide (LPS) increased myocardial functional recovery in hearts exposed to I/R (30 min/3 h) induced by coronary artery occlusion, partly through inhibition of NF-κB via increase of HSP70. Administration of QCT (100 mg/kg, i.p.) two hours before I/R injury decreased cardioprotection induced by LPS. In this study, QCT was used in the role of HSP70 inhibitor and the authors hypothesized that inhibition of HSP70 could attenuate the effect of LPS pretreatment [118]. However, this study might be criticized due to the use of LPS for cardioprotection, since normally, inflammation (including LPS-induced) causes negative consequences in the heart, e.g., may induce myocarditis.

Potential cardioprotective vs. cardiotoxic effects of QCT were tested also in vitro in cultured cardiomyocytes. In the study of Daubney et al. [84] increased concentrations of QCT (1–100 μM) for 24, 48 and 72 h were applied to differentiated H9c2 cardiomyocytes. MTT viability assay and LDH release testing showed that QCT induced cardiotoxic effects, which were the most evident after 48 h treatment in 30 and 100 μM concentration of QCT. After 72 h treatment, toxic effect of QCT was visible even at 10 μM concentration of QCT. Thus, in line with one of basic principles of toxicology "The dose makes the poison" ("*Sola dosis facit venenum*" by Paracelsus, 1538), experimental studies revealing cardiac effects of QCT indicated that prolonged exposure to high doses of flavonoids may lead to detrimental effects on cardiac cells, likely due to their possible pro-oxidant effects in dependence on the actual conditions [5,119].

7. Conclusions and Future Perspectives

Application of QCT and its derivatives in different cell culture and animal models of cardiac injury and their potential beneficial effects in preventing cardiac dysfunction due to cardiac I/R injury as well as other cardiac pathologies has been widely documented (Figure 3). Thus, QCT and its derivatives may represent promising cardioprotective substances for prevention/treatment for wide range of cardiac disease. On the other hand, metabolic comorbidities, at least diabetes mellitus type 2, might act as confounding factors for cardioprotection by QCT. In addition, non-metabolic factors such as ageing might also act as a confounding factor for cardioprotective effects of QCT. Thus, the age of the treated subject and presence of lifestyle-related comorbidities should be taken into consideration in potential use of QCT for prevention and/or treatment of cardiovascular disease in humans.

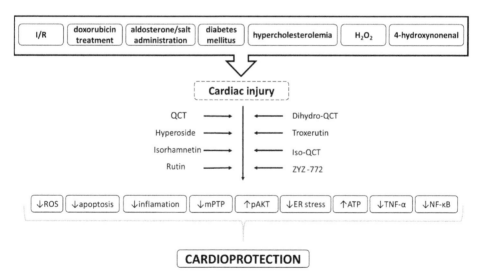

Figure 3. Scheme of potential cardioprotective effects of QCT and its derivatives in heart injury outlining the proposed molecular mechanisms involved in their action.

Despite promising experimental results pointing to potential beneficial cardiovascular effects of QCT, the results from human studies are still inconclusive due to very small number of clinical trials focused on cardiac effects of QCT and its derivatives. Thus, more studies with a stronger design and

Int. J. Mol. Sci. **2020**, 21, 1585

larger number of enrolled patients for testing different concentrations of QCT are needed to reveal real therapeutic potential of QCT in CVD. Finally, potential doubts based on reported negative effects of QCT should be considered in QCT application; especially proper dosage and application form must represent the golden rule of all QCT-based approaches aimed to treat CVD in humans.

Author Contributions: All authors wrote the draft of the manuscript and prepared the figures. M.B. supervised the writing project of the manuscript and finalized the manuscript. Funding for the project was acquired by M.B. All authors have read and agreed to the published version of the manuscript.

Funding: The infrastructure support for this project was provided by a grant from the Scientific Grant Agency of the Ministry of Education, Science, Research and Sport of the Slovak Republic and the Slovak Academy of Sciences VEGA no. 2/0104/20.

Acknowledgments: The authors thank Juraj Forró for his valuable help with graphical designing the Figures and Tables.

Conflicts of Interest: The authors declare no conflict of interest. The funders had no role in the design of the study; in the collection, analyses, or interpretation of data; in the writing of the manuscript, or in the decision to publish the results.

References

1. Lovegrove, J.A.; Stainer, A.; Hobbs, D.A. Role of flavonoids and nitrates in cardiovascular health. *Proc. Nutr. Soc.* **2017**, 76, 83–95. [CrossRef]
2. Hussain, T.; Tan, B.; Murtaza, G.; Liu, G.; Rahu, N.; Saleem Kalhoro, M.; Hussain Kalhoro, D.; Adebowale, T.O.; Usman Mazhar, M.; ur Rehman, Z.; et al. Flavonoids and type 2 diabetes: Evidence of efficacy in clinical and animal studies and delivery strategies to enhance their therapeutic efficacy. *Pharmacol. Res.* **2020**, 152, 104629. [CrossRef] [PubMed]
3. Maaliki, D.; Shaito, A.A.; Pintus, G.; El-Yazbi, A.; Eid, A.H. Flavonoids in hypertension: A brief review of the underlying mechanisms. *Curr. Opin. Pharmacol.* **2019**, 45, 57–65. [CrossRef]
4. Khan, H.; Ullah, H.; Martorell, M.; Valdes, S.E.; Belwal, T.; Tejada, S.; Sureda, A.; Kamal, M.A. Flavonoids nanoparticles in cancer: Treatment, prevention and clinical prospects. *Semin. Cancer Biol.* **2019**, 0–1. [CrossRef] [PubMed]
5. D'Andrea, G. Quercetin: A flavonol with multifaceted therapeutic applications? *Fitoterapia* **2015**, 106, 256–271. [CrossRef] [PubMed]
6. Miles, S.L.; McFarland, M.; Niles, R.M. Molecular and physiological actions of quercetin: Need for clinical trials to assess its benefits in human disease. *Nutr. Rev.* **2014**, 72, 720–734. [CrossRef] [PubMed]
7. Hashemzaei, M.; Far, A.D.; Yari, A.; Heravi, R.E.; Tabrizian, K.; Taghdisi, S.M.; Sadegh, S.E.; Tsarouhas, K.; Kouretas, D.; Tzanakakis, G.; et al. Anticancer and apoptosis-inducing effects of quercetin in vitro and in vivo. *Oncol. Rep.* **2017**, 38, 819–828. [CrossRef] [PubMed]
8. Yang, H.; Song, Y.; Liang, Y.; Li, R. Quercetin Treatment Improves Renal Function and Protects the Kidney in a Rat Model of Adenine-Induced Chronic Kidney Disease. *Med. Sci. Monit.* **2018**, 24, 4760–4766. [CrossRef]
9. Brüll, V.; Burak, C.; Stoffel-Wagner, B.; Wolffram, S.; Nickenig, G.; Müller, C.; Langguth, P.; Alteheld, B.; Fimmers, R.; Naaf, S.; et al. Effects of a quercetin-rich onion skin extract on 24 h ambulatory blood pressure and endothelial function in overweight-to-obese patients with (pre-)hypertension: A randomised double-blinded placebo-controlled cross-over trial. *Br. J. Nutr.* **2015**, 114, 1263–1277. [CrossRef]
10. Calabró, V.; Litterio, M.C.; Fraga, C.G.; Galleano, M.; Piotrkowski, B. Effects of quercetin on heart nitric oxide metabolism in l-NAME treated rats. *Arch. Biochem. Biophys.* **2018**, 647, 47–53. [CrossRef]
11. Kim, S.G.; Kim, J.R.; Choi, H.C. Quercetin-induced AMP-activated protein kinase activation attenuates vasoconstriction through LKB1-AMPK signaling pathway. *J. Med. Food* **2018**, 21, 146–153. [CrossRef] [PubMed]
12. Pereira, S.C.; Parente, J.M.; Belo, V.A.; Mendes, A.S.; Gonzaga, N.A.; do Vale, G.T.; Ceron, C.S.; Tanus-Santos, J.E.; Tirapelli, C.R.; Castro, M.M. Quercetin decreases the activity of matrix metalloproteinase-2 and ameliorates vascular remodeling in renovascular hypertension. *Atherosclerosis* **2018**, 270, 146–153. [CrossRef] [PubMed]

13. Barteková, M.; Čarnická, S.; Pancza, D.; Ondrejčáková, M.; Breier, A.; Ravingerová, T. Acute treatment with polyphenol quercetin improves postischemic recovery of isolated perfused rat hearts after global ischemia. *Can. J. Physiol. Pharmacol.* **2010**, *88*, 465–471. [CrossRef] [PubMed]

14. Barteková, M.; Šimončíková, P.; Fogarassyová, M.; Ivanová, M.; Okruhlicová, Ľ.; Tribulová, N.; Dovinová, I.; Barančík, M. Quercetin Improves Postischemic Recovery of Heart Function in Doxorubicin-Treated Rats and Prevents Doxorubicin-Induced Matrix Metalloproteinase-2 Activation and Apoptosis Induction. *Int. J. Mol. Sci.* **2015**, *16*, 8168–8185. [CrossRef] [PubMed]

15. Wang, Y.; Zhang, Z.Z.; Wu, Y.; Ke, J.J.; He, X.H.; Wang, Y.L. Quercetin postconditioning attenuates myocardial ischemia/reperfusion injury in rats through the PI3K/Akt pathway. *Braz. J. Med. Biol. Res.* **2013**, *46*, 861–867. [CrossRef] [PubMed]

16. Liu, H.; Guo, X.; Chu, Y.; Lu, S. Heart protective effects and mechanism of quercetin preconditioning on anti-myocardial ischemia reperfusion (IR) injuries in rats. *Gene* **2014**, *545*, 149–155. [CrossRef]

17. Castillo, R.L.; Herrera, E.A.; Gonzalez-Candia, A.; Reyes-Farias, M.; de la Jara, N.; Peña, J.P.; Carrasco-Pozo, C. Quercetin Prevents Diastolic Dysfunction Induced by a High-Cholesterol Diet: Role of Oxidative Stress and Bioenergetics in Hyperglycemic Rats. *Oxid. Med. Cell. Longev.* **2018**, *2018*, 1–14. [CrossRef]

18. Li, Y.; Yao, J.; Han, C.; Yang, J.; Chaudhry, M.T.; Wang, S.; Liu, H.; Yin, Y. Quercetin, Inflammation and Immunity. *Nutrients* **2016**, *8*, 167. [CrossRef]

19. Anand David, A.; Arulmoli, R.; Parasuraman, S. Overviews of biological importance of quercetin: A bioactive flavonoid. *Pharmacogn. Rev.* **2016**, *10*, 84.

20. Kaşıkcı, M.; Bağdatlıoğlu, N. Bioavailability of Quercetin. *Curr. Res. Nutr. Food Sci. J.* **2016**, *4*, 146–151. [CrossRef]

21. Gao, L.; Liu, G.; Wang, X.; Liu, F.; Xu, Y.; Ma, J. Preparation of a chemically stable quercetin formulation using nanosuspension technology. *Int. J. Pharm.* **2011**, *404*, 231–237. [CrossRef] [PubMed]

22. Konrad, M.; Nieman, D.C. *Evaluation of Quercetin as a Countermeasure to Exercise-Induced Physiological Stress*; Lamprecht, M., Ed.; CRC Press/Taylor & Francis: Abingdon, UK, 2015; ISBN 9781466567573.

23. Cai, X.; Fang, Z.; Dou, J.; Yu, A.; Zhai, G. Bioavailability of Quercetin: Problems and Promises. *Curr. Med. Chem.* **2013**, *20*, 2572–2582. [CrossRef] [PubMed]

24. Kumar, S.; Pandey, A.K. Chemistry and Biological Activities of Flavonoids: An Overview. *Sci. World J.* **2013**, *2013*, 1–16. [CrossRef] [PubMed]

25. Materska, M. Quercetin and its derivatives: Chemical structure and bioactivity—A review. *Pol. J. FOOD Nutr. Sci.* **2008**, *58*, 407–413.

26. Makino, T.; Shimizu, R.; Kanemaru, M.; Suzuki, Y.; Moriwaki, M.; Mizukami, H. Enzymatically Modified Isoquercitrin, α-Oligoglucosyl Quercetin 3-O-Glucoside, Is Absorbed More Easily than Other Quercetin Glycosides or Aglycone after Oral Administration in Rats. *Biol. Pharm. Bull.* **2009**, *32*, 2034–2040. [CrossRef]

27. Yang, B.; Liu, H.; Yang, J.; Gupta, V.K.; Jiang, Y. New insights on bioactivities and biosynthesis of flavonoid glycosides. *Trends Food Sci. Technol.* **2018**, *79*, 116–124. [CrossRef]

28. Ferreres, F.; Figueiredo, R.; Bettencourt, S.; Carqueijeiro, I.; Oliveira, J.; Gil-Izquierdo, A.; Pereira, D.M.; Valentão, P.; Andrade, P.B.; Duarte, P.; et al. Identification of phenolic compounds in isolated vacuoles of the medicinal plant Catharanthus roseus and their interaction with vacuolar class III peroxidase: An H2O2 affair? *J. Exp. Bot.* **2011**, *62*, 2841–2854. [CrossRef]

29. Wang, W.; Sun, C.; Mao, L.; Ma, P.; Liu, F.; Yang, J.; Gao, Y. The biological activities, chemical stability, metabolism and delivery systems of quercetin: A review. *Trends Food Sci. Technol.* **2016**, *56*, 21–38. [CrossRef]

30. Lesjak, M.; Beara, I.; Simin, N.; Pintać, D.; Majkić, T.; Bekvalac, K.; Orčić, D.; Mimica-Dukić, N. Antioxidant and anti-inflammatory activities of quercetin and its derivatives. *J. Funct. Foods* **2018**, *40*, 68–75. [CrossRef]

31. Lakhanpal, P.; Rai, D.K. Quercetin: A Versatile Flavonoid. *Internet J. Med. Updat. EJOURNAL* **2007**, *2*. [CrossRef]

32. Berardini, N.; Fezer, R.; Conrad, J.; Beifuss, U.; Carle, R.; Schieber, A. Screening of Mango (Mangifera indica L.) Cultivars for Their Contents of Flavonol O - and Xanthone C -Glycosides, Anthocyanins, and Pectin. *J. Agric. Food Chem.* **2005**, *53*, 1563–1570. [CrossRef]

33. Zheng, W.; Wang, S.Y. Oxygen Radical Absorbing Capacity of Phenolics in Blueberries, Cranberries, Chokeberries, and Lingonberries. *J. Agric. Food Chem.* **2003**, *51*, 502–509. [CrossRef]

34. Kuti, J.O.; Konuru, H.B. Antioxidant Capacity and Phenolic Content in Leaf Extracts of Tree Spinach (Cnidoscolus spp.). *J. Agric. Food Chem.* **2004**, *52*, 117–121. [CrossRef] [PubMed]

35. Chang, Q.; Wong, Y.-S. Identification of Flavonoids in Hakmeitau Beans (Vigna sinensis) by High-Performance Liquid Chromatography–Electrospray Mass Spectrometry (LC-ESI/MS). *J. Agric. Food Chem.* **2004**, *52*, 6694–6699. [CrossRef] [PubMed]
36. Kim, D.-O.; Chun, O.K.; Kim, Y.J.; Moon, H.-Y.; Lee, C.Y. Quantification of Polyphenolics and Their Antioxidant Capacity in Fresh Plums. *J. Agric. Food Chem.* **2003**, *51*, 6509–6515. [CrossRef] [PubMed]
37. Nemeth, K.; Piskula, M.K. Food Content, Processing, Absorption and Metabolism of Onion Flavonoids. *Crit. Rev. Food Sci. Nutr.* **2007**, *47*, 397–409. [CrossRef] [PubMed]
38. Gonçalves, B.; Landbo, A.-K.; Knudsen, D.; Silva, A.P.; Moutinho-Pereira, J.; Rosa, E.; Meyer, A.S. Effect of Ripeness and Postharvest Storage on the Phenolic Profiles of Cherries (Prunus avium L.). *J. Agric. Food Chem.* **2004**, *52*, 523–530. [CrossRef]
39. Slimestad, R.; Verheul, M.J. Seasonal Variations in the Level of Plant Constituents in Greenhouse Production of Cherry Tomatoes. *J. Agric. Food Chem.* **2005**, *53*, 3114–3119. [CrossRef]
40. Oomah, B.D.; Mazza, G. Flavonoids and Antioxidative Activities in Buckwheat. *J. Agric. Food Chem.* **1996**, *44*, 1746–1750. [CrossRef]
41. Price, K.R.; Casuscelli, F.; Colquhoun, I.J.; Rhodes, M.J.C. Composition and Content of Flavonol Gl y cosides in Broccoli Florets (Brassica olearacea) and their Fate during Cooking. *J. Sci. Food Agric.* **1998**, *468*, 468–472. [CrossRef]
42. Materska, M.; Perucka, I. Antioxidant Activity of the Main Phenolic Compounds Isolated from Hot Pepper Fruit (Capsicum annuum L.). *J. Agric. Food Chem.* **2005**, *53*, 1750–1756. [CrossRef]
43. Jürgenliemk, G.; Nahrstedt, A. Phenolic Compounds from Hypericum perforatum. *Planta Med.* **2002**, *68*, 88–91. [CrossRef] [PubMed]
44. Flamini, G.; Antognoli, E.; Morelli, I. Two flavonoids and other compounds from the aerial parts of Centaurea bracteata from Italy. *Phytochemistry* **2001**, *57*, 559–564. [CrossRef]
45. Özïpek, M.; Çaliş, İ.; Ertan, M.; Rüedi, P. Rhamnetin 3-p-coumaroylrhamninoside from Rhamnus petiolaris. *Phytochemistry* **1994**, *37*, 249–253. [CrossRef]
46. Olsson, M.E.; Gustavsson, K.-E.; Vågen, I.M. Quercetin and Isorhamnetin in Sweet and Red Cultivars of Onion (Allium cepa L.) at Harvest, after Field Curing, Heat Treatment, and Storage. *J. Agric. Food Chem.* **2010**, *58*, 2323–2330. [CrossRef] [PubMed]
47. Yao, L.; Datta, N.; Tomás-Barberán, F.A.; Ferreres, F.; Martos, I.; Singanusong, R. Flavonoids, phenolic acids and abscisic acid in Australian and New Zealand Leptospermum honeys. *Food Chem.* **2003**, *81*, 159–168. [CrossRef]
48. Hisanaga, A.; Mukai, R.; Sakao, K.; Terao, J.; Hou, D. Anti-inflammatory effects and molecular mechanisms of 8-prenyl quercetin. *Mol. Nutr. Food Res.* **2016**, *60*, 1020–1032. [CrossRef]
49. Crespy, V.; Morand, C.; Besson, C.; Manach, C.; Demigne, C.; Remesy, C. Quercetin, but not Its Glycosides, Is Absorbed from the Rat Stomach. *J. Agric. Food Chem.* **2002**, *50*, 618–621. [CrossRef]
50. Murota, K.; Shimizu, S.; Chujo, H.; Moon, J.; Terao, J. Efficiency of Absorption and Metabolic Conversion of Quercetin and Its Glucosides in Human Intestinal Cell Line Caco-2. *Arch. Biochem. Biophys.* **2000**, *384*, 391–397. [CrossRef]
51. Murota, K.; Shimizu, S.; Miyamoto, S.; Izumi, T.; Obata, A.; Kikuchi, M.; Terao, J. Unique Uptake and Transport of Isoflavone Aglycones by Human Intestinal Caco-2 Cells: Comparison of Isoflavonoids and Flavonoids. *J. Nutr.* **2002**, *132*, 1956–1961. [CrossRef]
52. Day, A.J.; Gee, J.M.; DuPont, M.S.; Johnson, I.T.; Williamson, G. Absorption of quercetin-3-glucoside and quercetin-4'-glucoside in the rat small intestine: The role of lactase phlorizin hydrolase and the sodium-dependent glucose transporter. *Biochem. Pharmacol.* **2003**, *65*, 1199–1206. [CrossRef]
53. Wolffram, S.; Blöck, M.; Ader, P. Quercetin-3-Glucoside Is Transported by the Glucose Carrier SGLT1 across the Brush Border Membrane of Rat Small Intestine. *J. Nutr.* **2002**, *132*, 630–635. [CrossRef] [PubMed]
54. Németh, K.; Plumb, G.W.; Berrin, J.-G.; Juge, N.; Jacob, R.; Naim, H.Y.; Williamson, G.; Swallow, D.M.; Kroon, P.A. Deglycosylation by small intestinal epithelial cell?-glucosidases is a critical step in the absorption and metabolism of dietary flavonoid glycosides in humans. *Eur. J. Nutr.* **2003**, *42*, 29–42. [CrossRef] [PubMed]

55. Aura, A.-M.; O'Leary, K.A.; Williamson, G.; Ojala, M.; Bailey, M.; Puupponen-Pimiä, R.; Nuutila, A.M.; Oksman-Caldentey, K.-M.; Poutanen, K. Quercetin Derivatives Are Deconjugated and Converted to Hydroxyphenylacetic Acids but Not Methylated by Human Fecal Flora in Vitro. *J. Agric. Food Chem.* **2002**, *50*, 1725–1730. [CrossRef]

56. Schoefer, L.; Mohan, R.; Schwiertz, A.; Braune, A.; Blaut, M. Anaerobic degradation of flavonoids by Clostridium orbiscindens. *Appl. Environ. Microbiol.* **2003**, *69*, 5849–5854. [CrossRef]

57. Galijatovic, A.; Walle, U.K.; Walle, T. Induction of UDP-glucuronosyltransferase by the flavonoids chrysin and quercetin in Caco-2 cells. *Pharm. Res.* **2000**, *17*, 21–26. [CrossRef]

58. Graf, B.A.; Ameho, C.; Dolnikowski, G.G.; Milbury, P.E.; Chen, C.; Blumberg, J.B. Rat Gastrointestinal Tissues Metabolize Quercetin. *J. Nutr.* **2006**, *136*, 39–44. [CrossRef]

59. Cao, Y.; Chen, Z.-J.; Jiang, H.; Chen, J. Computational Studies of the Regioselectivities of COMT-Catalyzed Meta -/ Para -O Methylations of Luteolin and Quercetin. *J. Phys. Chem. B* **2014**, *118*, 470–481. [CrossRef]

60. Williamson, G.; Kay, C.D.; Crozier, A. The Bioavailability, Transport, and Bioactivity of Dietary Flavonoids: A Review from a Historical Perspective. *Compr. Rev. Food Sci. Food Saf.* **2018**, *17*, 1054–1112. [CrossRef]

61. Murota, K.; Hotta, A.; Ido, H.; Kawai, Y.; Moon, J.; Sekido, K.; Hayashi, H.; Inakuma, T.; Terao, J. Antioxidant capacity of albumin-bound quercetin metabolites after onion consumption in humans. *J. Med. Investig.* **2007**, *54*, 370–374. [CrossRef]

62. Murota, K.; Cermak, R.; Terao, J.; Wolffram, S. Influence of fatty acid patterns on the intestinal absorption pathway of quercetin in thoracic lymph duct-cannulated rats. *Br. J. Nutr.* **2013**, *109*, 2147–2153. [CrossRef] [PubMed]

63. Arts, I.C.W.; Sesink, A.L.A.; Faassen-Peters, M.; Hollman, P.C.H. The type of sugar moiety is a major determinant of the small intestinal uptake and subsequent biliary excretion of dietary quercetin glycosides. *Br. J. Nutr.* **2004**, *91*, 841–847. [CrossRef]

64. Guo, Y.; Bruno, R.S. Endogenous and exogenous mediators of quercetin bioavailability. *J. Nutr. Biochem.* **2015**, *26*, 201–210. [CrossRef]

65. Kawabata, K.; Mukai, R.; Ishisaka, A. Quercetin and related polyphenols: New insights and implications for their bioactivity and bioavailability. *Food Funct.* **2015**, *6*, 1399–1417. [CrossRef] [PubMed]

66. Williamson, G.; Aeberli, I.; Miguet, L.; Zhang, Z.; Sanchez, M.-B.; Crespy, V.; Barron, D.; Needs, P.; Kroon, P.A.; Glavinas, H.; et al. Interaction of Positional Isomers of Quercetin Glucuronides with the Transporter ABCC2 (cMOAT, MRP2). *Drug Metab. Dispos.* **2007**, *35*, 1262–1268. [CrossRef] [PubMed]

67. Ulusoy, H.G.; Sanlier, N. A minireview of quercetin: From its metabolism to possible mechanisms of its biological activities. *Crit. Rev. Food Sci. Nutr.* **2019**, *0*, 1–14. [CrossRef] [PubMed]

68. Abrahamse, S.L.; Kloots, W.J.; van Amelsvoort, J.M.M. Absorption, distribution, and secretion of epicatechin and quercetin in the rat. *Nutr. Res.* **2005**, *25*, 305–317. [CrossRef]

69. Bali, E.; Ergin, V.; Rackova, L.; Bayraktar, O.; Küçükboyacı, N.; Karasu, Ç. Olive Leaf Extracts Protect Cardiomyocytes against 4-Hydroxynonenal-Induced Toxicity In Vitro: Comparison with Oleuropein, Hydroxytyrosol, and Quercetin. *Planta Med.* **2014**, *80*, 984–992. [CrossRef]

70. Chen, J.-Y.; Hu, R.-Y.; Chou, H.-C. Quercetin-induced cardioprotection against doxorubicin cytotoxicity. *J. Biomed. Sci.* **2013**, *20*, 95. [CrossRef]

71. Zhang, X.; Li, P.; Guo, S.; Wang, S.; Liu, D. Quantitation of β-carboline and quercetin in alligator weed (*Alternanthera philoxeroides* (Mart.) Griseb.) by LC-MS/MS and evaluation of cardioprotective effects of the methanol extracts. *Drug Discov. Ther.* **2018**, *12*, 341–346. [CrossRef]

72. Syama, H.P.; Arya, A.D.; Dhanya, R.; Nisha, P.; Sundaresan, A.; Jacob, E.; Jayamurthy, P. Quantification of phenolics in Syzygium cumini seed and their modulatory role on tertiary butyl-hydrogen peroxide-induced oxidative stress in H9c2 cell lines and key enzymes in cardioprotection. *J. Food Sci. Technol.* **2017**, *54*, 2115–2125. [CrossRef] [PubMed]

73. Li, C.; Wang, T.; Zhang, C.; Xuan, J.; Su, C.; Wang, Y. Quercetin attenuates cardiomyocyte apoptosis via inhibition of JNK and p38 mitogen-activated protein kinase signaling pathways. *Gene* **2016**, *577*, 275–280. [CrossRef] [PubMed]

74. Tang, L.; Peng, Y.; Xu, T.; Yi, X.; Liu, Y.; Luo, Y.; Yin, D.; He, M. The effects of quercetin protect cardiomyocytes from A/R injury is related to its capability to increasing expression and activity of PKCε protein. *Mol. Cell. Biochem.* **2013**, *382*, 145–152. [CrossRef] [PubMed]

75. Ai, X.; Lu, W.; Zeng, K.; Li, C.; Jiang, Y.; Tu, P. Microfluidic Coculture Device for Monitoring of Inflammation-Induced Myocardial Injury Dynamics. *Anal. Chem.* **2018**, *90*, 4485–4494. [CrossRef]
76. Lozano, O.; Lázaro-Alfaro, A.; Silva-Platas, C.; Oropeza-Almazán, Y.; Torres-Quintanilla, A.; Bernal-Ramírez, J.; Alves-Figueiredo, H.; García-Rivas, G. Nanoencapsulated Quercetin Improves Cardioprotection during Hypoxia-Reoxygenation Injury through Preservation of Mitochondrial Function. *Oxid. Med. Cell. Longev.* **2019**, *2019*, 1–14. [CrossRef]
77. Cote, B.; Carlson, L.J.; Rao, D.A.; Alani, A.W.G. Combinatorial resveratrol and quercetin polymeric micelles mitigate doxorubicin induced cardiotoxicity in vitro and in vivo. *J. Control. Release* **2015**, *213*, 128–133. [CrossRef]
78. Dong, L.Y.; Chen, F.; Xu, M.; Yao, L.P.; Zhang, Y.J.; Zhuang, Y. Quercetin attenuates myocardial ischemia-reperfusion injury via downregulation of the HMGB1-TLR4-NF-κB signaling pathway. *Am. J. Transl. Res.* **2018**, *10*, 1273–1283.
79. Huang, L.; He, H.; Liu, Z.; Liu, D.; Yin, D.; He, M. Protective Effects of Isorhamnetin on Cardiomyocytes Against Anoxia/Reoxygenation-induced Injury Is Mediated by SIRT1. *J. Cardiovasc. Pharmacol.* **2016**, *67*, 526–537. [CrossRef]
80. Shu, Z.; Yang, Y.; Yang, L.; Jiang, H.; Yu, X.; Wang, Y. Cardioprotective effects of dihydroquercetin against ischemia reperfusion injury by inhibiting oxidative stress and endoplasmic reticulum stress-induced apoptosis via the PI3K/Akt pathway. *Food Funct.* **2019**, *10*, 203–215. [CrossRef]
81. Wang, Y.; Zhong, L.; Liu, X.; Zhu, Y. ZYZ-772 Prevents Cardiomyocyte Injury by Suppressing Nox4-Derived ROS Production and Apoptosis. *Molecules* **2017**, *22*, 331. [CrossRef]
82. Xiao, R.; Xiang, A.-L.; Pang, H.-B.; Liu, K.-Q. Hyperoside protects against hypoxia/reoxygenation induced injury in cardiomyocytes by suppressing the Bnip3 expression. *Gene* **2017**, *629*, 86–91. [CrossRef] [PubMed]
83. Cao, H.; Xu, H.; Zhu, G.; Liu, S. Isoquercetin ameliorated hypoxia/reoxygenation-induced H9C2 cardiomyocyte apoptosis via a mitochondrial-dependent pathway. *Biomed. Pharmacother.* **2017**, *95*, 938–943. [CrossRef] [PubMed]
84. Daubney, J.; Bonner, P.L.; Hargreaves, A.J.; Dickenson, J.M. Cardioprotective and Cardiotoxic Effects of Quercetin and Two of Its In Vivo Metabolites on Differentiated H9c2 Cardiomyocytes. *Basic Clin. Pharmacol. Toxicol.* **2015**, *116*, 96–109. [CrossRef] [PubMed]
85. Allawadhi, P.; Khurana, A.; Sayed, N.; Kumari, P.; Godugu, C. Isoproterenol-induced cardiac ischemia and fibrosis: Plant-based approaches for intervention. *Phyther. Res.* **2018**, *32*, 1908–1932. [CrossRef]
86. Kumar, M.; Kasala, E.R.; Bodduluru, L.N.; Kumar, V.; Lahkar, M. Molecular and biochemical evidence on the protective effects of quercetin in isoproterenol-induced acute myocardial injury in rats. *J. Biochem. Mol. Toxicol.* **2017**, *31*, e21832. [CrossRef]
87. Ballmann, C.; Denney, T.S.; Beyers, R.J.; Quindry, T.; Romero, M.; Amin, R.; Selsby, J.T.; Quindry, J.C. Lifelong quercetin enrichment and cardioprotection in Mdx/Utrn +/− mice. *Am. J. Physiol. Circ. Physiol.* **2017**, *312*, H128–H140. [CrossRef]
88. Arumugam, S.; Thandavarayan, R.A.; Arozal, W.; Sari, F.R.; Giridharan, V.V.; Soetikno, V.; Palaniyandi, S.S.; Harima, M.; Suzuki, K.; Nagata, M.; et al. Quercetin offers cardioprotection against progression of experimental autoimmune myocarditis by suppression of oxidative and endoplasmic reticulum stress via endothelin-1/MAPK signalling. *Free Radic. Res.* **2012**, *46*, 154–163. [CrossRef]
89. Shahbaz, A.U.; Kamalov, G.; Zhao, W.; Zhao, T.; Johnson, P.L.; Sun, Y.; Bhattacharya, S.K.; Ahokas, R.A.; Gerling, I.C.; Weber, K.T. Mitochondria-targeted Cardioprotection in Aldosteronism. *J. Cardiovasc. Pharmacol.* **2011**, *57*, 37–43. [CrossRef]
90. Putakala, M.; Gujjala, S.; Nukala, S.; Bongu, S.B.R.; Chintakunta, N.; Desireddy, S. Cardioprotective effect of Phyllanthus amarus against high fructose diet induced myocardial and aortic stress in rat model. *Biomed. Pharmacother.* **2017**, *95*, 1359–1368. [CrossRef]
91. Fadda, L.M.; Attia, H.A.; Al-Rasheed, N.M.; Ali, H.M.; Al-Rasheed, N.M. Roles of some antioxidants in modulation of cardiac myopathy induced by sodium nitrite via down-regulation of mRNA expression of NF-κB, Bax, and flt-1 and suppressing DNA damage. *Saudi Pharm. J.* **2018**, *26*, 217–223. [CrossRef]
92. Wiseman, R.L.; Zhang, Y.; Lee, K.P.K.; Harding, H.P.; Haynes, C.M.; Price, J.; Sicheri, F.; Ron, D. Flavonol Activation Defines an Unanticipated Ligand-Binding Site in the Kinase-RNase Domain of IRE1. *Mol. Cell* **2010**, *38*, 291–304. [CrossRef] [PubMed]

93. Zhu, X.; Xiong, T.; Liu, P.; Guo, X.; Xiao, L.; Zhou, F.; Tang, Y.; Yao, P. Quercetin ameliorates HFD-induced NAFLD by promoting hepatic VLDL assembly and lipophagy via the IRE1a/XBP1s pathway. *Food Chem. Toxicol.* **2018**, *114*, 52–60. [CrossRef] [PubMed]
94. Binder, P.; Wang, S.; Radu, M.; Zin, M.; Collins, L.; Khan, S.; Li, Y.; Sekeres, K.; Humphreys, N.; Swanton, E.; et al. Pak2 as a Novel Therapeutic Target for Cardioprotective Endoplasmic Reticulum Stress Response. *Circ. Res.* **2019**, *124*, 696–711. [CrossRef] [PubMed]
95. Liu, X.; Yu, Z.; Huang, X.; Gao, Y.; Wang, X.; Gu, J.; Xue, S. Peroxisome proliferator-activated receptor γ (PPARγ) mediates the protective effect of quercetin against myocardial ischemia-reperfusion injury via suppressing the NF-κB pathway. *Am. J. Transl. Res.* **2016**, *8*, 5169–5186.
96. Jin, H.-B.; Yang, Y.-B.; Song, Y.-L.; Zhang, Y.; Li, Y.-R. Protective roles of quercetin in acute myocardial ischemia and reperfusion injury in rats. *Mol. Biol. Rep.* **2012**, *39*, 11005–11009. [CrossRef]
97. Tang, J.; Lu, L.; Liu, Y.; Ma, J.; Yang, L.; Li, L.; Guo, H.; Yu, S.; Ren, J.; Bai, H.; et al. Quercetin improve ischemia/reperfusion-induced cardiomyocyte apoptosis in vitro and in vivo study via SIRT1/PGC-1α signaling. *J. Cell. Biochem.* **2019**, *120*, 9747–9757. [CrossRef]
98. Ma, C.; Jiang, Y.; Zhang, X.; Chen, X.; Liu, Z.; Tian, X. Isoquercetin ameliorates myocardial infarction through anti-inflammation and anti-apoptosis factor and regulating TLR4-NF-κB signal pathway. *Mol. Med. Rep.* **2018**, *17*, 6675–6680. [CrossRef]
99. Shu, L.; Zhang, W.; Huang, C.; Huang, G.; Su, G. Troxerutin Protects Against Myocardial Ischemia/Reperfusion Injury Via Pi3k/Akt Pathway in Rats. *Cell. Physiol. Biochem.* **2017**, *44*, 1939–1948. [CrossRef]
100. Badalzadeh, R.; Baradaran, B.; Alihemmati, A.; Yousefi, B.; Abbaszadeh, A. Troxerutin Preconditioning and Ischemic Postconditioning Modulate Inflammatory Response after Myocardial Ischemia/Reperfusion Injury in Rat Model. *Inflammation* **2017**, *40*, 136–143. [CrossRef]
101. Saliu, J.A.; Oyeleye, S.I.; Olasehinde, T.A.; Oboh, G. Modulatory effects of stonebreaker (Phyllanthus amarus) and bitter gourd (Momordica charantia) on enzymes linked with cardiac function in heart tissue of doxorubicin-stressed rats. *Drug Chem. Toxicol.* **2019**, *0545*, 1–9. [CrossRef]
102. Annapurna, A.; Reddy, C.S.; Akondi, R.B.; Rao, S.R.C. Cardioprotective actions of two bioflavonoids, quercetin and rutin, in experimental myocardial infarction in both normal and streptozotocin-induced type I diabetic rats. *J. Pharm. Pharmacol.* **2009**, *61*, 1365–1374. [CrossRef] [PubMed]
103. Roslan, J.; Giribabu, N.; Karim, K.; Salleh, N. Quercetin ameliorates oxidative stress, inflammation and apoptosis in the heart of streptozotocin-nicotinamide-induced adult male diabetic rats. *Biomed. Pharmacother.* **2017**, *86*, 570–582. [CrossRef] [PubMed]
104. Najafi, M.; Noroozi, E.; Javadi, A.; Badalzadeh, R. Anti-arrhythmogenic and anti-inflammatory effects of troxerutin in ischemia/reperfusion injury of diabetic myocardium. *Biomed. Pharmacother.* **2018**, *102*, 385–391. [CrossRef] [PubMed]
105. Seferović, P.M.; Paulus, W.J. Clinical diabetic cardiomyopathy: A two-faced disease with restrictive and dilated phenotypes. *Eur. Heart J.* **2015**, *36*, 1718–1727. [CrossRef]
106. Soman, S.; Rajamanickam, C.; Rauf, A.A.; Madambath, I. Molecular mechanisms of the antiglycative and cardioprotective activities of Psidium guajava leaves in the rat diabetic myocardium. *Pharm. Biol.* **2016**, *54*, 3078–3085. [CrossRef]
107. Ulasova, E.; Perez, J.; Hill, B.G.; Bradley, W.E.; Garber, D.W.; Landar, A.; Barnes, S.; Prasain, J.; Parks, D.A.; Dell'Italia, L.J.; et al. Quercetin prevents left ventricular hypertrophy in the Apo E knockout mouse. *Redox Biol.* **2013**, *1*, 381–386. [CrossRef]
108. Zhang, J.; Liang, R.; Wang, L.; Yan, R.; Hou, R.; Gao, S.; Yang, B. Effects of an aqueous extract of Crataegus pinnatifida Bge. var. major N.E.Br. fruit on experimental atherosclerosis in rats. *J. Ethnopharmacol.* **2013**, *148*, 563–569. [CrossRef]
109. Ferenczyova, K.; Kalocayova, B.; Kindernay, L.; Jelemensky, M.; Balis, P.; Berenyiova, A.; Zemancikova, A.; Farkasova, V.; Sykora, M.; Tothova, L.; et al. Quercetin Exerts Age-Dependent Beneficial Effects on Blood Pressure and Vascular Function, But Is Inefficient in Preventing Myocardial Ischemia-Reperfusion Injury in Zucker Diabetic Fatty Rats. *Molecules* **2020**, *25*, 187. [CrossRef]
110. Knekt, P.; Jarvinen, R.; Reunanen, A.; Maatela, J. Flavonoid intake and coronary mortality in Finland: A cohort study. *BMJ* **1996**, *312*, 478–481. [CrossRef]
111. Malishevskaia, I.V.; Ilashchuk, T.A.; Okipniak, I.V. [Therapeutic efficacy of quercetin in patients with is ischemic heart disease with underlying metabolic syndrome]. *Georg. Med. News* **2013**, *225*, 67–71.

112. Chekalina, N.I.; Shut, S.V.; Trybrat, T.A.; Burmak, Y.H.; Petrov, Y.Y.; Manusha, Y.I.; Kazakov, Y.M. Effect of quercetin on parameters of central hemodynamics and myocardial ischemia in patients with stable coronary heart disease. *Wiad. Lek.* **2017**, *70*, 707–711. [PubMed]

113. Zahedi, M.; Ghiasvand, R.; Feizi, A.; Asgari, G.; Darvish, L. Does quercetin improve cardiovascular risk factors and inflammatory biomarkers in women with type 2 diabetes: A double-blind randomized controlled clinical trial. *Int. J. Prev. Med.* **2013**, *4*, 777–785. [PubMed]

114. Dower, J.I.; Geleijnse, J.M.; Gijsbers, L.; Zock, P.L.; Kromhout, D.; Hollman, P.C.H. Effects of the pure flavonoids epicatechin and quercetin on vascular function and cardiometabolic health: A randomized, double-blind, placebo-controlled, crossover trial. *Am. J. Clin. Nutr.* **2015**, *101*, 914–921. [CrossRef] [PubMed]

115. Serban, M.C.; Sahebkar, A.; Zanchetti, A.; Mikhailidis, D.P.; Howard, G.; Antal, D.; Andrica, F.; Ahmed, A.; Aronow, W.S.; Muntner, P.; et al. Effects of Quercetin on Blood Pressure: A Systematic Review and Meta-Analysis of Randomized Controlled Trials. *J. Am. Heart Assoc.* **2016**, *5*, 1–16. [CrossRef] [PubMed]

116. Kondratiuk, V.E.; Synytsia, Y.P. Effect of quercetin on the echocardiographic parameters of left ventricular diastolic function in patients with gout and essential hypertension. *Wiad. Lek.* **2018**, *71*, 1554–1559.

117. Yadav, H.N.; Singh, M.; Sharma, P.L. Pharmacological inhibition of GSK-3β produces late phase of cardioprotection in hyperlipidemic rat: Possible involvement of HSP 72. *Mol. Cell. Biochem.* **2012**, *369*, 227–233. [CrossRef]

118. Yao, Y.; Zhang, G.; Zhang, Y.; Li, W.; Wang, C.; Yin, C.; Zhang, F. Lipopolysaccharide pretreatment protects against ischemia/reperfusion injury via increase of HSP70 and inhibition of NF-κB. *Cell Stress Chaperones* **2011**, *16*, 287–296.

119. Eren-Guzelgun, B.; Ince, E.; Gurer-Orhan, H. In vitro antioxidant/prooxidant effects of combined use of flavonoids. *Nat. Prod. Res.* **2018**, *32*, 1446–1450. [CrossRef]

International Journal of
Molecular Sciences

Review

Beneficial Properties of Green Tea Catechins

Claudia Musial [1], Alicja Kuban-Jankowska [1] and Magdalena Gorska-Ponikowska [1,2,3,*]

[1] Department of Medical Chemistry, Medical University of Gdansk, 80-211 Gdansk, Poland;
claudia.musial@gumed.edu.pl (C.M.); alicja.kuban-jankowska@gumed.edu.pl (A.K.-J.)
[2] Department of Biophysics, Institute of Biomaterials and Biomolecular Systems, University of Stuttgart,
70569 Stuttgart, Germany
[3] Euro-Mediterranean Institute of Science and Technology, 90139 Palermo, Italy
* Correspondence: magdalena.gorska-ponikowska@gumed.edu.pl

Received: 13 January 2020; Accepted: 29 February 2020; Published: 4 March 2020

Abstract: Green tea (*Camellia sinesis*) is widely known for its anticancer and anti-inflammatory properties. Among the biologically active compounds contained in *Camellia sinesis*, the main antioxidant agents are catechins. Recent scientific research indicates that the number of hydroxyl groups and the presence of characteristic structural groups have a major impact on the antioxidant activity of catechins. The best source of these compounds is unfermented green tea. Depending on the type and origin of green tea leaves, their antioxidant properties may be uneven. Catechins exhibit the strong property of neutralizing reactive oxygen and nitrogen species. The group of green tea catechin derivatives includes: epicatechin, epigallocatechin, epicatechin gallate and epigallocatechin gallate. The last of these presents the most potent anti-inflammatory and anticancer potential. Notably, green tea catechins are widely described to be efficient in the prevention of lung cancer, breast cancer, esophageal cancer, stomach cancer, liver cancer and prostate cancer. The current review aims to summarize the potential anticancer effects and molecular signaling pathways of major green tea catechins. It needs to be clearly emphasized that green tea as well as green tea catechols cannot replace the standard chemotherapy. Nonetheless, their beneficial effects may support the standard anticancer approach.

Keywords: green tea; *Camellia sinensis*; catechins; cancer stem cells; anticancer theraphy

1. Introduction

Camellia sinensis (L.) is one of the oldest and the most popular drinks in the world. Green tea is classified mainly because of the tradition of production of green tea leaf processing, the place of origin as well as by the type of soil on which the bushes have grown. Green tea is grown mainly in Japan, China and Taiwan. The main difference between green tea and black tea is the technological process of their production [1–4].

There are many types of green tea that are classified according to their taste and antioxidant properties. The most popular type of green tea consumed is Sencha, most often made in Japan [5–7]. After proper treatment, the Bancha, Matcha and Gyokuro species are made from Sencha tea. Bancha infusion, compared to Sencha infusion, contains much less caffeine, as well as L-theanine, the amino acid responsible for the formation of proteins responsible for the production of neurotransmitters, insulin and adrenaline [7]. The infusion of Matcha green tea leaves, in contrast to other types of infusions, has the highest amount of caffeine and L-theanine [7]. Available scientific studies indicate that L-theanine significantly modifies the effects of caffeine, reducing its stimulant effect, positively affecting brain work, improving cognitive functions, mood and concentration, and additionally, decreasing blood pressure [6]. Matcha tea has two forms: Matcha–Usucha and Macha–Koicha. Among the Japanese types of green tea infusions, Mecha, Genmaicha, Kukicha, Kamairicha, Kariganech, Konch,

Kokeicha, Fukamushicha and Tamaryokucha also stand out. Chinese types of green tea include: Gunpowder, Chun Mee, Lung Ching, Mao Feng, and China Sencha, a Chinese variety of Japanese Sencha infusion [3,4,7].

The technological process has a major impact on the antioxidant potential of green tea. Compared to black tea, green tea has a much higher catechins content. This is a consequence of oxidation of catechins to theaflavins during the fermentation process. In addition, the important fact is that the higher the catechins content in tea, the higher the antioxidant activity. The number of polyphenolic compounds, including catechins, depends on the cultivation conditions of *Camellia sinensis*—climatic as well as agro-technical. It is also noteworthy that as the temperature rises, the antioxidant activity of the green tea infusion increases [6,7]. The percentage content of green tea is not constant, but depends on different environmental factors including growing conditions, soil, climatic conditions, or other external factors such as: light factors, geography, microbes or temperature [4–7].

The group of catechins (flavan-3-ol) belonging to the group of flavonoids contained in tea include: (−)-epigallocatechin-3-gallate (EGCG), (−)-epicatechin-3-gallate (ECG), (−)-epigallocatechin (EGC) and (−)-epicatechin (EC). Flavonoids are one of the most common and diverse groups of polyphenols. The presence of numerous hydroxyl groups in the molecules gives them strong antioxidant properties [1,2]. The chemical composition of green tea includes more than ten groups of compounds. The main components are phenolic acids, polyphenolic compounds (which include catechins), as well as amino acids, proteins and fats [8–13].

Notably, the best source of catechins is unfermented green tea. Depending on the type and origin of green tea leaves, their antioxidant properties may be uneven [13–16]. Catechins also occur naturally in black tea, coffee, berries, grapes and wine.

Due to the numerous health-promoting properties of catechins, it is recommended to include particularly products containing catechins in the daily diet [17]. Anti-inflammatory and antioxidant as well as chemopreventive activity are considered as the most important action of the catechin group [13–18].

The basic functions of catechins include their antioxidant effects: scavenging of reactive oxygen species, inhibition of the formation of free radicals and lipid peroxidation. Available literature data indicate that the antioxidant activity of catechins contained in green tea and their significant impact on the prevention of civilization diseases are largely dependent on the presence of structural groups in the molecules, as well as the number of hydroxyl groups [3,4]. Green tea may exert the prevention effect in various types of cancer including lung, esophagus, stomach, intestinal, pancreatic, breast, prostate or bladder cancers [14–17].

However, it is worth taking into consideration the oxidative potential of catechins, for example, when using green tea in the form of dietary supplements, as a result of which there is a possibility for the formation of very highly reactive metabolites with quinone structure. Quinones, as a result of redox reactions, have also the potential to generate high amounts of reactive oxygen species [19].

2. Health-Promoting Properties of Green Tea

As mentioned above, green tea is not produced as a result of fermentation, unlike the production of black tea, during which fermentation to Oolong takes place (which is partially fermented). The process of full fermentation into black tea is a result of the influence of enzymes on catechin polyphenols found in the leaves of the tea bush [14]. The technology of processing *Camellia sinensis* leaves makes each type of tea have a different effect and has other biologically active ingredients and health-promoting properties [14,15].

The health-promoting properties of green tea are due to the presence of polyphenols, in particular, flavonols and flavanols. Clinical studies, in vivo and in vitro experiments, confirm their antioxidant and anti-inflammatory effects. Catechins are the dominant polyphenols in green tea, whose antioxidant activities result from the neutralization of free nitrogen and oxygen radicals, as well as the ability to chelate metal ions in redox reactions. Numerous scientific studies indicate the antitumor effects of polyphenols contained in green tea leaves due to inhibition of cell division as well as the induction of phase II antioxidant enzymes, e.g., superoxide dismutase, glutathione-*S*-transferase as well as glutathione peroxidase and reductase. The described result concerns the research on the effects of polyphenols on oxidative stress in vivo. The study showed that consumption of green tea within 4 months in an amount of four glasses per day reduced urinary levels of 8-hydroxydeoxyguanosine. The effects of green tea polyphenols on inhibition of the growth of cancer cells and reduction of the risk of cancer are confirmed by numerous scientific studies in the field of prostate, pancreatic, breast and stomach cancers [14–16]. It is worth emphasizing that green tea may support chemotherapeutic as well as preventive effects, however, it cannot replace pharmacological treatment. Notably, polyphenols, including catechins, are able to induce cancer cell death while not affecting healthy cells [9,14,17].

3. The Chemical Composition of Green Tea

From a chemical point of view, green tea has a protein content of about 15–20%, which include amino acids such as L-theanine [10], tyrosine, tryptophan, threonine, 5-*N*-ethylglutamine, glutamic acid, serine, glycine, valine, leucine, aspartic acid, lysine and arginine. It also contains trace elements such as magnesium, chromium, manganese, calcium, copper, zinc, iron, selenium, sodium cobalt or nickel, and carbohydrates such as glucose, cellulose and sucrose [9–18,20,21]. In addition, green tea is rich in sterols and lipids—linoleic and α-linolenic acid, and vitamins B2, B3, C—of which the most is in Gyokuro tea (about 10 mg) and Sencha (4 mg), vitamin E and trace amounts of vitamin K. Vitamin A only occurs in Matcha tea. It is also important that green tea is extremely rich in macroelements; it is a source of fluorine, iodine as well as phosphorus. The diphenylpropanoid skeleton ($C_6C_3C_6$) content is also typical feature of green tea [10–12]. In addition, green tea is rich in xanthine bases, which include theophylline and caffeine [20], as well as pigments such as carotenoids and chlorophyll. It is worth noting that the chemical composition of green tea also includes phenolic acids, which include gallic acid and volatile compounds including alcohols, esters, hydrocarbons and aldehydes. Phenolic acids, which include proanthocyanidins, as well as gallic acid esters with monosaccharides, have a huge impact on the qualities of green tea infusion.

The phenolic acids mentioned earlier belong to the group of polyphenols, together with flavonoids, flavandiols and flavols. Available data indicate that these compounds can constitute up to 30% of the dry matter of green tea. Catechins are the standard green tea flavonoids. Green tea contains a much higher amount of catechins than black tea or Oolong. As mentioned above, the group of catechins include EGCG, ECG, EGC and EC [10–13]. Below (Figure 1) are the chemical structure of green tea catechins. In addition to the number of hydroxyl groups, their distribution is equally important, taking into account the antioxidant activity of catechins [16]. Catechins, with a catechol group have lower antioxidant potential compared to catechins with a pyrogalol group. However, the antioxidant efficacy of catechins depends not only on the chemical structure, but also on the environmental conditions [10–18].

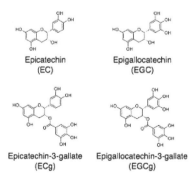

Figure 1. This figure presents chemical structure of green tea catechins.

The individual chemical components of green tea have a fundamentally different effect on particular types of cancer. Available data indicate that ascorbic acid, arginine, proline, lysine and EGCG were reported to have a positive effect on tumor growth reduction [12–17].

On figure below (Figure 2), we present the chemical composition of green tea, broken down into lipids, amino acids, trace elements, phenolic acids, vitamins, carbohydrates and volatile compounds.

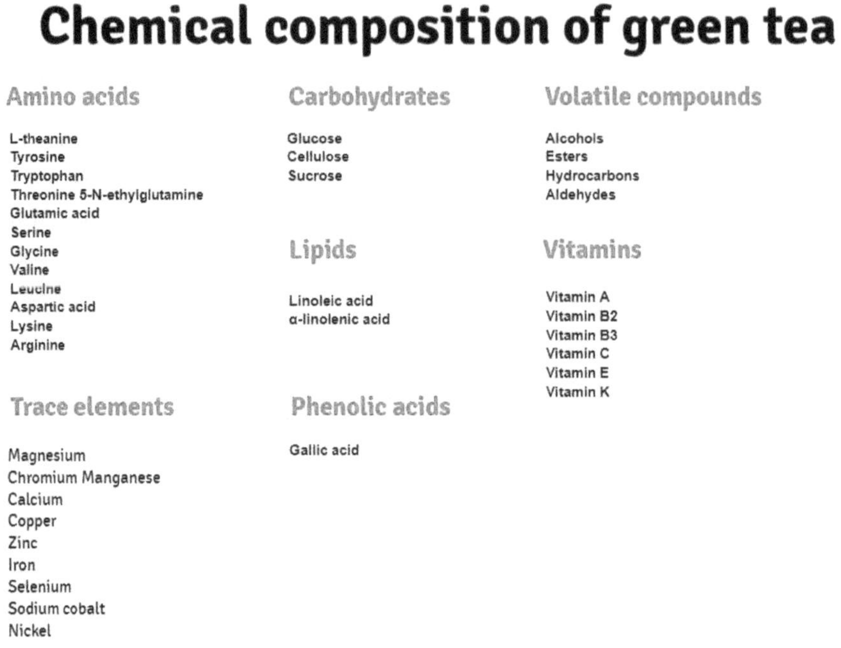

Chemical composition of green tea

Amino acids

L-theanine
Tyrosine
Tryptophan
Threonine 5-N-ethylglutamine
Glutamic acid
Serine
Glycine
Valine
Leucine
Aspartic acid
Lysine
Arginine

Trace elements

Magnesium
Chromium Manganese
Calcium
Copper
Zinc
Iron
Selenium
Sodium cobalt
Nickel

Carbohydrates

Glucose
Cellulose
Sucrose

Lipids

Linoleic acid
α-linolenic acid

Phenolic acids

Gallic acid

Volatile compounds

Alcohols
Esters
Hydrocarbons
Aldehydes

Vitamins

Vitamin A
Vitamin B2
Vitamin B3
Vitamin C
Vitamin E
Vitamin K

Figure 2. Chemical compounds of green tea.

4. Catechins: Modes of Action

EGCG is so far the best studied catechin derivative. The amount of catechins in green tea depends primarily on its variety, the method of its cultivation and leaf processing, as well as the brewing time and temperature. Studies show that catechins achieve the highest stability in the range of pH between 4 and 6 [9–13].

Available data indicate antitumor [9], antioxidant [17], anti-inflammatory [22], anti-microbial, anti-viral [23–25], anti-diabetic, anti-obesity and hypotensive effects [23–25] of catechins. Their beneficial effects on Gram-positive and Gram-negative bacteria, viruses, fungi and prions also need to be emphasized [1].

Catechins also act as the metal ion chelators for copper ions and iron ions. The specific chemical structure of polyphenols (the presence of a minimum of five hydroxyl groups) contained in green tea has a significant impact on the antioxidant capacity [26–29]. Chelation of transition metal ions is possible due to the di/tri-hydroxy structure of the B and D rings [26], as well as the meta-5,7-dihydroxy group at the A ring [1,30,31]. However, under specific conditions, they may have pro-oxidative effects [32]. The control of catechins under intracellular pool of nitro-oxidative stress is mainly responsible for their anticancer properties [33]. Therefore, polyphenolic compounds that bring health-promoting properties for the body can also result in the opposite effects if very high doses of catechins are used [19]. The result is induction of pro-oxidative stress, as well as oxygen damage to cellular components. In addition, polyphenols also have a pro-oxidative effect in the presence of tyrosinase or peroxidase, i.e., oxidizing enzymes. In addition, the pro-oxidative effect is closely related to inflammatory processes [19]. Analogously to the antioxidant properties, the pro-oxidizing properties of catechins depend identically on such factors as the number of hydroxyl groups in the molecule. During the process of polyphenol oxidation, cellular molecules are damaged by reactive oxygen species as well as electrophilic quinones. This factor is crucial in the etiopathogenesis of degenerative diseases and a carcinogenic process [19].

Catechins, as well as other active ingredients derived from green tea, can also repair DNA damage caused by UVB radiation. Available data point to the high effectiveness of green tea active ingredients in order to prevent ultraviolet radiation damage to the skin [20].

5. Anticancer Potential of Green Tea Catechins Based on In Vitro and In Vivo Studies

The most potent bioactive ingredient in green tea is EGCG, containing eight hydroxyl groups, named as the main green tea polyphenol [20,34,35]. The cell-death-inducing effect of catechins has been previously confirmed in prostate cancer animal model [34]. Many studies have been conducted to confirm the induction of apoptosis and cell cycle arrest by EGCG, e.g., in colon cancer HCT-116 cells [36,37]. It is believed that the main antitumor mechanism of EGCG is the inhibition of metalloproteinase activity. This hypothesis has been supported by study indicating the reduction of prostate cancer metastases after oral supplementation of green tea catechins [33]. Green tea catechols were also proven to inhibit lung melanoma metastasis in animal model [35]. Moreover, a positive relationship between green tea intake and the development of bladder cancer was also reported. There are also studies confirming the preventive function of colorectal adenoma after consuming ten cups of green tea of 150 mL each [35].

Breast cancer is one of the most common cancers around the world among the female population, breast cancer cells have been repeatedly subjected to scientific and clinical research to determine the effect of green tea catechin derivatives, including chemo-preventive as well as synergistic effects along with chemotherapy [38]. It is well known that the main catechins of green tea may induce anti-angiogenic and anti-proliferative effects in cancer cells, which results in their potential chemo-preventive properties. The effectiveness of green tea catechins in patients with breast cancer has been evaluated in a clinical trial, using Polyphenon E as a supplementation, consisting of succeeding catechins: EC, EGC, ECG, and the main EGCG [38]. Each capsule contained a decaf EGCG mixture with 200 mg content. During the I phase of the clinical trial, a limit of 1200 mg EGCG was established as acceptable for future safety. The study was conducted on a group of patients with breast cancer lacking the hormone receptor [38].

Lung cancer is currently the most common malignancy in the world. The effect of oral supplementation of EGCG on H1299 human non-small cell lung cancer xenograft in case of animal (mice) models have been evidenced. Research results indicate an increase in apoptosis in cancer cell death as well as inhibition of tumor growth in lung cancer [39]. In addition, oral supplementation of EGCG induced the formation of reactive oxygen species in the mitochondria of lung cancer cells, possibly due to the limited number of antioxidant enzymes in these cells [39]. It was proven that catechins derived from green tea, while added to the medium used in cell culture, increase level of oxidative stress, leading to apoptosis [34].

Therefore, many in vivo studies determine the effect of the amount of consuming green tea on the reduction of incidence of malignant tumors, including colorectal cancer, stomach cancer, liver cancer [19] or lung cancer [38]. These results concern drinking more than ten cups of green tea infusions per day [40]. However, on the other side, one study indicates an increased risk of developing bladder cancer when consuming five to nine cups of green tea infusions per day. Another interesting result of the study carried out by the Taniguchi group is the oral consumption of the main catechins of green tea, EGCG, and its positive anticancer effect established in melanoma animal model [41].

The anticancer potential of EGCG has also been studied in cancer stem cells [33]. Stem cells, or precursor cells, are characterized by the ability to proliferate, i.e., self-renew, and maintain a constant, unchanging number of cells; they also have the ability to differentiate into an appropriate cell type. Notably, green tea extract and EGCG inhibit cell growth in these cellular and animal models [42,43].

In vivo and in vitro studies report that cancer stem cells are responsible for cancer renewal as well as metastasis [33]. Available data indicate that tumor stem cells overcome the epithelial–mesenchymal transition during the metastasis process [33]. This process allows the cancer cells to move towards the blood vessels. It is noteworthy that cancer stem cells, when compared to a cancer cell, show a much greater capacity for oncogenesis [33]. After analyzing the available scientific research on the use of green tea catechins on cancer stem cells, we found information indicating the effect of Matcha green tea catechins on the oxidative phosphorylation of MCF-7 breast cancer stem cells [33]. In addition, treatment with Matcha green tea extract of MCF-7 breast cancer cells also affects the regulation of the cell cycle, and causes a significant effect on the IL-8 pathway involved in the proliferation and angiogenesis of migratory cancer cells [33].

Molecular Signaling Pathways in Anticancer Effects of Green Tea Catechins

Cell signaling pathways, responsible for maintaining a homeostasis between cell proliferation and death, have emerged as rational targets for anticancer strategies.

As mentioned above, green tea catechins, especially the most potent EGCG, induce apoptosis in different cancer models. Notably, it is able to induce both intrinsic (mitochondrial) and extrinsic (death receptor) apoptotic pathways [44]. Nuclear condensation, caspase-3 activation, and poly(ADP)ribose polymerase cleavage are the main apoptotic features observed after treatment with green tea catechols [45]. In addition, the anticancer mechanism of EGCG also includes activation of BAX, depolarization of mitochondrial membranes, and cytochrome c release into cytosol [46].

The induction of cell cycle arrest and apoptosis are the main strategies of regulating cell proliferation. Indeed, green tea catechols regulate both the G1/S and G2/M transition and inhibit an increase in the number of cells and DNA synthesis [44]. Importantly, EGCG induces apoptosis and cell cycle arrest in many cancer cells without affecting normal cells [12]. EGCG directly inhibits the cyclin-dependent kinases which is the primary event in cell cycle progression [44]. EGCG also induces the expression of p21 and p27 while decreasing the expression of cyclin D1 and the phosphorylation of retinoblastoma [44].

The molecular signaling pathways regulated by green tea catechols resulting in their pro-apoptotic and anti-proliferative effects include, among others, inhibition of nuclear factor-κB (NF-κB) which is the crucial oxidative stress-sensitive transcription factor [14,35] NF-κB plays a critical role in the regulation of a variety of genes important in cellular responses, including inflammation, proliferation and cancer cell death. In addition, catechins contained in green tea, and above all the main catechin EGCG, activate endothelial nitric oxide synthase (eNOS) [42,47].

Inhibition of the mitogen-activated protein kinases (MAPKs), ERK, JNK, and p38 is implicated in many patho-physiological processes, such as cell proliferation, differentiation, and cancer cell death [39,46]. In addition, EGCG is known to lead to the induction of apoptosis in cancer cells by inhibiting tumor necrosis factor α activity (TNF-α) [42].

Another molecular signaling pathway event regulated by green tea catechols is the inhibition of the epidermal growth factor receptor (EGFR)-mediated signal transduction pathway. EGFR is a plasma membrane glycoprotein with an extracellular ligand-binding domain, a single transmembrane region, and an intracellular domain that exhibits intrinsic tyrosine kinase activity. Overexpression of EGFR produces a neoplastic phenotype in tumor cells. Notably, EGCG inhibits the activation of the EGFR, HER2, and multiple downstream signaling pathways in colon cancer cell lines [12,35].

Notably, molecular signaling pathways of green tea catechols involve the additional inhibition of insulin-like growth factor-I (IGF I)-mediated signal transduction pathway [12]. As evidenced, green tea catechins significantly reduce IGF-I protein levels in prostate cancer animal models [48].

Available literature data indicate that polyphenols derived from green tea exert their antitumor activity due to modification of histones, micro-RNA as well as DNA methylation [40]. Figure 3 presents a summary of molecular signaling pathways of green tea catechin.

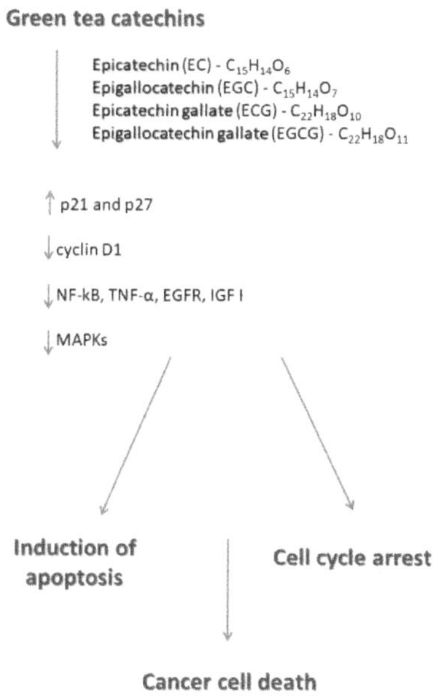

Green tea catechins

Epicatechin (EC) - $C_{15}H_{14}O_6$
Epigallocatechin (EGC) - $C_{15}H_{14}O_7$
Epicatechin gallate (ECG) - $C_{22}H_{18}O_{10}$
Epigallocatechin gallate (EGCG) - $C_{22}H_{18}O_{11}$

↑ p21 and p27

↓ cyclin D1

↓ NF-kB, TNF-α, EGFR, IGF I

↓ MAPKs

Induction of apoptosis   **Cell cycle arrest**

Cancer cell death

Figure 3. Summary of molecular signaling pathways of green tea catechin.

6. Differences between Black Tea and Green Tea

Black tea significantly differs from green tea, primarily in terms of chemical composition as well as the fermentation and oxidation process. Black tea, like green tea, is rich in a number of catechins as well as theaflavin; namely, Theaflavin (TF1), Theaflavin-3-monogallate (TF2a), Theaflavin-3′-monogallate (TF2b), and Theaflavin-3,3′-digallate (TF3). Numerous articles describe the molecular mechanism of black tea extraction, as well as individual theaflavins. According to the data, black tea in addition to catechins and theaflavins consists of phenolic acids, flavanols, tearubigins, amino acids, proteins, methylxanthine, and mineral compounds and volatile substances [49]. However, it is known that both tearubingins and theaflavins are products of the tea polyphenols.

The main molecular mechanisms of black tea polyphenols include the activation of mitochondrial cell death signaling pathways and reactive oxygen species-scavenging effects. The molecular effects of polyphenols contained in black tea additionally include activation of nuclear factor erythroid 2-related factor 2 (Nrf2), which is responsible for controlling gene expression as well as regulating antioxidant and detoxifying enzymes [12,14,35,48–50]. Notably, the anti-estrogenic impact of black tea consumption may significantly reduce the risk of malignant neoplasms in women [51].

Theaflavin 1 was found to prevent lung tumorigenesis via induction of apoptosis, down-regulation of fatty acid synthase and COX-2 in cellular and animal models. Theaflavin 2 induced cell death by regulating BAX and p53 protein in the HeLa and WI38VA cervical cancer cell line [45,52,53]. On figure below (Figure 4), we present a comparison of polyphenol content in green and black tea, broken down into theaflavins and catechins.

Int. J. Mol. Sci. **2020**, *21*, 1744

Polyphenol compounds of green and black tea

Green tea

- Epicatechin (EC)
- Epigallocatechin (EGC)
- Epicatechin gallate (ECG)
- Epigallocatechin gallate (EGCG)

Black tea

- Theaflavin (TF1)
- Theaflavin-3-monogallate (TF2a)
- Theaflavin-3'-monogallate (TF2b)
- Theaflavin-3,3'-digallate (TF3)

Figure 4. Comparison of polyphenol content in green and black tea.

7. Conclusions and Future Perspectives

A number of reports suggesting the beneficial effect of green tea polyphenols on cancer prognosis and prevention as an adjunct to pharmacological treatment have been reported [6,9].

There is a lot of in vivo evidence confirming that consumption of green tea in the form of a drink or dietary supplement exerts the anticancer properties [43,47,54]. The other valuable properties of green tea catechols involve their anti-viral, anti-bacterial, anti-aging, and hypotensive effects [4,5,9,12,27]. Nonetheless, it needs to be clearly emphasized that green tea as well as green tea catechins cannot replace standard chemotherapy. However, their beneficial effects may support anticancer effects and can be used as an adjunct [43,47,54,55].

All in all, polyphenols, and especially the main catechin of green tea, EGCG, brings promising results in the prevention of breast, lung, prostate, stomach, and pancreatic cancers.

Author Contributions: Conceptualization M.G.-P.; writing—original draft preparation M.G.-P. and C.M.; writing—review and editing M.G.-P., C.M., A.K.-J.; graphical part—M.G.-P. and C.M.; supervision M.G.-P.; project administration M.G.-P.; funding acquisition M.G.-P. All authors have read and agreed to the published version of the manuscript.

Funding: The manuscript publication and the studies concerning anticancer influence of green tea catechols were funded by the MN grant No. 01-0420/08/259 from Medical University of Gdansk (Gdansk, Poland) and Polish Ministry of Science and Higher Education. The funders had no role in study design, data collection and analysis, decision to publish, or preparation of the article.

Acknowledgments: Magdalena Gorska-Ponikowska kindly acknowledges being a guest scientist in the Stephan Nussberger lab at Stuttgart University (Stuttgart, Germany); and in the Francesco Cappello lab at Euro-Mediterranean Institute of Science and Technology (Palermo, Italy).

Conflicts of Interest: The authors declare no conflict of interest.

References

1. Cardoso, R.R.; Neto, R.O.; Dos Santos D'Almeida, C.T.; Nascimento, C.T.; Pressete, C.G.; Azevedo, L.; Martino, H.S.D.; Cameron, L.C.; Ferreira, M.S.L.; Barros, F.A.R. Kombuchas from green and black teas have different phenolic profile, which impacts their antioxidant capacities, antibacterial and antiproliferative activities. *Food Res. Int.* **2020**, *128*, 108782. [CrossRef] [PubMed]
2. Steinmann, J.; Buer, J.; Pietschmann, T.; Steinmann, E. Anti-infective properties of epigallocatechin-3-gallate (EGCG), a component of green tea. *Br. J. Pharmacol.* **2013**, *168*, 1059–1073. [CrossRef] [PubMed]
3. Chantre, P.; Lairon, D. Recent finding of green tea extract AR25 (Exolise) and its activity for the treatment of obesity. *Phytomedicine* **2002**, *9*, 3–8. [CrossRef] [PubMed]
4. Leung, L.K.; Su, Y.; Chen, R. Thea flavins in black tea and catechins in green tea are equally effective antioxidants. *J. Nutr.* **2001**, *131*, 2248–2251. [CrossRef] [PubMed]

5.	Zhang, C.; Suen, C.L.C.; Yang, C.; Quek, S.Y. Antioxidant capacity and major polyphenol composition of teas as affected by geographical location, plantation elevation and leaf grade. *Food Chem.* **2018**, *244*, 109–119. [CrossRef]

6.	Yanagimoto, K.; Ochi, H.; Lee, K.G.; Shibamoto, T. Antioxidative activities of volatile extracts from green tea, oolong tea, and black tea. *J. Agric. Food Chem.* **2003**, *51*, 7396–7401. [CrossRef] [PubMed]

7.	Juneja, L.R.; Chu, D.-C.; Okubo, T. L-theanine—A unique amino acid of green tea and its relaxation effect in humans. *Trends Food Sci. Technol.* **1999**, *10*, 199–204. [CrossRef]

8.	Yoshizawa, S.; Horiuchi, T.; Sugimura, M. Penta-o-galloyl-β-D-glucose and epigallocatechin gallate: Cancer prevention agent. Phenolic Compunds in Food and Health II. Antioxidant and cancer prevention. Washington DC. *Am. Chem. Soc.* **1992**, *2*, 118–119.

9.	Beltz, L.A.; BayerD, K.; Moss, A.L.; Simet, I.M. Mechanisms of cancer prevention by green and black tea polyphenols. *Anticancer Agents Med. Chem.* **2006**, *6*, 389–406. [CrossRef]

10.	Graham, H.N. Green tea composition, consumption, and polyphenol chemistry. *Prev. Med.* **1992**, *21*, 334–350. [CrossRef]

11.	Komatsu, Y.; Suematsu, S.; Hisanobu, Y.; Saigo, H.; Matsuda, R.; Hara, K. Effects of pH and temperature on reaction kinetics of catechins in green tea infusion. *Biosci. Biotechnol. Biochem.* **1993**, *57*, 907–910. [CrossRef]

12.	Ahmad, N.; Makhtar, H. Green tea polyphenols and cancer: Biologic mechanisms and implications. *Nutr. Rev.* **1999**, *57*, 78–83. [CrossRef] [PubMed]

13.	Tadano, N.; Du, C.; Yumoto, F.; Morimoto, S.; Ohta, M.; Xie, M.; Nagata, K.; Zhan, D.; Lu, Q.; Miwa, Y. Biological Actions of Green Tea Catechins on Cardiac Troponin C Br. *J. Pharmacol.* **2010**, *161*, 1034–1043.

14.	Gupta, D.A.; Bhaskar, D.J.; Gupta, R.K. Green tea: A review on its natural anti-oxidant therapy and cariostatic benefits. *Biol. Sci. Pharm. Res.* **2014**, *2*, 8–12.

15.	Bernatoniene, J.; Kopustinskiene, D.M. The Role of Catechins in Cellular Responses. *Molecular* **2018**, *23*, 965. [CrossRef]

16.	Masek, A.; Chrzescijanska, E.; Latos, M.; Zaborski, M.; Podsedek, A. Antioxidant and antiradical properties of green tea extract compounds. *Int. J. Electrochem. Sci.* **2017**, *12*, 6600–6610. [CrossRef]

17.	Singh, B.N.; Shankar, S.; Srivastava, R.K. Green Tea Catechin, Epigallocatechin-3-Gallate (EGCg), Mechanisms, Perspectives and Clinical Applications. *Biochem. Pharmacol.* **2011**, *82*, 1807–1821. [CrossRef]

18.	Yang, Y.; Zhang, T. Antimicrobial Activities of Tea Polyphenol on Phytopathogens: A Review. *Molecules* **2019**, *24*, 816. [CrossRef]

19.	Schulze, J.; Melzer, L.; Smith, L.; Teschke, R. Green Tea and Its Extracts in Cancer Prevention and Treatment. *Beverages* **2017**, *3*, 17. [CrossRef]

20.	Ye, Y.; Yan, J.; Cui, J.; Mao, S.; Li, M.; Liao, X. Dynamic changes in amino acids, catechins, caffeine and gallic acid in green tea during withering. *J. Food Compos Anal.* **2018**, *66*, 98–108. [CrossRef]

21.	Ahn, W.S.; Yoo, J.; Huh, S.W.; Kim, C.K.; Lee, J.M.; Namkoong, S.E.; Bae, S.M.; Lee, I.P. Protective effect of green tea extract (polyphenon E and EGCG) on human cervical lesions. *Eur. J. Cancer Prev.* **2003**, *12*, 383–390. [CrossRef] [PubMed]

22.	Yang, C.S.; Lambert, J.D.; Sang, S. Antioxidative and anticarcinogenic activities of tea polyphenols. *Arch. Toxicol.* **2009**, *83*, 11–21. [CrossRef] [PubMed]

23.	Hamilton-Miller, J.M.T. Anti-cariogenic properties of tea (*Camellia sinensis*). *J. Med. Microbiol.* **2001**, *2001. 50*, 299–302. [CrossRef]

24.	Maity, R.; Chatterjee, M.; Banejee, A.; Das, A.; Mishra, R.; Mazumder, S.; Chanda, N. Gold nanoparticle-assisted enhancement in the anti-cancer properties of theaflavin against human ovarian cancer cells. *Mater. Sci. Eng. C Mater. Biol. Appl.* **2019**, *104*, 109909. [CrossRef] [PubMed]

25.	Subramani, C.; Natesh, R.K. Molecular mechanisms and biological implications of green tea polyphenol, (-)-epigallocatechin-3-gallate. *Int. J. Pharma Biosci. Technol.* **2003**, *1*, 54–63.

26.	Botten, D.; Fugallo, G.; Fraternali, F.; Molteni, C. Structural Properties of Green Tea Catechins. *J. Phys. Chem. B* **2015**, *119*, 12860–12867. [CrossRef] [PubMed]

27.	Jigisha, A.; Nishant, R.; Navin, K. Green tea: A magical herb with miraculous outcomes. *Int. Res. J. Pharm.* **2012**, *3*, 139–148.

28.	Koch, W.; Kukula-Koch, W.; Komsta, Ł.; Marzec, Z.; Szwerc, W.; Główniak, K. Green tea quality evaluation based on its catechins and metals composition in combination with chemometric analysis. *Molecules* **2018**, *23*, 1689. [CrossRef]

29. Barbosa, D.S. Green tea polyphenolic compounds and human health. *J. Verbr. Lebensm.* **2007**, *2*, 407–413. [CrossRef]

30. Ambigaipalan, P.; Young, W.; Shahidi, F. Epigallocatechin (EGC) esters as potential sources of antioxidants. *Food Chem.* **2020**, *309*, 125609. [CrossRef]

31. Lawless, M.W.; O'Byrne, K.J.; Gray, S.G. Targeting oxidative stress in cancer. *Expert Opin. Ther. Targets* **2010**, *14*, 1225–1245. [CrossRef] [PubMed]

32. Kellogg, J.J.; Graf, T.N.; Paine, M.F.; McCune, J.S.; Kvalheim, O.M.; Oberlies, N.H.; Cech, N.B. Comparison of Metabolomics Approaches for Evaluating the Variability of Complex Botanical Preparations: Green Tea (*Camellia sinensis*) as a Case Study. *J. Nat. Prod.* **2017**, *80*, 1457–1466. [CrossRef] [PubMed]

33. Bonuccelli, G.; Sotgia, F.; Lisanti, M.P. Matcha green tea (MGT) inhibits the propagation of cancer stem cells (CSCs), by targeting mitochondrial metabolism, glycolysis, and multiple cell signaling pathways. *Aging* **2018**, *10*, 1867–1883. [CrossRef] [PubMed]

34. Sharifi-Rad, M.; Pezzani, R.; Redaelli, M.; Zorzan, M.; Imran, M.; Ahmed Khalil, A.; Salehi, B.; Sharopov, F.; Cho, W.C.; Sharifi-Rad, J. Preclinical Pharmacological Activities of Epigallocatechin-3-gallate in Signaling Pathways: An Update on Cancer. *Molecules* **2020**, *25*, 467. [CrossRef]

35. Khan, N.; Mukhtar, H. Tea and health: Studies in humans. *Curr. Pharm. Des.* **2013**, *19*, 6141–6147. [CrossRef]

36. Yoshida, G.J.; Saya, H. Therapeutic strategies targeting cancer stem cells. *Cancer Sci.* **2016**, *107*, 5–11. [CrossRef]

37. Toden, S.; Tran, H.M.; Tovar-Camargo, O.A.; Okugawa, Y.; Goel, A. Epigallocatechin-3-gallate targets cancer stem-like cells and enhances 5-fluorouracil chemosensitivity in colorectal cancer. *Oncotarget* **2016**, *7*, 16158–16170. [CrossRef]

38. Fu, H.; He, J.; Mei, F.; Zhang, Q.; Hara, Y.; Ryota, S. Lung cancer inhibitory effect of epigallocatechin-3-gallate is dependent on its presence in a complex mixture (polyphenon E). *Cancer Prev. Res. (Phila)* **2009**, *2*, 531–537. [CrossRef]

39. Fujiki, H.; Watanabe, T.; Sueoka, E.; Rawangkan, A.; Suganuma, M. Cancer Prevention with Green Tea and Its Principal Constituent, EGCG: From Early Investigations to Current Focus on Human Cancer Stem Cells. *Mol. Cells* **2018**, *41*, 73–82.

40. Bag, A.; Bag, N. Tea Polyphenols and Prevention of Epigenetic Aberrations in Cancer. *J. Nat. Sci. Biol. Med.* **2018**, *9*, 2–5. [CrossRef]

41. Li, Q.; Zhao, H.F.; Zhang, Z.F.; Liu, Z.G.; Pei, X.R.; Wang, J.B.; Cai, M.Y. Long-term administration of green tea catechins prevents age-related spatial learning and memory decline in C57BL/6 J mice by regulating hippocampal cyclic amp-response element binding protein signaling cascade. *Neuroscience* **2009**, *159*, 1208–1215. [CrossRef] [PubMed]

42. Okabe, S.; Ochiai, Y.; Aida, M.; Park, K.; Kim, S.J.; Nomura, T.; Suganuma, M.; Fujiki, H. Mechanistic aspects of green tea as a cancer preventive: Effect of components on human stomach cancer cell lines. *Jpn. J. Cancer Res.* **1999**, *90*, 733–739. [CrossRef]

43. Reygaert, W.C. Green tea catechins: Their use in treating and preventing infectious diseases. *BioMed Res. Int.* **2018**. [CrossRef] [PubMed]

44. Liu, S.M.; Ou, S.Y.; Huang, H.H. Green tea polyphenols induce cell death in breast cancer MCF-7 cells through induction of cell cycle arrest and mitochondrial-mediated apoptosis. *Univ. Sci. B* **2017**, *18*, 89–98. [CrossRef] [PubMed]

45. Gosslau, A.; En Jao, D.L.; Huang, M.T. Effects of the black tea polyphenol theaflavin-2 on apoptotic and inflammatory pathways in vitro and in vivo. *Mol. Nutr. Food Res.* **2011**, *55*, 198–208. [CrossRef]

46. Lambert, J.D.; Elias, R.J. The antioxidant and pro-oxidant activities of green tea polyphenols: A role in cancer prevention. *Arch. Biochem. Biophys.* **2010**, *501*, 65–72. [CrossRef]

47. Pervin, M.; Unno, K.; Takagaki, A.; Isemura, M.; Nakamura, Y. Function of green tea catechins in the brain: Epigallocatechin gallate and its metabolites. *Int. J. Mol. Sci.* **2019**, *20*, 3630. [CrossRef]

48. Adhami, V.M.; Siddiqui, I.A.; Ahmad, N.; Gupta, S.; Mukhtar, H. Oral consumption of green tea polyphenols inhibits insulin-like growth factor-I-induced signaling in an autochthonous mouse model of prostate cancer. *Cancer Res.* **2004**, *64*, 8715–8722. [CrossRef]

49. Pan, M.H.; Lai, C.S.; Wang, H.; Ho, C.H.; Li, S. Black tea in chemo-prevention of cancer and other human diseases. *Food Sci. Hum. Well.* **2013**, *2*, 12–21. [CrossRef]

50. Singh Bhalla, H.; Kaur, J.; Arora, A.; Kumar, N. Comparative study of Anti-oxidant activity of green, black, white and oolong tea. *World J. Pharm. Res.* **2018**, *7*, 514–523.
51. Kapiszewska, M.; Miskiewicz, M.; Ellison, P.T. High tea consumption diminishes salivary 17beta-estradiol concentration in Polish women. *Br. J. Nutr.* **2006**, *95*, 989–995. [CrossRef] [PubMed]
52. Sheng, J.; Shi, W.; Guo, H.; Long, W.; Wang, Y.; Qi, J.; Liu, J.; Xu, Y. The Inhibitory Effect of (-)-Epigallocatechin-3-Gallate on Breast Cancer Progression via Reducing SCUBE2 Methylation and DNMT Activity. *Molecules* **2019**, *24*, 2899. [CrossRef] [PubMed]
53. Yeh, C.W.; Chen, W.J.; Chiang, C.T. Suppression of fatty acid synthase in MCF-7 breast cancer cells by tea and tea polyphenols: A possible mechanism for their hypolipidemic effects. *Pharm. J.* **2003**, *3*, 267–276. [CrossRef]
54. Niedzwiecki, A.; Roomi, M.W.; Kalinovsky, T.; Rath, M. Anticancer efficacy of polyphenols and their combinations. *Nutrients* **2016**, *8*, 552. [CrossRef] [PubMed]
55. Guo, Y.; Zhi, F.; Chen, P.; Zhao, K.; Xiang, H.; Mao, Q. Green tea and the risk of prostate cancer: A systematic review and meta-analysis. *Medicine* **2017**, *96*, e6426. [CrossRef]

Review

Functional Ingredients From *Brassicaceae* Species: Overview and Perspectives

Daniela Ramirez [1,2], Angel Abellán-Victorio [3], Vanesa Beretta [1], Alejandra Camargo [1,2] and Diego A. Moreno [3,*]

[1] Laboratorio de Cromatografía para Agroalimentos, Facultad de Ciencias Agrarias, UNCuyo, Mendoza 54 261, Argentina; danielaandrearamirez2511@gmail.com (D.R.); vanesaberetta@hotmail.com (V.B.); alebcamargo@gmail.com (A.C.)

[2] Instituto de Biología Agrícola de Mendoza, CONICET Mendoza 54 261, Argentina

[3] Phytochemistry and Healthy Foods Laboratory, Department of Food Science and Technology, Spanish National Research Council for Scientific Research (CEBAS-CSIC), Murcia 30100, Spain; avictorio@cebas.csic.es

* Correspondence: dmoreno@cebas.csic.es

Received: 20 February 2020; Accepted: 13 March 2020; Published: 15 March 2020

Abstract: *Brassicaceae* vegetables are important crops consumed worldwide due to their unique flavor, and for their broadly recognized functional properties, which are directly related to their phytochemical composition. Isothiocyanates (ITC) are the most characteristic compounds, considered responsible for their pungent taste. Besides ITC, these vegetables are also rich in carotenoids, phenolics, minerals, and vitamins. Consequently, Brassica's phytochemical profile makes them an ideal natural source for improving the nutritional quality of manufactured foods. In this sense, the inclusion of functional ingredients into food matrices are of growing interest. In the present work, *Brassicaceae* ingredients, functionality, and future perspectives are reviewed.

Keywords: *Brassicaceae*; ingredients; phytochemicals; functionality

---

1. *Brassicaceae* Family: A Rich Mine of Bioactive Phytochemicals

Brassicaceae family vegetables have an ample worldwide distribution, which can be found in all continents except Antarctica [1–4]. One of the most striking features of this botanical family is the presence of several kinds of secondary metabolites with a distinctive taste, and also interesting bioactivities. The most deeply studied are the glucosinolates (GSL) and their breakdown products, isothiocyanates and indoles [5–7]. Moreover, these species are also rich and possess unique profiles of phenolic compounds, carotenoids, and other groups of less studied compounds such as phytoalexins, terpenes, phytosteroids, and tocopherols, here reviewed.

1.1. Phenolic Compounds

Phenolic compounds are a large class of plant secondary metabolites characterized by having at least one aromatic ring with one or more hydroxyl groups attached, showing a diversity of structures, ranging from rather simple and low molecular weight structures to complex polymeric compounds. More than 8000 phenolic compounds have been reported on plant kingdom [8]. Phenolic compounds are very important regarding the quality of plant-based foods since they are involved in flavor features (e.g., astringency), and they are responsible for the color of some fruits and vegetables and also because they serve as substrates for enzymatic deterioration [9,10]. Finally, phenolic compounds are considered to contribute to the health benefits associated with dietary consumption of *Brassicaceae* species such as antioxidant capacity, anticarcinogenic power, anti-aggregation activity, activation of detoxification enzymes, among others (*Brassicaceae* bioactive properties are reviewed and discussed in Section 3 of the present study). The most important phenolic compounds present in *Brassicacea* family vegetables are the flavonoids and the hydroxycinnamic acids [8]. Among flavonoids, the most important group corresponds to the flavonols. Quercetin, kaempferol, isorhamnetin, and cyanidin are the most representative flavonols in these species, but their qualitative and quantitative profiles vary significantly among species. For example, cauliflower main phenolic compounds are quercetin aglycon and catechins, but in white cabbage, the main compound are kaempferol glucosides and epicatechins [11,12]. The phenolic profile can also vary within the same plant species according to the plant organ being studied; for example, cruciferous sprouts can contain from 2 to 10 times more phenolic compound when compared with roots and inflorescences, which are the most common plant organ consumed [13]. Recently, Fusari et al. (2019) reported for the first time important levels of *t*-resveratrol-*a p*-terostilbene phenolic compound extensively reported as a potent antioxidant molecule-in several members of this botanical family, reaching, for example, 84 μg/g dry weight level in rocket leaves (*Eruca sativa* L.) [12,14].

Another group of phenolic compounds frequently detected in *Brassicaceae* vegetables is the hydroxycinnamic acid group, which is characterized by the C6–C3 structure and can be found free or conjugated with sugars or with other acids. The most common in this species are ferulic acid, sinapic acid, caffeic acid, and *p*-coumaric acid, but as occur with flavonols, this varies significantly according to the plant species considered. For example, sinapic acid is the main hydroxycinnamic acid present in rocket salad but is absent in red cherry and daikon radishes [11]. Another example of this considerable variation among species is ferulic acid, which represents the main hydroxycinnamic acid for red cabbage but is absent in radish and rocket leaves [12]. In Figure 1, the chemical structure of the phenolic compounds usually present in *Brassicaceae* is shown.

Anthocyanins have also been reported in *Brassicaceae* vegetables. For example, the red or violet pigmentation of red cabbage, purple cauliflower, or red radishes is caused by anthocyanins. The major type of anthocyanins differs among species. While red radish contains mainly cyanidin and peonidin anthocyanins acylated with aromatic acids [15], red cabbage and broccoli sprouts contain mainly cyaniding glucosides derivatives [16]. Besides, Lo Scalzo et al. (2008) [17] found that the *p*-coumaryl and feruloyl esterified forms of cyanidin-3-sophoroside-5-glucoside were predominant in cauliflower, while the sinapyl one was mostly present in red cabbage. In another study, Otsuki (2002) [18] found 12 different anthocyanins in radish roots, 6 of them corresponding to the pelargonidin derivatives. In red cabbage cultivars, the predominant anthocyanins resulted in being nonacylated cyanidin- glucosides [19]. Altogether, these results indicate that anthocyanins, as with other phenolic compounds, vary according to the vegetable species, the plant organ, and the cultivars of the single species considered.

1.2. Organosulfur Compounds

Among the organosulfur compounds accumulated by cruciferous vegetables, glucosinolates (GSL)-sulfur-containing glycosides- are the main secondary metabolites found. Their presence is evidenced whenever its tissue is disrupted, and their breakdown products are the principal responsible for the sharp and bitter-tasting flavors of these vegetables. There have been described in plant kingdom more than 120 different GSL, but in *Brassicaceae*, the amount reaches around 96, of which some are unique of some specific gender or species [20]. While genetic factors determining mainly the type of GSL, environmental factors influence the amount of them. The induction of GSL following abiotic or biotic stresses has frequently been described in order to increase the phytochemicals levels when GSL are hydrolyzed by myrosinase (thioglucoside glucohydrolase, EC 3.2.1.147) upon tissue disruption, numerous breakdown products are formed, including isothiocyanates (ITCs), thiocyanates, nitriles, ascorbigen, indoles, oxazolidine-2-thiones, and epithioalkanes depending upon different factors like pH, temperature, presence of myrosinase-interacting protein, and availability of ferrous ion [21]. Among the different GLS-degradation products formed, the most abundantly formed at physiological pH are the ITCs, which are also considered the main responsible for cruciferous foods bioactivity. Since ITCs are very unstable, their health benefits depend on numerous variables related to several factors, such as the initial GSL concentration, cooking processes, amount of vegetable intake, and human metabolism.

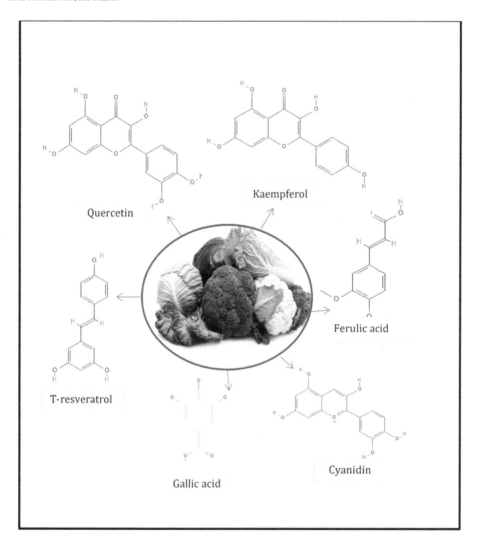

Figure 1. Phenolic compounds present in members of *Brassicaceae* [12].

Because the GSL profile varies between different species and the hydrolysis conditions determine the identity and amount of ITC compounds formed, it is possible to find in the literature many ITC profiles for each species, and these profiles do not always coincide with each other. ITC profiles for each cruciferous vegetable have been extensively reviewed [22–25], and the reported information highly variable according to the extraction. It is also important to keep in mind that the majority of GLS will not always give rise to its ITC profile. For example, in radish, it has consistently been reported that the majority GLS is glucoraphasatin; however, the raphasatin levels found when the ITC profile was studied, were negligible or non-quantifiable because of the extraction conditions and the hydrolysis affecting the results, especially if the medium is polar or aqueous [26]. Furthermore, the ITC profile of each cruciferous species varies according to the cultivar or variety considered and also according to the plant tissue found [27,28]. For example, in rocket leaves, the main ITC generally detected corresponds to sativin [29], but in rocket seeds, the main ITC detected have been erucin and sulforaphane (SFN) [30]. Accordingly, in radish seeds and sprouts, the main ITC detected was sulforaphene according to several reports [13,27,28,31] (Figure 2), but in radish roots, the chief ITC have been raphasatin and sulforaphene [27,32]. In Figure 2, a graphical example of the ITC variation inside a single plant is schematized. The foregoing demonstrates that, in order to inform the ITC profile of a cruciferous vegetable, it is very important to consider, in addition to the species, the cultivation, the plant organ under study, and the extraction and detection techniques in order to make inferences and comparisons among studies.

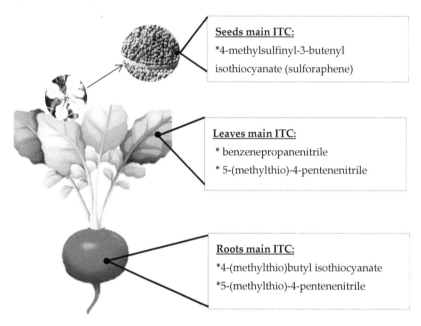

Seeds main ITC:
*4-methylsulfinyl-3-butenyl isothiocyanate (sulforaphene)

Leaves main ITC:
* benzenepropanenitrile
* 5-(methylthio)-4-pentenenitrile

Roots main ITC:
*4-(methylthio)butyl isothiocyanate
*5-(methylthio)-4-pentenenitrile

Figure 2. Schematic representation of different isothiocyanate (ITC) profiles in several radish plant organs.

1.3. Carotenoids

Carotenoids are highly pigmented phytochemicals that possess a C40 backbone structure and are classified as symmetrical tetraterpenes. They are produced in many plants and microorganisms, and they can be yellow, orange, or red pigments. Some carotenoids such as β-carotene and α-carotene and β-cryptoxanthin have provitamin A activity since they act as precursors of vitamin A and, therefore, acquires an important function as a human health promoter. These compounds have been extensively studied for their health-enhancing properties and also for their biological functions as attractants to pollinators, as photoprotection pigments, and as light-harvesting pigments. Similarly, to phenolic compounds, the accumulation of carotenoids in cruciferous is regulated by the environment, tissue type, and developmental stage [33,34]. These groups of bioactive compounds have not been deeply characterized for *Brassicaceae* species, but it has been reported that the predominant ones are β-carotene and luteolin, but variable amounts of zeaxanthin, cryptoxanthin, neoxanthin, and violaxanthin have also been detected [35–37]. Other reports have found that carotenoid-containing cruciferous vegetables include kale (*Brassica oleracea* L. convar. Acephala var. sabellica), brussels sprouts, broccoli, cauliflower, red cabbage, white cabbage, pakchoi (Brassica rapa subsp. chinensis), and kohlrabi (Brassica oleracea var. ganglyoides) [38,39]. Kale is considered the richest cruciferous source of this compound, surpassing cabbage in about 40 times [35]. Among these, kale stands out for its high contents, not only within the cruciferous but also when compared to other vegetables, resulting in one of the main dietary source of carotenoids [35,40,41]. Kale main carotenoids have been proposed to be zeaxantin and luteolin [40] but important differences were found among several kale cultivars [42]. Carotenoid profile among *Brassicaceae* species varies greatly; for example, broccoli contains mainly β-carotene and luteolin [43], cabbage contains mainly luteolin, followed by β-carotene, zeaxantin, and α-carotene [44].

1.4. Other Terpenes Present in Brassicaceae Vegetables

Other naturally occurring terpenes compounds that can be found in *Brassicaceae* vegetables are tocotrienols and tocopherols. According to Podsedeck (2007) [45], the descending order of total tocopherols and tocotrienol content in Brassica vegetables is as follows: broccoli > broccoli sprouts > cabbage. Furtheremore, Kurilich et al. (1999) [46] reported that kale was the best source among other *Brassicaceae* vegetables of α-tocopherol and γ-tocopherol. Beside *Brassicaceae* vegetables, these compounds have also been reported in oils and cereals [47]. These phytochemicals have been extensively researched due to its anticarcinogenic properties [48,49]. Another bioactivity extensively reported in these lipid-soluble compounds is the antioxidant activity through hydrogen atom transference [50].

Phytosterols are another important terpene subclass. It has been reported to possess anti-inflammatory, anti-neoplastic, anti-pyretic, and immune-modulating activity. Also, it has been reported that phytosterols reduce serum or plasma total cholesterol and low-density lipoprotein (LDL) cholesterol [51]. Among cruciferous vegetables, Brassica napus L., known as rapeseed, is the most abundant natural source of phytosterols, reaching levels of up to 9.79 gr/kg oil [52]. Another rich source of phytosterols among cruciferous vegetables is Brassica Juncea, of which, according to the cultivar analyzed, different compositions and levels of phytosterol can be detected [53].

1.5. Phytoalexins

These groups of compounds were described initially in 1940 and are considered phenolic-related compounds with highly diverse chemical structures and several bioactivities, including anti-cancer properties. They possess low molecular weight and are thought to serve as an important defense mechanism for the plant [54,55]. *Brassicaceae* members containing phytoalexins present an indolic ring with C3 substitutions with N and S atoms, which confers a unique structure among other vegetables. The proposed biosynthetic pathway for phytoalexins formation includes brassinin formations from GSL; thereafter, other related phytoalexins are produced from brassinin. Klein and Sattely (2017) [55] reported that over 30 compounds arise from oxidative tailoring and rearrangement of Brassinin. Among edible cruciferous, phytoalexins have been reported in *Brassica napus* [56], *Brassica oleracea* [57], *Brassica Juncea* [58], *Sinapsis alba* [59], *Wasabi japonica* [60], and in *Raphanus sativus* [61].

1.6. Alkaloids

Alkaloids are secondary metabolites of plants synthesized from amino acids. These nitrogen compounds have been reported in several *Brassicaceae* species, including *Capsella bursa pastoris*, *Lepidium cartilacineum*, *Nasturtium montanum*, and *Raphanus sativus*, among others [62]. Among edible *Brassicaceae* alkaloid compounds have also been reported in a cabbage cultivar collection [63], in cabbage seeds by Mohammed (2014) [64], in cauliflower leaves [65], in broccoli florets [66]. and red cabbage florets [67]. Besides, a screening of tropane alkaloids—a class of alkaloids typically found in *Solanaceae* vegetables—in 43 different *Brassicaceae* species reveal that 18 of them presented alkaloid of different structures, and the authors proposed that alkaloid compounds are typical secondary cruciferous metabolites [68].

As described above, the *Brassicacea* family is characterized by the presence of GSL and the isothiocyanates that are exclusive of this family. Also, *Brassicacea* stands out because they possess phytochemicals of multiple chemical groups, being these species' excellent sources of bioactive compounds that have been studied throughout history. Currently, modern analytical techniques allow us to expand the knowledge about new compounds and metabolites. Consequently, it is possible to understand that each species, each Brassica-derived product, is themselves a mixture of multiple components. For this reason, an exhaustive determination of their phytochemical profiles must be made in each case.

2. "Functional" Foods Based on Brassicas: Concepts and Relevance for Development of New Products

2.1. Origin of the "Functional Food" Concept

The origin of the concept of functional food dates to 1980 with the introduction of the concept "FOSHU" (Foods for Specified Human Health) in Japan. This tag system pretended, for first time in the world, to regulate the employment of health claims in the market [69]. From this point, the regulation of functional foods has been in constant evolution in Europe by the EFSA (European Food Safety Authority), in the USA by the FDA (United States Food and Drug Administration), or in Canada by the CFIA (Health Canada's Food Directorate and the Canadian Food Inspection Agency), among others [70–72]. Nowadays, different unofficial definitions and concepts of functional foods coexist, being dependent of diverse factors: the country of the origin, in the case of a food product; the main characteristics of the manufacturing and the main use of this product; the specific criteria of an author, in the case of an article [73]. In this sense, a global definition can be outlined, based on specific definitions collected in recent literature [74]: A functional food must have a nutritional function that contributes to nutritional benefit on the consumer health, besides have been subjected to a technological process, in order to add a beneficial ingredient or eliminate a harmful one. In addition, it is interesting to mention the concept "nutraceutical" (classified by the European Union like "dietary supplement") [75], a kind of functional product with a specific format similar to medicines (e.g., pills, tablets), like [76]. However, it would be a priority to clarify the limit between medicine and functional foods or nutraceuticals: it is possible to establish a mandatory common characteristic, and, without discussion, that is the preventive and non-resolving nature of functional foods against different diseases.

In general terms and due to the information exposed, it is feasible to establish the next division of this group of products:

- Functional foods with an added (or enhanced) ingredient that is associated with a health benefit. Example: milk chocolate enriched with kale [77].
- Functional foods without an ingredient (naturally present in the original product) with a health risk associated. Example: reduced fat/cholesterol mayonnaise [78]. Nutraceuticals example: microencapsulation of polyphenols extracted from red chicory and red cabbage [79]

Nowadays, consumers have introduced several modifications in their nutritional habits, due to the growing concern about health. This fact could explain the recent popularization of food products based on functional ingredients, including products based on Brassicas vegetables [80]. However, the introduction of new concepts like bioaccessibility ("digestibility") and bioavailability has caused a strong controversy due to the questionable functionality of these food products in scientific reality [81]. In fact, the responsible regulations of health claims demand studies in vivo to allow legal commercialization, in addition to official controls in vitro that guarantees the presence of the compounds, related to the health claim of the commercial product and the capacity of the organism to use such compounds.

2.2. Functional Foods Based on Brassica Vegetables

Dietary intake of Brassicas has shown a relevant influence in the control and incidence of diverse diseases like cancer, hypertension, diabetes, chronic inflammation, or oxidative stress, among others [82]. These benefits are associated to specific compounds with active properties over human health, such as polyphenols or GSL, previously described in Section 1.

In this sense, fresh products such as broccoli or cabbage have reached a high production level nowadays, which leads to a high amount of by-products with interesting potential as biocompound sources. This valorization process is especially relevant in popular crops like broccoli, which represents 34% of total cruciferous production in the world, according to the Food and Agriculture Organization Corporate Statistical Database (FAOSTAT, 2017, www.fao.org/faostat/es/). Broccoli floret, the edible part, represents just 15% of the total vegetable, producing 85% (stems and leaves) of valuable by-products [83]. Other Brassica species by-products have been studied as sources of bioactive compounds, among them red radish or kale, among others [84].

Recent work has focused on the increase of the total quantity of bioactive compounds found in Brassica species by elicitation in order to enhance health benefits. In this way, biotic (plant hormones), and abiotic (e.g., LED light, temperature, humidity, irrigation) elicitors, have been applied to improve the quantity of polyphenols and GSL in broccoli sprouts (Brassica oleracea L. var. Italica), red radish sprouts (Raphanus sativus cv. Rambo), or chinese cabbage (Brassica rapa ssp. pekinensis), among others [85,86].

In light of improving the manufacturing of these functional foods, efforts have been focused, on one hand, in the optimization of isolation and elicitation of these bioactive compounds from Brassicas and, on the other hand, in the use of the by-products generated by the industry, to obtain socio-economically sustainable products [87–89].

3. Functionality: What Has Been Demonstrated and What Remains to Be Study

The development of functional foods or functional ingredients is possible thanks to the interaction of three actors: (1) consumers demanding healthy foods, (2) the industrial sector motivated to elaborate and labelling their food products with a functional claim, and (3) the scientific sector which is responsible to obtain the knowledge to support those claims. Scientific substantiations of claims are performed by taking into account the totality of the available pertinent scientific data and by weighing up the evidence. To support these claims, scientific evidence on functional assessment procedures is needed, as well as toxicological evaluations and standardize analytical methodologies for functional component quantification [90]. The European Commission Regalement indicates a ranking of tests that can be done to support health statements of certain products. These tests consider, among others, whether a specific effect attributed to the product is representative in a target population, and if the quantity of the food and pattern of consumption required to obtain the claimed effect could reasonably be achieved as part of a balanced diet. In order of decreasing preference, the "most reliable" would be the products that would have demonstrated their benefits in experimental trials in humans. For that reason, among all the available information on the functional properties of *Brassicaceae*, we consider in the first instance, those that involve the results of epidemiological studies. A bibliographic search was made with the keys "epidemiology" + "*Brassicaceae*" + "functional property" in the last ten years. It follows that from the spectrum of functional properties attributed to this botanical family, biological properties related to chemoprevention of cancer are the most evaluated (40%), followed very far by properties related to the prevention of cardiovascular diseases (6.6%) and antidiabetics (5.7%). These results allow us, a priori, to warn of the areas in which there is a shortage of epidemiological data.

In this regard, the extent of information supporting the benefits of consuming cruciferous vegetables is plenty and rather proven. However, when analyzing the functionality of *Brassicaceae*-based products, epidemiological results are scarce. The studies that can be found in this regard focus mainly on product development, and the study of in vitro properties associated with some bioactive compounds present in the final product. Alvarez-Jubete et al. (2013), for example, determined the glucosinolate and isothiocyanate contents as the antioxidant capacity of a Broccoli-based soup [91]. Other authors have evaluated different biological activities of *Brassicaceae* juices. Broccoli sprout juice has been studied as a potential therapeutic strategy for Alzheimer's disease [92]. A broccoli–cabbage juice was also efficient as a lowering LDL-cholesterol agent [93]. The antibacterial properties against food-borne bacteria of *Brassica oleracea* juice have also been addressed [94]. Furthermore, Brussels sprouts juice affects the balance of colorectal cell proliferation and death in an animal model of colorectal neoplasia [95]. Even though these findings help to give birth to the idea that certain products and ingredients have potential functionality, clinical and epidemiological studies that yield more accurate findings regarding a real health-claim are still lacking.

Unlike the above, there is plenty of epidemiological evidence indicating that cruciferous vegetable (CV) consumption has health-promoting effects on the consumers. Although *Brassicaceae* vegetables are associated with numerous biological properties, such as antioxidant, anti-inflammatory, anti-diabetic, neuroprotective, and cholesterol-lowering effects, the cancer-protective effects stand out from the other [93]. It has been proven that CV is protective against a range of cancers, GSL and their breakdown products being considered the biologically active constituents [96].

Meta-analysis are useful tools that allow statistical comparison of results among a large number of research articles that have common variables [97]. In other words, they serve to organize and simplify the findings concerning a specific subject, identifying broad trends and patterns. In this case, updated meta-analysis related to chemopreventive properties associated with CV intake were examined in order to get closer to valid health claims. Data on epidemiological studies were taken from an exhaustive review carried out using the most common and broad search engines available online up to 2010. The databases considered were SCOPUS, SCIENCE.GOV, and SCHOLAR GOOGLE. The current paper limits itself to an overview of epidemiological data on cancers with high incidence and mortality such as lung, colon, prostate, gastric, breast, and ovarium. Based on other reviews, like the one published by Van Poppel et al. (2000) [98], two types of epidemiological studies were considered. On one side, prospective cohort studies, in which diets of large groups of people are recorded, using surveys, and then, these people are controlled for disease occurrence. On the other hand, retrospective case–control studies were also considered. They are based on interviews or questionnaires to estimate dietary patterns in the near or distant past. Data from patients are then compared with data from disease-free controls.

As a result of this search in the most important data bases regarding scientific reports and articles, using as key words the terms "meta-analysis isothiocyanates", up to 15,000 results appeared in SCHOLAR GOOGLE, but fewer results appeared in SCOPUS and SCIENCE.GOV. It must be point out that not all these results are meta-analysis per se, given that the term "analysis" is also included in the search. Therefore, most results are related to in-vitro or in vivo studies, and not precisely epidemiological studies, like the ones we are interested in. Table 1 shows the most relevant up-dated meta-analysis carried out, considering CV or ITC intake.

Table 1. Latest most relevant evidence for the association of CV/ITC/GLS intake and cancer preventive effects.

Functional Property Addressed in the Meta-Analysis/Health Claim	Bioactive Compounds/Vegetables/Ingredients to Which the Bioactivity Is Attributed	Reference
Chemoprevention of melanoma	Isothiocyanates	[99]
May reduce ovarian cancer	Cruciferous vegetables	[100]
Protect against colon cancer	Cruciferous vegetables	[101]
May decrease risk of renal cancer	Cruciferous vegetables	[102]
Might be inversely associated with pancreatic cancer	Cruciferous vegetables	[103]
Chemoprevention activities against bladder cancer	Isothiocyanates	[104]
Inversely associated with type 2 diabetes	Cruciferous vegetables	[105]
Inversely associated with lung cancer	Cruciferous vegetables	[106]
Inversely associated with breast cancer	Glucosinolates (GSL) and isothiocyanates (ITC)	[107]
Decreased risk of renal cell carcinoma	Cruciferous vegetables	[102]
May reduce risk of developing lung cancer in females	Cruciferous vegetables	[108]
Decreased risk of developing colorectal and gastric cancer	Cruciferous vegetables	[109]
Chemoprevention of breast cancer	Sulforaphane (SFN)/Epicatechin Gallate	[110]
Weakly and inversely associated with lung cancer	Cruciferous vegetables	[111]

Lung cancer derived from tobacco consumption is responsible for approximately 22% of cancer deaths [112]. Regarding this type of cancer, back in 2009, Lam et al. [111] started to systematize the available evidence through a meta-analysis based on epidemiological studies focusing on the potential gene–diet interaction between cruciferous vegetable intake and GSTM1 and GSTT1 (genes involved in detoxification). Back then, the evidence weakly showed an inverse association between lung cancer and CV consumption. Since then, dozens of case–control and cohort studies have been published. Liu et al. (2013) gathered this information to make an emphasis in lung cancer incidence in females, more specifically in Chinese women aged 40 to 70 years, through a prospective cohort study, which added to previous observational evidence up to 2011 [108]. In that occasion, it was observed that CV consumption might reduce the risk of lung cancer in women, especially in non-smoker ones. More recently, Zhang et al. (2018) concluded that CV intake was inversely associated with lung cancer risk. However, they recognized that current evidence is still limited and more short-term clinical Phase II and III trials are needed to elucidate further whether the inverse association reported for CV intake is due to ITC content or other bioactive compounds.

On the other side, cancers related to colorectum, gastric, oesophagus, and oropharyngeal tissues constitute one of the most common causes of death from cancer throughout the world [112]. In regards to this type of cancers, a literature review and meta-analysis carried out by Johnson et al. (2018) [109] proved that higher consumption of CV might reduce the risk of colorectal and gastric cancers by approximately 8% and 19%, respectively. These protective effects in the colorectal tissues are hypothesized to be associated with genetic polymorphism of regulating genes of the glutathione S-transferase enzyme expression; however, evidence is inconclusive on this point. That is why further epidemiological studies with accurate dietary exposure measurements need to be done. A previous study carried out by Tse et al. (2012) also suggested the value of CV intake when considering colon preventive properties. In that meta-analysis, including 33 articles, results showed a statistically significant inverse association between CV intake and colon cancer. Broccoli, particularly, stood out from other species.

Following this line of research, pancreatic cancer is responsible for 4.5% of the total number of deaths in 2018 [112]. In 2015, Li [103] showed that cruciferous plant consumption might be inversely associated with pancreatic cancer risk. Nevertheless, given that the number of studies included in this research is scarce, further evidence needs to be included in future meta-analyses.

On another note, breast cancer is the second most common cancer diagnosed in the entire world. Given this high incidence, joint efforts are being made to prevent the development of this disease, and CV intake has been proven as a chemopreventive strategy against breast cancer cells. Gianfredi et al. (2017) [110] identified sulforaphane (SFN) and epigallocathechin gallate as modulators of epigenetic events in one breast cancer cell line, therefore interfering with tumor growth rate. The following year, Zhang et al. (2018) [107] conducted a case–control study among Chinese women, proving that CV providing GLS and ITC showed a significant statistically inverse association with breast cancer risk. Despite these promising results, future prospective epidemiological studies are needed to positively assess a breast cancer prevention claim concerning CV or CV ingredient consumption. Another woman-affecting disease is ovarian cancer. In regards to this ailment, Hu et al. (2015) [100] showed that CV intake was also effective to prevent this disease.

Cancers affecting the urinary system are also affected by *Brassicaceae* vegetable consumption. Liu et al. (2013) [102] proved the consumption of these vegetables might decrease the risk of renal cancer, and in 2015, Veeranki and colleagues [104], concluded that ITCs have chemopreventive activities against bladder cancer.

As can be appreciated, there are cumulatively epidemiological studies suggesting that cancer rates are associated with environmental factors, more precisely in this case with diet. Numerous researches have attempted to identify the dietary agents that may inhibit the multistage process of carcinogenesis [113]. In this sense, plenty of evidence regarding naturally occurring compounds that have shown cancer-preventive effects in experimental models is available. Particularly in *Brassicaceae* species, as several investigations show, isothiocyanates are the ones responsible for the chemopreventive activities [114]. There are other phytochemicals such as flavonoids present in Brassica species, that have cancer related properties; however, isothiocyanates are by far the ones with the greatest chemopreventive power [114]. Figure 3 shows the mechanism of actions during carcinogenesis process affected by ITCs.

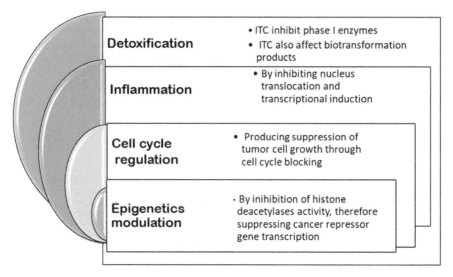

Figure 3. Mechanisms of action and signalling pathways implied for inhibiting carcinogenesis affected by isothiocyanates.

Due to the wide range of GLS breakdown products that can be found in nature, it is not surprising that the number of cancer preventive mechanisms is so diverse. However, it must be noted that there is a dose-dependency in these responses generally; induction of cytoprotective genes and inhibition of CYP activity occurs at low compounds concentrations, whereas activation of cell cycle arrest and apoptosis occurs at higher levels of phytochemicals. Another major problem exists in interpreting experiments when using vegetable extracts because of their variable composition. Hence, uncertainty about attributing biological effects to specific phytochemicals exists. It is also important to consider the bioavailability of GLS breakdown products, which makes the interpretation of in vitro data more complex [115].

In summary, there is abundant scientific evidence that supports functional activities for the vegetables of the *Brassicaceas* family. However, the number of results related to *Brassicaceae* derived-products is lower. In agreement with point (2), each *Brassicaceae*-product (e.g., ingredient, phytotherapeutic, functional food) possesses a unique mixture of bioactive compounds that consequently evidences a spectrum of biological activities because of an additive/synergistic mechanism. From here arises the importance of studying each product particularly.

4. Food Products and Ingredients Enriched in Bioactives from *Brassicaceae*

The functional food market based on *Brassicaceae* vegetables is relatively recent. However, it contains interesting potential to offer new food products and formats with beneficial effects on health. In this sense, consumers, especially young adults and children, show some adversity in relation to the organoleptic characteristics, like the flavor of many cruciferous such as broccoli or radish [116]. For this reason, diverse new products based on functional ingredients from cruciferous families have been developed to facilitate the inclusion of this group of nutrients to the diet, into different and original formats (e.g., smoothies, soups, breads) [88]. In this way, the manufacturing of these new food products can include the use of by-products, or side-streams, to also reach a better environmental and socio-economic balance [117]. In addition, diverse nutraceuticals like broccoli pills, tablets, or powders have been commercialized to compensate for the absence of this group of vegetables in the diet [118].

Broccoli, cabbage, and kale are predominant in the search for new functional products based on Brassica vegetables (Table 2), due to their phytochemical composition and the extensive knowledge collected in the scientific literature until this moment. The processing of food to obtain the new functional products can cause diverse changes (advantageous or disadvantageous) into the food matrix. This is crucial for the design of novel food products. In this sense, it has been seen that the addition of broccoli to baked crackers improved the nutritional properties of the final product, whilst the addition of broccoli to a juice results in important losses of sulphoraphane (Table 2). On the other hand, the use of byproducts is promising, not only because of the use of non-marketable material but also for showing the advantages of using agro-waste instead of edible florets.

Table 2. Diverse experimental products based on functional ingredients from *Brassicaceae*.

Functional Food	Nutrients and Bioactive Compounds	Effects of Processing on Bioactive Compounds	References
Juice from Broccoli sprouts (*Brassica oleracea* L. var. *botrytis* subvar. *cymosa*)	SFN and Glucoraphanin (GRA)	Less amount of SFN present than expected from GRA dosage / Lost of GLS/ITC during processing	[88]
Lentil flour fortified bread with addition of kale (*Brassica oleracea* var. *sabellica*) and pea leaves	Carotenoids, Chlorophylls Flavonoid glycosides Hydroxycinnamic acid derivatives	Less quantities of carotenoids and chlorophylls. Formation of derivatives (pheophytins) / Losses of flavonoid glycosides and hydroxycinnamic acid derivatives	[119]
Muffins enriched with dietary fiber from kimchi byproducts	Dietary fiber	Enhanced of antioxidant capacity by adding kimchi fiber / Decrease of color, height, and volume of the muffins / Increased of hardness due to the weakening of gluten	[120]
Milk chocolate enriched with kale (*Brassica oleracea* var. *acephala*) and grapes	Phenolic compounds Dietary fiber Minerals	Some phenolic compounds transferred from kale or grapes to milk chocolate. However, the antiradical activity was not increased / Enhanced total amount of fiber and minerals due to the addition of kale powder	[77]
Broccoli puree inoculated with lactic acid	Phenolic compounds GLS	Phytochemical total content was enhanced due to the fermentation of the lactic bacteria. / The total content of sugar was lower than original broccoli puree	[121]
Broccoli puree inoculated with lactic acid	GRA SFN-nitrile	Improved stability of SFN / Improved antioxidant capacity / Preferential formation of SFN-nitrile (less potential as inducer of phase II detoxification enzymes than SFN) instead of SFN.	[122]
Broccoli soup with microalgae addition	Phenolic compounds	Improved antioxidant capacity due to the incorporation of the microalgae rich in bioaccessible phenolic compounds / Preferential formation of SFN-nitrile instead of SFN.	[123]
Croquets with addition of red and green cabbage aqueous extract	Phenolic compounds	Improved antioxidant activity, better in croquets with green cabbage than croquets with red cabbage / Organoleptic analysis indicates acceptability for consumers	[124]
"Kimchi" Prepared with Amtap Baechu Cabbage salted in Brine Solution	Gluconasturtin β-carotene, Pyropheophorbide A	Increase of the anticancer effect of "kimchi"	[125]
Baked crackers with addition of broccoli byproducts	Phenolic compounds Dietary fiber GLS	Improved antioxidant capacity / Organoleptic properties unaffected by elaboration	[126]
Puree and juice made with Broccoli by-products (powder)	Epigallocatechin gallate	Improved antioxidant anticancer and anti-inflammatory activity by increased Epigallocatechin-gallate in puree / Juices is not an optimal carrier of Epigallocatechin-gallate	[127]
Sponge cake with substitution of white flour (10% and 20%) by White Cabbage byproduct powder	Total dietary fiber	Increase of dietary fiber / Decrease of total quantity of fat and carbohydrates / Slight but acceptable decrease of organoleptic properties	[128]
Microencapsulation of polyphenols extracted from red chicory and red cabbage (nutraceutical)	Phenolic compounds	Stabilization of pH-dependent light-absorption properties of polyphenols / Improvement of the thermal stability of polyphenols, mostly from red cabbage	[79]
Microencapsulated SFN from broccoli seed extracts (nutraceutical)	SFN	Powdered complex from Arabic gum and gelatin for encapsulating SFN from broccoli seeds.	[129]
Microencapsulated of Broccoli ingredient (nutraceutical)	Phenolic compounds Chlorophylls Carotenoids	Powdered complex obtained by coacervation for the stability of chlorophylls content / Odor masking effects to improved acceptability for consumer	[130]

Natural food matrix contents and bioactive compounds and grants the food the capacity to be adsorbed and metabolized by the organism [131]. However, the addition (or isolation) of some bioactive compound functional food products is not a guaranty of bioaccessibility and bioavailability, and more work is necessary to elucidate solutions against their insufficient presence in new products [132]. On the other hand, the food industry is trying to reduce the food processing to obtain products more similar to fresh-food: the concept called "minimally processed foods". One example is broccoli hummus, which has shown promising nutritional values [133]. However, it is necessary to clearly establish the difference between fresh products and minimally processed foods to avoid the systematic and total consumption of fruits and vegetables instead off ready-to-eat fruits and salads, among other processed foods in the diet that, in addition, would result in an important impact on the environmental.

5. Food Products and Ingredients from *Brassica* spp.—Certain Commercialization Aspects

It is true that certain functional foods result in interesting physiological effects (Table 2), but it is necessary to stress that the novel developed "functional food" products cannot replace the nutritive qualities of fresh food [134]. Nevertheless, numerous food products are commercialized as "alternatives" for the consumption of *Brassica* vegetables, such as vegetable powdered formulas (broccoli https://www.bulkpowders.es/brocoli-en-polvo.html) or kale powder https://saludmediterranea.com/products/kale-col-rizada-en-polvo-salud-viva) in convenient but expensive formats (200 g >10 EUR/unit). We can ask ourselves if these are really necessary products, considering these prices. One kg of fresh broccoli (heads) is between EUR 1–2 in the supermarket, the sample place where these other products are sold in different shelves or areas of the store to highlight these added-valude products. Besides the price tag, the effects of industrial processing to obtain the products (e.g., powders) could degrade the phytochemical profile (and the label of these products sometimes is difficult to understand for the consumers) and the composition on the marketed products may be far distant from the natural content of the fresh produce for a given bioactive, and therefore, much less effective.

Taking in consideration the mentioned situation, there is more interest so far in those foods that are minimally processed—once the organoleptic barrier is overpassed for the consumption of these smelly vegetable family—and ready-to-eat salads, sprouts and germinates of different cruciferous species are growing in demand and presence in the stores, even in countries that were not top consumers (such as USA or UK), as in the Mediterranean European countries [135,136], even in snack formats [137]. Therefore, there is a wide range of possibilities to exploit commercially.

When it comes to nutraceuticals or products alike, the situation is quite similar; their potential for specific population groups and pathophysiological situations where they can be used as coadjuvants is clear because of the isolation of the bioactive compounds in pharma-grade products such as pills, powders, capsules, but involving the elimination of the food matrix; in many circumstances, the isolated bioactive is not as bioavailable or metabolically active as in the natural food matrix [138].

The research in this area of functional foods and ingredients for new therapeutic applications keeps going further with the evaluation of functionalities in different chronic diseases; but many more studies will be needed to ascertain the "functionality" of these new products. For this reason, it is important to think about the population target these products are intended for: is the consumption of nutraceuticals for the general population really necessary or advisable? Will his trend lead consumers to avoid or dramatically reduce the consumption of fresh foods? If the current evidence from clinical studies and epidemiological data are still not totally clear or not totally acceptable for many of these new products, which are always much more expensive than fresh food, should we keep the wheel spinning and keep working hard on these products because of their (so far unclear) potential, or should we push for much more work from scientific research in collaboration with dietary and nutrition advice on eating a more sustainable, safe, and rich diet with plenty of "naturally functional" fresh foods (e.g., cruciferous sprouts, fresh foods enriched in bioactives) that would definitively contribute to wellbeing? Many open fronts remain waiting for answers in this global era of plants for food and health.

Author Contributions: Conceptualization, A.C. and D.A.M.; investigation, all authors; writing—review, all authors; visualization and editing, D.R., A.C., and D.A.M.; supervision and project administration, A.C.; funding acquisition, A.C. and D.A.M. All authors have read and agreed to the published version of the manuscript.

Funding: This research was partially supported by Fundación Seneca, Murcia Regional Agency for Science and Technology, Project 20855/PI/18; and by Secretaría de Investigación, Internacionales y Posgrado de la Universidad Nacional de Cuyo. Project SIIP 06/A690. Res. 4142/2019.

Conflicts of Interest: The authors declare no conflict of interest. The funders had no role in the design of the study; in the collection, analyses, or interpretation of data; in the writing of the manuscript, or in the decision to publish the results.

Abbreviations

GSL   Glucosinolates
ITC   Isothiocyanates
CV   Cruciferous vegetables
SFN   Sulforaphane
GRA   Glucoraphanin

References

1. Jiménez-Morales, P.; Sánchez-León, G.; Vargas-Rincón, C. La Producción de Metabolitos Secundarios en la Familia Brassicaceae. *Rev. Fac. Ciencias Básicas* **2014**, *9*, 282.
2. Branca, F.; Argento, S.; Alessandro, T. Assessing genetic reserves in Sicily (Italy): The Brassica wild relatives case study. In *Agrobiodiversity Conservation: Securing the Diversity of Crop Wild Relatives and Landraces*; Maxted, N., Ehsan Dulloo, M., Ford-Lloyd, B.V., Frese, L., Iriondo, J.M., Pinheiro de Carvalho, M.A.A., Eds.; CABI: Wallingford, Oxfordshire, UK, 2012; pp. 52–58.
3. Pinheiro de Carvalho, M.Â. *Agrobiodiversity Conservation: Securing the Diversity of Crop Wild Relatives and Landraces*; CABI: Wallingford, Oxfordshire, UK, 2012.
4. Branca, F.; Chiarenza, L.; Ragusa, L.; Argento, S. Morphological Characterization of the ECPGR Wild Brassica Species Collection. Acta horticulturae. *Acta Hortic.* **2013**, *1005*, 157–164. [CrossRef]
5. Argento, S.; Melilli, M.G.; Branca, F. Enhancing Greenhouse Tomato-Crop Productivity by Using Brassica macrocarpa Guss. Leaves for Controlling Root-Knot Nematodes. *Agronomy* **2019**, *9*, 820. [CrossRef]
6. Branca, F.; Lucia, R.; Alessandro, T.; Lo Scalzo, R.; Picchi, V.; Argento, S. The Glucosinolates and Variation of Antioxidant Compounds in Seeds and Sprouts of Broccoli (*Brassica oleracea* L. var. *italica*) and Rocket (*Eruca sativa* L.) in Relation to Temperature and Germinative Stage. *Acta Hortic.* **2013**, *1005*, 271–278. [CrossRef]
7. Galletti, S.; Bagatta, M.; Branca, F.; Argento, S.; De Nicola, G.R.; Cianchetta, S.; Iori, R.; Ninfali, P. Isatis canescens is a rich source of glucobrassicin and other health-promoting compounds. *J. Sci. Food Agric.* **2015**, *95*, 158–164. [CrossRef]
8. Cartea, M.E.; Francisco, M.; Soengas, P.; Velasco, P. Phenolic Compounds in *Brassica* Vegetables. *Molecules* **2011**, *16*, 251–280. [CrossRef]
9. Cheynier, V. Phenolic compounds: From plants to foods. *Phytochem. Rev.* **2012**, *11*, 153–177. [CrossRef]
10. Todaro, A.; Cavallaro, R.; Argento, S.; Branca, F.; Spagna, G. Study and Characterization of Polyphenol Oxidase from Eggplant (*Solanum melongena* L.). *J. Agric. Food Chem.* **2011**, *59*, 11244–11248. [CrossRef]
11. Li, Z.; Lee, H.W.; Liang, X.; Liang, D.; Wang, Q.; Huang, D.; Ong, C.N. Profiling of Phenolic Compounds and Antioxidant Activity of 12 Cruciferous Vegetables. *Molecules* **2018**, *23*, 1139. [CrossRef]
12. Fusari, C.; Beretta, H.; Locatelli, D.; Nazareno, M.; Camargo, A. Seasonal isothiocyanates variation and market availability of Brassicaceae species consumed in Mendoza. *Rev. Fac. Cienc. Agrar.* **2019**, *51*, 403–408.
13. Baenas, N.; Gómez-Jodar, I.; Moreno, D.A.; García-Viguera, C.; Periago, P.M. Broccoli and radish sprouts are safe and rich in bioactive phytochemicals. *Postharvest Biol. Technol.* **2017**, *127*, 60–67. [CrossRef]
14. Loedolff, B.; Brooks, J.; Stander, M.; Peters, S.; Kossmann, J. High light bio-fortification stimulates de novo synthesis of resveratrol in Diplotaxis tenuifolia (wild rocket) micro-greens. *Funct. Foods Health Dis.* **2017**, *7*, 859–872. [CrossRef]

15. Matera, R.; Gabbanini, S.; De Nicola, G.R.; Iori, R.; Petrillo, G.; Valgimigli, L. Identification and analysis of isothiocyanates and new acylated anthocyanins in the juice of *Raphanus sativus* cv. *Sango sprouts*. *Food Chem.* **2012**, *133*, 563–572. [CrossRef] [PubMed]

16. Moreno, D.A.; Pérez-Balibrea, S.; Ferreres, F.; Gil-Izquierdo, Á.; García-Viguera, C. Acylated anthocyanins in broccoli sprouts. *Food Chem.* **2010**, *123*, 358–363. [CrossRef]

17. Lo Scalzo, R.; Genna, A.; Branca, F.; Chedin, M.; Chassaigne, H. Anthocyanin composition of cauliflower (*Brassica oleracea* L. var. *botrytis*) and cabbage (*B. oleracea* L. var. *capitata*) and its stability in relation to thermal treatments. *Food Chem.* **2008**, *107*, 136–144. [CrossRef]

18. Otsuki, T.; Matsufuji, H.; Takeda, M.; Toyoda, M.; Goda, Y. Acylated anthocyanins from red radish (*Raphanus sativus* L.). *Phytochemistry* **2002**, *60*, 79–87. [CrossRef]

19. Wiczkowski, W.; Szawara-Nowak, D.; Topolska, J. Red cabbage anthocyanins: Profile, isolation, identification, and antioxidant activity. *Food Res. Int.* **2013**, *51*, 303–309. [CrossRef]

20. Anjum, N.A.; Gill, S.S.; Ahmad, I.; Pacheco, M.; Duarte, A.C.; Umar, S.; Khan, N.A.; Pereira, M.E. The Plant Family Brassicaceae: An Introduction. In *The Plant Family Brassicaceae: Contribution Towards Phytoremediation*; Anjum, N.A., Ahmad, I., Pereira, M.E., Duarte, A.C., Umar, S., Khan, N.A., Eds.; Springer: Dordrecht, The Netherlands, 2012; pp. 1–33.

21. Bell, L.; Yahya, H.N.; Oloyede, O.O.; Methven, L.; Wagstaff, C. Changes in rocket salad phytochemicals within the commercial supply chain: Glucosinolates, isothiocyanates, amino acids and bacterial load increase significantly after processing. *Food Chem.* **2017**, *221*, 521–534. [CrossRef]

22. Traka, M.; Mithen, R.J.P.R. Glucosinolates, isothiocyanates and human health. *Phytochem. Rev.* **2009**, *8*, 269–282. [CrossRef]

23. Fahey, J.W.; Zalcmann, A.T.; Talalay, P. The chemical diversity and distribution of glucosinolates and isothiocyanates among plants. *Phytochemistry* **2001**, *56*, 5–51. [CrossRef]

24. Cartea, M.E.; Velasco, P.J.P.R. Glucosinolates in Brassica foods: Bioavailability in food and significance for human health. *Phytochem. Rev.* **2008**, *7*, 213–229. [CrossRef]

25. Dinkova-Kostova, A.T.; Kostov, R.V. Glucosinolates and isothiocyanates in health and disease. *Trends Mol. Med.* **2012**, *18*, 337–347. [CrossRef]

26. Baenas, N.; Piegholdt, S.; Schloesser, A.; Moreno, D.A.; García-Viguera, C.; Rimbach, G.; Wagner, A.E. Metabolic Activity of Radish Sprouts Derived Isothiocyanates in *Drosophila melanogaster*. *Int. J. Mol. Sci.* **2016**, *17*, 251. [CrossRef] [PubMed]

27. Blažević, I.; Mastelić, J. Glucosinolate degradation products and other bound and free volatiles in the leaves and roots of radish (*Raphanus sativus* L.). *Food Chem.* **2009**, *113*, 96–102. [CrossRef]

28. Yi, G.; Lim, S.; Chae, W.B.; Park, J.E.; Park, H.R.; Lee, E.J.; Huh, J.H. Root Glucosinolate Profiles for Screening of Radish (*Raphanus sativus* L.) Genetic Resources. *J. Agric. Food Chem.* **2016**, *64*, 61–70. [CrossRef] [PubMed]

29. Fechner, J.; Kaufmann, M.; Herz, C.; Eisenschmidt, D.; Lamy, E.; Kroh, L.W.; Hanschen, F.S. The major glucosinolate hydrolysis product in rocket (*Eruca sativa* L.), sativin, is 1,3-thiazepane-2-thione: Elucidation of structure, bioactivity, and stability compared to other rocket isothiocyanates. *Food Chem.* **2018**, *261*, 57–65. [CrossRef]

30. Franco, P.; Spinozzi, S.; Pagnotta, E.; Lazzeri, L.; Ugolini, L.; Camborata, C.; Roda, A. Development of a liquid chromatography–electrospray ionization–tandem mass spectrometry method for the simultaneous analysis of intact glucosinolates and isothiocyanates in Brassicaceae seeds and functional foods. *J. Chromatogr. A* **2016**, *1428*, 154–161. [CrossRef]

31. Kuang, P.; Song, D.; Yuan, Q.; Yi, R.; Lv, X.; Liang, H. Separation and purification of sulforaphene from radish seeds using macroporous resin and preparative high-performance liquid chromatography. *Food Chem.* **2013**, *136*, 342–347. [CrossRef]

32. Kim, J.-W.; Kim, M.-B.; Lim, S.-B. Formation and Stabilization of Raphasatin and Sulforaphene from Radish Roots by Endogenous Enzymolysis. *Prev. Nutr. Food Sci.* **2015**, *20*, 119–125. [CrossRef]

33. Yu, B.; Lydiate, D.J.; Young, L.W.; Schäfer, U.A.; Hannoufa, A.J.T.R. Enhancing the carotenoid content of Brassica napus seeds by downregulating lycopene epsilon cyclase. *Transgenic Res.* **2008**, *17*, 573–585. [CrossRef]

34. Frede, K.; Schreiner, M.; Baldermann, S. Light quality-induced changes of carotenoid composition in pak choi *Brassica rapa* ssp. *chinensis*. *J. Photochem. Photobiol. B Biol.* **2019**, *193*, 18–30. [CrossRef] [PubMed]

35. Nilsson, J.; Olsson, K.; Engqvist, G.; Ekvall, J.; Olsson, M.; Nyman, M.; Åkesson, B. Variation in the content of glucosinolates, hydroxycinnamic acids, carotenoids, total antioxidant capacity and low-molecular-weight carbohydrates in *Brassica* vegetables. *J. Sci. Food Agric.* **2006**, *86*, 528–538. [CrossRef]

36. Zhang, B.; Liu, C.; Wang, Y.; Yao, X.; Wang, F.; Wu, J.; King, G.J.; Liu, K. Disruption of a Carotenoid Cleavage Dioxygenase 4 gene converts flower colour from white to yellow in *Brassica* species. *New Phytol.* **2015**, *206*, 1513–1526. [CrossRef] [PubMed]

37. Guzman, I.; Yousef, G.G.; Brown, A.F. Simultaneous Extraction and Quantitation of Carotenoids, Chlorophylls, and Tocopherols in Brassica Vegetables. *J. Agric. Food Chem.* **2012**, *60*, 7238–7244. [CrossRef] [PubMed]

38. Park, W.T.; Kim, J.K.; Park, S.; Lee, S.-W.; Li, X.; Kim, Y.B.; Uddin, M.R.; Park, N.I.; Kim, S.-J.; Park, S.U. Metabolic Profiling of Glucosinolates, Anthocyanins, Carotenoids, and Other Secondary Metabolites in Kohlrabi (*Brassica oleracea* var. *gongylodes*). *J. Agric. Food Chem.* **2012**, *60*, 8111–8116. [CrossRef] [PubMed]

39. Chun, J.-H.; Kim, N.-H.; Seo, M.-S.; Jin, M.; Park, S.U.; Arasu, M.V.; Kim, S.-J.; Al-Dhabi, N.A. Molecular characterization of glucosinolates and carotenoid biosynthetic genes in Chinese cabbage (*Brassica rapa* L. ssp. *pekinensis*). *Saudi J. Biol. Sci.* **2018**, *25*, 71–82. [CrossRef]

40. Walsh, R.P.; Bartlett, H.; Eperjesi, F. Variation in Carotenoid Content of Kale and Other Vegetables: A Review of Pre- and Post-harvest Effects. *J. Agric. Food Chem.* **2015**, *63*, 9677–9682. [CrossRef]

41. Abdel-Aal, E.-S.M.; Akhtar, H.; Zaheer, K.; Ali, R. Dietary Sources of Lutein and Zeaxanthin Carotenoids and Their Role in Eye Health. *Nutrients* **2013**, *5*, 1169–1185. [CrossRef]

42. Mageney, V.; Baldermann, S.; Albach, D.C. Intraspecific Variation in Carotenoids of *Brassica oleracea* var. *sabellica*. *J. Agric. Food Chem.* **2016**, *64*, 3251–3257. [CrossRef]

43. Fernández-León, M.F.; Fernández-León, A.M.; Lozano, M.; Ayuso, M.C.; González-Gómez, D. Identification, quantification and comparison of the principal bioactive compounds and external quality parameters of two broccoli cultivars. *J. Funct. Foods* **2012**, *4*, 465–473. [CrossRef]

44. Kaulmann, A.; André, C.M.; Schneider, Y.-J.; Hoffmann, L.; Bohn, T. Carotenoid and polyphenol bioaccessibility and cellular uptake from plum and cabbage varieties. *Food Chem.* **2016**, *197*, 325–332. [CrossRef] [PubMed]

45. Podsędek, A. Natural antioxidants and antioxidant capacity of *Brassica* vegetables: A review. *LWT—Food Sci. Technol.* **2007**, *40*, 1–11. [CrossRef]

46. Kurilich, A.C.; Tsau, G.J.; Brown, A.; Howard, L.; Klein, B.P.; Jeffery, E.H.; Kushad, M.; Wallig, M.A.; Juvik, J.A. Carotene, Tocopherol, and Ascorbate Contents in Subspecies of *Brassica oleracea*. *J. Agric. Food Chem.* **1999**, *47*, 1576–1581. [CrossRef] [PubMed]

47. Dan, L.; Yi, Y.; Yongxin, L.; Chengjun, S. Analysis of Tocopherols and Tocotrienols in Pharmaceuticals and Foods: A Critical Review. *Curr. Pharm. Anal.* **2015**, *11*, 66–78. [CrossRef]

48. Yu, W.; Simmons-Menchaca, M.; Gapor, A.; Sanders, B.G.; Kline, K. Induction of apoptosis in human breast cancer cells by tocopherols and tocotrienols. *Nutr. Cancer* **1999**, *33*, 26–32. [CrossRef]

49. Mo, H.; Elson, C.E. Apoptosis and Cell-Cycle Arrest in Human and Murine Tumor Cells Are Initiated by Isoprenoids. *J. Nutr.* **1999**, *129*, 804–813. [CrossRef]

50. Lampi, A.-M.; Kamal-Eldin, A.; Piironen, V. Tocopherols and tocotrienols from oil and cereal grains. *Funct. Foods Biochem. Process. Asp.* **2002**, 1–38.

51. Ling, W.H.; Jones, P.J.H. Dietary phytosterols: A review of metabolism, benefits and side effects. *Life Sci.* **1995**, *57*, 195–206. [CrossRef]

52. Gül, M.; Amar, S. Sterols and the phytosterol content in oilseed rape (*Brassica napus* L.). *J. Cell & Mol. Biol.* **2006**, *5*, 71–79.

53. Sharma, A.; Rai, P.K.; Prasad, S. GC–MS detection and determination of major volatile compounds in *Brassica juncea* L. leaves and seeds. *Microchem. J.* **2018**, *138*, 488–493. [CrossRef]

54. Ahuja, I.; Kissen, R.; Bones, A.M. Phytoalexins in defense against pathogens. *Trends Plant Sci.* **2012**, *17*, 73–90. [CrossRef] [PubMed]

55. Klein, A.P.; Sattely, E.S. Biosynthesis of cabbage phytoalexins from indole glucosinolate. *Proc. Natl. Acad. Sci. USA* **2017**, *114*, 1910–1915. [CrossRef] [PubMed]

56. Pedras, M.S.C.; Zheng, Q.-A.; Gadagi, R.S.; Rimmer, S.R. Phytoalexins and polar metabolites from the oilseeds canola and rapeseed: Differential metabolic responses to the biotroph Albugo candida and to abiotic stress. *Phytochemistry* **2008**, *69*, 894–910. [CrossRef] [PubMed]

57. Pedras, M.S.C.; Adio, A.M.; Suchy, M.; Okinyo, D.P.O.; Zheng, Q.-A.; Jha, M.; Sarwar, M.G. Detection, characterization and identification of crucifer phytoalexins using high-performance liquid chromatography with diode array detection and electrospray ionization mass spectrometry. *J. Chromatogr. A* **2006**, *1133*, 172–183. [CrossRef] [PubMed]

58. Pedras, M.S.C.; Ahiahonu, P.W.K. Metabolism and detoxification of phytoalexins and analogs by phytopathogenic fungi. *Phytochemistry* **2005**, *66*, 391–411. [CrossRef]

59. Pedras, M.S.C.; Montaut, S.; Zaharia, I.L.; Gai, Y.; Ward, D.E. Transformation of the host-selective toxin destruxin B by wild crucifers: Probing a detoxification pathway. *Phytochemistry* **2003**, *64*, 957–963. [CrossRef]

60. Pedras, M.S.C.; Sorensen, J.L.; Okanga, F.I.; Zaharia, I.L. Wasalexins A and B, new phytoalexins from wasabi: Isolation, synthesis, and antifungal activity. *Bioorganic Med. Chem. Lett.* **1999**, *9*, 3015–3020. [CrossRef]

61. Monde, K.; Takasugi, M.; Shirata, A. Three sulphur-containing stress metabolites from Japanese radish. *Phytochemistry* **1995**, *39*, 581–586. [CrossRef]

62. Nee, M. *Plant Alkaloids: A Guide to Their Discovery and Distribution*; Raffauf, R.F., Ed.; Brittonia: New York, NY, USA, 1998; Volume 50, p. 55.

63. Guriya, R.; Moon, A.; Talreja, K. Phytochemical profiling and characterization of bioactive compounds from *Brassica oleracea*. *Int. J. Pharmacogn. Phytochem. Res.* **2015**, *7*, 825–831.

64. Khalid, A.; Mohammed, A.D.; Al-Maliki, M. Effect of phenolic and alkaloid compounds extracted from *Brassica oleracea* var. *capitata* seed on glucose level in blood of alloxan- induced diabetes rabbits. *World J. Exp. Biosci.* **2014**, *2*, 24–29.

65. Yannai, S. *Dictionary of Food*; CRC Press: Boca Raton, FL, USA, 2003.

66. Shah, M.A.; Sarker, M.M.R.; Gousuddin, M. Antidiabetic Potential of *Brassica oleracea* var. *italica* in Type 2 Diabetic Sprague Dawley (sd) Rats. *Int. J. Pharmacogn. Phytochem. Res.* **2016**, *8*, 462–469.

67. Chauhan, E.S.T.; Tiwari, A.; Singh, A. Phytochemical screening of red cabbage (*Brassica oleracea*) powder and juice—A comparative study. *J. Med. Plants Stud.* **2016**, *4*, 196–199.

68. Brock, A.; Herzfeld, T.; Paschke, R.; Koch, M.; Dräger, B. Brassicaceae contain nortropane alkaloids. *Phytochemistry* **2006**, *67*, 2050–2057. [CrossRef] [PubMed]

69. Villaño, D.; Gironés-Vilapana, A.; García-Viguera, C.; Moreno, D.A. Development of Functional Foods. In *Innovation Strategies in the Food Industry*; Galanakis, C.M., Ed.; Academic Press: Cambridge, MA, USA, 2016; Chapter 10; pp. 191–210. [CrossRef]

70. Serafini, M.; Stanzione, A.; Foddai, S. Functional foods: Traditional use and European legislation. *Int. J. Food Sci. Nutr.* **2012**, *63*, 7–9. [CrossRef]

71. Bagchi, D. Nutraceutical and Functional Food Regulations in the United States and Around the World. In *Nutraceutical and Functional Food Regulations in the United States and Around the World*; Bagchi, D., Ed.; Academic Press: San Diego, CA, USA, 2008; pp. ix–xii. [CrossRef]

72. Powers, J.-P.; Farrell, M.; McMullin, C.; Retik, L.; White, J. Regulation of dietary supplements and functional foods in Canada. In *Nutraceutical and Functional Food Regulations in the United States and around the World (Third Edition)*; Bagchi, D., Ed.; Academic Press: San Diego, CA, USA, 2019; Chapter 17; pp. 235–252. [CrossRef]

73. Baenas, N.; Abellán, Á.; Rivera, S.; Moreno, D.A.; García-Viguera, C.; Domínguez-Perles, R. Foods and Suplements. In *Polyphenols: Properties, Recovery and Applications*; Elsevier: Amsterdam, The Netherlands, 2018; pp. 327–362.

74. Bigliardi, B.; Galati, F. Innovation trends in the food industry: The case of functional foods. *Trends Food Sci. Technol.* **2013**, *31*, 118–129. [CrossRef]

75. Poli, A.; Barbagallo, C.M.; Cicero, A.F.G.; Corsini, A.; Manzato, E.; Trimarco, B.; Bernini, F.; Visioli, F.; Bianchi, A.; Canzone, G.; et al. Nutraceuticals and functional foods for the control of plasma cholesterol levels. An intersociety position paper. *Pharmacol. Res.* **2018**, *134*, 51–60. [CrossRef]

76. Fuentes-Alventosa, J.M. *Caracterización de Componentes Bioactivos del Espágarrago Verde: Obtención de Ingredientes Funcionales a Partir de Los Subproductos Generados Durante su Transformación Industrial*; University of Cordoba: Cordoba, Spain, 2010.

77. Carvalho, J.C.S.; Romoff, P.; Lannes, S.C.d.S. Improvement of nutritional and physicochemical proprieties of milk chocolates enriched with kale (*Brassica olereacea* var. *acephala*) and grape (*Vitis vinifera*). *Food Sci. Technol.* **2018**, *38*, 551–560. [CrossRef]

78. Ouraji, M.; Alimi, M.; Motamedzadegan, A.; Shokoohi, S. Faba bean protein in reduced fat/cholesterol mayonnaise: Extraction and physico-chemical modification process. *J. Food Sci. Technol.* **2020**. [CrossRef]

79. Zanoni, F.; Primiterra, M.; Angeli, N.; Zoccatelli, G. Microencapsulation by spray-drying of polyphenols extracted from red chicory and red cabbage: Effects on stability and color properties. *Food Chem.* **2020**, *307*, 125535. [CrossRef]

80. Singh, N.; Aditika; Rani, S.; Chaurasia, O.P. Vegetable Microgreens Farming in High-Altitude Region of Trans-Himalayas to Maintain Nutritional Diet of Indian Troops. *Proc. Natl. Acad. Sci. India Sect. B Biol. Sci.* **2019**. [CrossRef]

81. Granado-Lorencio, F.; Herrero-Barbudo, C.; Acién-Fernández, G.; Molina-Grima, E.; Fernández-Sevilla, J.M.; Pérez-Sacristán, B.; Blanco-Navarro, I. In vitro bioaccesibility of lutein and zeaxanthin from the microalgae Scenedesmus almeriensis. *Food Chem.* **2009**, *114*, 747–752. [CrossRef]

82. Baenas, N.; Fusari, C.; Moreno, D.A.; Valero, D.; García-Viguera, C. Biostimulation of bioactive compounds in radish sprouts (Raphanus sativus 'Rambo') by priming seeds and spray treatments with elicitors. *ISHS Acta Hortic.* **2017**, 659–663. [CrossRef]

83. Liu, M.; Zhang, L.; Ser, S.L.; Cumming, J.R.; Ku, K.-M. Comparative Phytonutrient Analysis of Broccoli By-Products: The Potentials for Broccoli By-Product Utilization. *Molecules* **2018**, *23*, 900. [CrossRef] [PubMed]

84. Baenas, N.; Marhuenda, J.; García-Viguera, C.; Zafrilla, P.; Moreno, D.A. Influence of Cooking Methods on Glucosinolates and Isothiocyanates Content in Novel Cruciferous Foods. *Foods* **2019**, *8*, 257. [CrossRef] [PubMed]

85. Baenas, N.; Villaño, D.; García-Viguera, C.; Moreno, D.A. Optimizing elicitation and seed priming to enrich broccoli and radish sprouts in glucosinolates. *Food Chem.* **2016**, *204*, 314–319. [CrossRef]

86. Zang, Y.X.; Ge, J.L.; Huang, L.H.; Gao, F.; Lv, X.S.; Zheng, W.-W.; Hong, S.-B.; Zhu, Z.-J. Leaf and root glucosinolate profiles of Chinese cabbage (*Brassica rapa* ssp. *pekinensis*) as a systemic response to methyl jasmonate and salicylic acid elicitation. *J. Zhejiang Univ. Sci. B* **2015**, *16*, 696–708. [CrossRef]

87. Krupa-Kozak, U.; Drabińska, N.; Rosell, C.M.; Fadda, C.; Anders, A.; Jeliński, T.; Ostaszyk, A. Broccoli leaf powder as an attractive by-product ingredient: Effect on batter behaviour, technological properties and sensory quality of gluten-free mini sponge cake. *Food Sci. Tehnol.* **2019**, *54*, 1121–1129. [CrossRef]

88. Liang, J.L.; Yeow, C.C.; Teo, K.C.; Gnanaraj, C.; Chang, Y.P. Valorizing cabbage (Brassica oleracea L. var. capitata) and capsicum (*Capsicum annuum* L.) wastes: In vitro health-promoting activities. *J. Food Sci. Technol.* **2019**, *56*, 4696–4704. [CrossRef]

89. Ferreira, S.S.; Passos, C.P.; Cardoso, S.M.; Wessel, D.F.; Coimbra, M.A. Microwave assisted dehydration of broccoli by-products and simultaneous extraction of bioactive compounds. *Food Chem.* **2018**, *246*, 386–393. [CrossRef]

90. Yang, Y. Scientific Substantiation of Functional Food Health Claims in China. *J. Nutr.* **2008**, *138*, 1199S–1205S. [CrossRef]

91. Alvarez-Jubete, L.; Valverde, J.; Kehoe, K.; Reilly, K.; Rai, D.K.; Barry-Ryan, C. Development of a Novel Functional Soup Rich in Bioactive Sulforaphane Using Broccoli (*Brassica oleracea* L. ssp. *italica*) Florets and Byproducts. *Food Bioprocess Technol.* **2014**, *7*, 1310–1321. [CrossRef]

92. Masci, A.; Mattioli, R.; Costantino, P.; Baima, S.; Morelli, G.; Punzi, P.; Giordano, C.; Pinto, A.; Donini, L.M.; d'Erme, M.; et al. Neuroprotective Effect of *Brassica oleracea* Sprouts Crude Juice in a Cellular Model of Alzheimer's Disease. *Oxid. Med. Cell Longev.* **2015**, *2015*, 781938. [CrossRef] [PubMed]

93. Saban Guler, M.; Sanlier, N. The Benefits of Brassica Vegetables on Human Health. *J. Hum. Heal. Res.* **2012**, *1*, 104.

94. Brandi, G.; Amagliani, G.; Schiavano, G.F.; De Santi, M.; Sisti, M. Activity of *Brassica oleracea* Leaf Juice on Foodborne Pathogenic Bacteria. *J. Food Prot.* **2006**, *69*, 2274–2279. [CrossRef] [PubMed]

95. Smith, T.K.; Mithen, R.; Johnson, I.T. Effects of *Brassica* vegetable juice on the induction of apoptosis and aberrant crypt foci in rat colonic mucosal crypts in vivo. *Carcinogenesis* **2003**, *24*, 491–495. [CrossRef]

96. McNaughton, S.A.; Marks, G.C. Development of a food composition database for the estimation of dietary intakes of glucosinolates, the biologically active constituents of cruciferous vegetables. *Br. J. Nutr.* **2003**, *90*, 687–697. [CrossRef]

97. Herron, J.D.; Nurrenbern, S.C. Chemical Education Research: Improving Chemistry Learning. *J. Chem. Educ.* **1999**, *76*, 1353. [CrossRef]

98. Van Poppel, G.; Verhagen, D.T.; Verhagen, H.; Goldbohm, R.A. Brassica vegetables and cancer prevention: Epidemiology and mechanisms. *Adv. Exp. Med. Biol.* **2000**, *472*, 159–168.

99. Mitsiogianni, M.; Koutsidis, G.; Mavroudis, N.; Trafalis, D.T.; Botaitis, S.; Franco, R.; Zoumpourlis, V.; Amery, T.; Galanis, A.; Pappa, A.; et al. The Role of Isothiocyanates as Cancer Chemo-Preventive, Chemo-Therapeutic and Anti-Melanoma Agents. *Antioxidants* **2019**, *8*, 106. [CrossRef]

100. Hu, J.; Hu, Y.; Hu, Y.; Zheng, S. Intake of cruciferous vegetables is associated with reduced risk of ovarian cancer: A meta-analysis. *Asia Pac. J. Clin. Nutr.* **2015**, *24*, 101–109.

101. Tse, G.; Eslick, G.D. Cruciferous Vegetables and Risk of Colorectal Neoplasms: A Systematic Review and Meta-Analysis. *Nutr. Cancer* **2014**, *66*, 128–139. [CrossRef] [PubMed]

102. Liu, B.; Mao, Q.; Wang, X.; Zhou, F.; Luo, J.; Wang, C.; Lin, Y.; Zheng, X.; Xie, L. Cruciferous Vegetables Consumption and Risk of Renal Cell Carcinoma: A Meta-Analysis. *Nutr. Cancer* **2013**, *65*, 668–676. [CrossRef] [PubMed]

103. Li, L.Y.; Luo, Y.; Lu, M.D.; Xu, X.W.; Lin, H.D.; Zheng, Z.Q. Cruciferous vegetable consumption and the risk of pancreatic cancer: A meta-analysis. *World J. Surg. Oncol.* **2015**, *13*, 44. [CrossRef] [PubMed]

104. Abbaoui, B.; Lucas, C.R.; Riedl, K.M.; Clinton, S.K.; Mortazavi, A. Cruciferous Vegetables, Isothiocyanates, and Bladder Cancer Prevention. *Mol. Nutr. Food Res.* **2018**, *62*, e1800079. [CrossRef]

105. Jia, X.; Zhong, L.; Song, Y.; Hu, Y.; Wang, G.; Sun, S. Consumption of citrus and cruciferous vegetables with incident type 2 diabetes mellitus based on a meta-analysis of prospective study. *Prim. Care Diabetes* **2016**, *10*, 272–280. [CrossRef]

106. Zhang, Z.; Bergan, R.; Shannon, J.; Slatore, C.G.; Bobe, G.; Takata, Y. The Role of Cruciferous Vegetables and Isothiocyanates for Lung Cancer Prevention: Current Status, Challenges, and Future Research Directions. *Mol. Nutr. Food Res.* **2018**, *62*, 1700936. [CrossRef]

107. Zhang, N.-Q.; Ho, S.C.; Mo, X.-F.; Lin, F.-Y.; Huang, W.-Q.; Luo, H.; Huang, J.; Zhang, C.-X. Glucosinolate and isothiocyanate intakes are inversely associated with breast cancer risk: A case–control study in China. *Br. J. Nutr.* **2018**, *119*, 957–964. [CrossRef]

108. Wu, Q.J.; Xie, L.; Zheng, W.; Vogtmann, E.; Li, H.L.; Yang, G.; Ji, B.T.; Gao, Y.T.; Shu, X.O.; Xiang, Y.B. Cruciferous vegetables consumption and the risk of female lung cancer: A prospective study and a meta-analysis. *Ann. Oncol.* **2013**, *24*, 1918–1924. [CrossRef]

109. Johnson, I.T. Cruciferous Vegetables and Risk of Cancers of the Gastrointestinal Tract. *Mol. Nutr. Food Res.* **2018**, *62*, 1701000. [CrossRef]

110. Gianfredi, V.; Vannini, S.; Moretti, M.; Villarini, M.; Bragazzi, N.L.; Izzotti, A.; Nucci, D. Sulforaphane and Epigallocatechin Gallate Restore Estrogen Receptor Expression by Modulating Epigenetic Events in the Breast Cancer Cell Line MDA-MB-231: A Systematic Review and Meta-Analysis. *Lifestyle Genom.* **2017**, *10*, 126–135. [CrossRef]

111. Lam, T.K.; Gallicchio, L.; Lindsley, K.; Shiels, M.; Hammond, E.; Tao, X.G.; Chen, L.; Robinson, K.A.; Caulfield, L.E.; Herman, J.G.; et al. Cruciferous vegetable consumption and lung cancer risk: A systematic review. *Cancer Epidemiol. Biomark. Prev.* **2009**, *18*, 184–195. [CrossRef] [PubMed]

112. International Agency for Research on Cancer (IARC); World Health Organization. *All Cancers Data Sheet*; International Agency for Research on Cancer: Lyon, France, 2018; Volume 876.

113. Murillo, G.; Mehta, R.G. Cruciferous vegetables and cancer prevention. *Nutr. Cancer* **2014**, *41*, 17–28. [CrossRef] [PubMed]

114. Gründemann, C.; Huber, R. Chemoprevention with isothiocyanates—From bench to bedside. *Cancer Lett.* **2018**, *414*, 26–33. [CrossRef] [PubMed]

115. Hayes, J.D.; Kelleher, M.O.; Eggleston, I.M. The cancer chemopreventive actions of phytochemicals derived from glucosinolates. *Eur. J. Nutr.* **2008**, *47*, 73–88. [CrossRef]

116. Cox, D.N.; Poelman, A.A.M. Towards greater vegetable consumption: Change the product or change the person? Case studies of two vegetable commodities. *Food Res. Int.* **2015**, *69*, 348–356. [CrossRef]

117. Domínguez-Perles, R.; Martínez-Ballesta, M.C.; Carvajal, M.; García-Viguera, C.; Moreno, D.A. Broccoli-Derived By-Products—A Promising Source of Bioactive Ingredients. *J. Food Sci.* **2010**, *75*, C383–C392. [CrossRef]

118. Drabińska, N.; Ciska, E.; Szmatowicz, B.; Krupa-Kozak, U. Broccoli by-products improve the nutraceutical potential of gluten-free mini sponge cakes. *Food Chem.* **2018**, *267*, 170–177. [CrossRef]

119. Klopsch, R.; Baldermann, S.; Voss, A.; Rohn, S.; Schreiner, M.; Neugart, S. Narrow-Banded UVB Affects the Stability of Secondary Plant Metabolites in Kale (*Brassica oleracea* var. *sabellica*) and Pea (*Pisum sativum*) Leaves Being Added to Lentil Flour Fortified Bread: A Novel Approach for Producing Functional Foods. *Foods* **2019**, *8*, 427. [CrossRef]

120. Heo, Y.; Kim, M.-J.; Lee, J.-W.; Moon, B. Muffins enriched with dietary fiber from kimchi by-product: Baking properties, physical–chemical properties, and consumer acceptance. *Food Sci. Nutr.* **2019**, *7*, 1778–1785. [CrossRef]

121. Ye, J.-H.; Huang, L.-Y.; Terefe, N.S.; Augustin, M.A. Fermentation-based biotransformation of glucosinolates, phenolics and sugars in retorted broccoli puree by lactic acid bacteria. *Food Chem.* **2019**, *286*, 616–623. [CrossRef] [PubMed]

122. Cai, Y.X.; Wang, J.H.; McAuley, C.; Augustin, M.A.; Terefe, N.S. Fermentation for enhancing the bioconversion of glucoraphanin into sulforaphane and improve the functional attributes of broccoli puree. *J. Funct. Foods* **2019**, *61*, 103461. [CrossRef]

123. Lafarga, T.; Acién-Fernández, F.G.; Castellari, M.; Villaró, S.; Bobo, G.; Aguiló-Aguayo, I. Effect of microalgae incorporation on the physicochemical, nutritional, and sensorial properties of an innovative broccoli soup. *LWT* **2019**, *111*, 167–174. [CrossRef]

124. Ashfaq, F.; Butt, M.S.; Bilal, A.; Tehseen, S.; Suleria, H.A.R. Effect of cabbage or its aqueous extract incorporated croquettes on chemical composition and storage stability in relation to antioxidant potential and sensory profile. *J. Food Process. Preserv.* **2020**, *44*, e14291. [CrossRef]

125. Song, G.-H.; Park, E.-S.; Lee, S.-M.; Park, D.-B.; Park, K.-Y. Beneficial Outcomes of Kimchi Prepared with Amtak Baechu Cabbage and Salting in Brine Solution: Anticancer Effects in Pancreatic and Hepatic Cancer Cells. *J. Environ. Pathol. Toxicol. Oncol.* **2018**, *37*, 151–161. [CrossRef] [PubMed]

126. Lafarga, T.; Gallagher, E.; Bademunt, A.; Bobo, G.; Echeverria, G.; Viñas, I.; Aguiló-Aguayo, I. Physiochemical and nutritional characteristics, bioaccessibility and sensory acceptance of baked crackers containing broccoli co-products. *Int. J. Food Sci. Technol.* **2019**, *54*, 634–640. [CrossRef]

127. Shi, M.; Ying, D.-Y.; Hlaing, M.M.; Ye, J.-H.; Sanguansri, L.; Augustin, M.A. Development of broccoli by-products as carriers for delivering EGCG. *Food Chem.* **2019**, *301*, 125301. [CrossRef]

128. Prokopov, T.; Goranova, Z.; Baeva, M.; Slavov, A.; Galanakis, C.M. Effects of powder from white cabbage outer leaves on sponge cake quality. *Int. Agrophys.* **2015**, *29*, 493–500. [CrossRef]

129. García-Saldaña, J.S.; Campas-Baypoli, O.N.; López-Cervantes, J.; Sánchez-Machado, D.I.; Cantú-Soto, E.U.; Rodríguez-Ramírez, R. Microencapsulation of sulforaphane from broccoli seed extracts by gelatin/gum arabic and gelatin/pectin complexes. *Food Chem.* **2016**, *201*, 94–100. [CrossRef]

130. Sánchez, F.M.; García, F.; Calvo, P.; Bernalte, M.J.; González-Gómez, D. Optimization of broccoli microencapsulation process by complex coacervation using response surface methodology. *Innov. Food Sci. Emerg. Technol.* **2016**, *34*, 243–249. [CrossRef]

131. Soler-Rivas, C.; Marín, F.R.; Santoyo, S.; García-Risco, M.R.; Señoráns, F.J.; Reglero, G. Testing and Enhancing the in Vitro Bioaccessibility and Bioavailability of Rosmarinus officinalis Extracts with a High Level of Antioxidant Abietanes. *J. Agric. Food Chem.* **2010**, *58*, 1144–1152. [CrossRef] [PubMed]

132. Riar, H.; Khatkar, S.; Khatkar, A.; Arora, N.; Mann, S.; Panghal, A.; Kumar, S. The conceptual understanding of nutrikinetics: A futuristic approach for designing health foods. *Nutr. Food Sci.* **2019**. [CrossRef]

133. Klug, T.V.; Martínez-Hernández, G.B.; Collado, E.; Artés, F.; Artés-Hernández, F. Effect of Microwave and High-Pressure Processing on Quality of an Innovative Broccoli Hummus. *Food Bioprocess Technol.* **2018**, *11*, 1464–1477. [CrossRef]

134. Valenzuela, B.A.; Valenzuela, R.; Sanhueza, J.; Morales, I.G. Alimentos funcionales, nutracéuticos y foshu: ¿Vamos hacia un nuevo concepto de alimentación? Revista chilena de nutrición. *Rev. Chil. Nutr.* **2014**, *41*, 198–204. [CrossRef]

135. Cai, Y.X.; Augustin, M.A.; Jegasothy, H.; Wang, J.H.; Terefe, N.S. Mild heat combined with lactic acid fermentation: A novel approach for enhancing sulforaphane yield in broccoli puree. *Food Funct.* **2020**, *11*, 779–786. [CrossRef] [PubMed]

136. Mazzucotelli, C.A.; González-Aguilar, G.A.; Villegas-Ochoa, M.A.; Domínguez-Avila, A.J.; Ansorena, M.R.; Di Scala, K.C. Chemical characterization and functional properties of selected leafy vegetables for innovative mixed salads. *J. Food Biochem.* **2018**, *42*, e12461. [CrossRef]

137. Barakat, H.; Reim, V.; Rohn, S. Stability of saponins from chickpea, soy and faba beans in vegetarian, broccoli-based bars subjected to different cooking techniques. *Food Res. Int.* **2015**, *76*, 142–149. [CrossRef]

138. Atwell, L.L.; Hsu, A.; Wong, C.P.; Stevens, J.F.; Bella, D.; Yu, T.-W.; Pereira, C.B.; Löhr, C.V.; Christensen, J.M.; Dashwood, R.H.; et al. Absorption and chemopreventive targets of sulforaphane in humans following consumption of broccoli sprouts or a myrosinase-treated broccoli sprout extract. *Mol. Nutr. Food Res.* **2015**, *59*, 424–433. [CrossRef]

International Journal of
Molecular Sciences

Article

δ-Tocotrienol, Isolated from Rice Bran, Exerts an Anti-Inflammatory Effect via MAPKs and PPARs Signaling Pathways in Lipopolysaccharide-Stimulated Macrophages

Junjun Shen [1], Tao Yang [1], Youzhi Xu [1], Yi Luo [2], Xinyue Zhong [1], Limin Shi [1], Tao Hu [1], Tianyi Guo [1], Ying Nie [1], Feijun Luo [1,*] and Qinlu Lin [1,*]

1   Hunan Key Laboratory of Grain-Oil Deep Process and Quality Control, Hunan Key Laboratory of Processed Food for Special Medical Purpose, College of Food Science and Engineering, National Engineering Laboratory for Deep Process of Rice and Byproducts, Central South University of Forestry and Technology, Changsha 410004, Hunan, China; shenjunjun@yeah.net (J.S.); yangtao807@163.com (T.Y.); xuyouzhi123@hotmail.com (Y.X.); zhongxinyue111@163.com (X.Z.); Shilm6666@126.com (L.S.); hutao0829@hotmail.com (T.H.); guotianyib11@hotmail.com (T.G.); ny198722@hotmail.com (Y.N.)
2   Department of Clinic Medicine, Xiangya School of Medicine, Central South University, Changsha 410008, Hunan, China; YiLuo603@hotmail.com
*   Correspondence: luofeijun888@csuft.edu.cn (F.L.); linqinlu@hotmail.com (Q.L.); Tel.: +86-731-8562-3240 (F.L. & Q.L.)

Received: 12 September 2018; Accepted: 1 October 2018; Published: 4 October 2018

Abstract: δ-Tocotrienol, an important component of vitamin E, has been reported to possess some physiological functions, such as anticancer and anti-inflammation, however their molecular mechanisms are not clear. In this study, δ-tocotrienol was isolated and purified from rice bran. The anti-inflammatory effect and mechanism of δ-tocotrienol against lipopolysaccharides (LPS) activated pro-inflammatory mediator expressions in RAW264.7 cells were investigated. Results showed that δ-tocotrienol significantly inhibited LPS-stimulated nitric oxide (NO) and proinflammatory cytokine (TNF-α, IFN-γ, IL-1β and IL-6) production and blocked the phosphorylation of c-Jun N-terminal kinase (JNK) and extracellular regulated protein kinases 1/2 (ERK1/2). δ-Tocotrienol repressed the transcriptional activations and translocations of nuclear factor-kappa B (NF-κB) and activator protein-1 (AP-1), which were closely related with downregulated cytokine expressions. Meanwhile, δ-tocotrienol also affected the PPAR signal pathway and exerted an anti-inflammatory effect. Taken together, our data showed that δ-tocotrienol inhibited inflammation via mitogen-activated protein kinase (MAPK) and peroxisome proliferator-activated receptor (PPAR) signalings in LPS-stimulated macrophages.

Keywords: rice bran; δ-tocotrienol; inflammation; MAPKs; PPARs; RAW264.7

1. Introduction

Inflammation is a significant mechanism of the immune pathogenesis and against different harmful stimuli [1]. Inflammation may result in tissue injury, infection and stress or exposure to bacterial components, such as lipopolysaccharide (LPS) [2,3]. LPS is a component of the cell wall of gram-negative bacteria and was used to induce the cell inflammation model in macrophage RAW264.7. During inflammatory response, macrophages play an important role to provide a defense against the foreign stimuli. Macrophages take part in the inflammatory process through regulating a series of inflammatory cytokines, such as tumor necrosis factor-α (TNF-α), interferon-γ (INF-γ), interleukin-1β (IL-1β), IL-6 and IL-8 [4]. On the other hand, macrophages also stimulate the expressions and secretions of inflammatory mediators, including nitric oxide (NO) and prostaglandin E2 (PGE2). NO release is controlled by inducible NO synthase (iNOS) and PGE2 secretion is synthesized by cyclooxygenase-2 (COX-2) [5]. Although the cellular signaling pathways and molecular mechanisms of the inflammation response are very complicated, mitogen-activated protein kinase (MAPK) is an important pathway in the initiation and development of the inflammation process. MAPKs are the specific protein family of serine/threonine kinases, which can transmit signal by sequential phosphorylation events. Meanwhile, lipids play essential roles in almost all inflammation processes [6,7]. Peroxisome proliferator-activated receptors (PPARs) are key important transcript factors which are involved in lipid metabolism and inflammation, and PPAR pathway is closely related with developing chronic inflammation, diabetes, obesity, hypertension and hyperlipidemia [8–11]. PPAR super family contains α-, γ-, δ-, (PPARα, PPARγ and PPARδ), which are ligand-regulated transcription factors and belong to the nuclear hormone receptors [7]. Specific ligands like unsaturated fatty acids participate in the regulation of physical metabolic pathways. Interestingly, δ-tocotrienol is an unsaturated fatty acid [12,13]. Although PPARs have many similarities among each different isoform, they have their own particular functions, tissue distributions, biomedical properties and unique reactions to different ligands [14,15]. PPAR signaling can also activate activator protein-1 (AP-1) and activate mitogen-activated protein kinase (MAPK) signaling, which forms a complex signal pathway net via cross-talking different pathways in the response. However, the complex mechanism of inflammation is still not clear [15,16].

δ-Tocotrienol is a bioactive component of rice, which is a common staple food consumed worldwide [17,18]. Since rice is the most important crop around the world harvested from over 100 countries, its components including rice starch, δ-tocotrienol and other vitamins deserve more attention [19]. Rice bran is an important by-product of rice acquired from rice milling process. Rice bran and its components exert multiple biological effects [17,18]. δ-Tocotrienol is a member of vitamin E family which can be extracted from rice bran. δ-Tocotrienol can also obtained from some plant resources such as palm, coconut and grains like oat, wheat, maize and rye [20–22]. Vitamin E compounds family has members named α-, β-, γ-, δ- tocopherols and α-, β-, γ-, δ-tocotrienol, all of the eight chemically distinct isomers constitute vitamin E [23–25]. Unlike saturated tocopherols, tocotrienols are unsaturated forms of vitamin E and own an isoprenoid side chain. δ-Tocotrienol was found to take part in a lot of health-promoting functions which include anti-diabetic, cholesterol-lowering, anticancer, antihyperlipidemic, immunomodulatory effects, antioxidant and anti-inflammation, but its molecular mechanism is not clear [26].

In this study, we used an LPS-induced macrophage inflammation model to evaluate the anti-inflammation function of δ-tocotrienol and explore if δ-tocotrienol inhibits inflammation through MAPK and PPAR pathways. Moreover, we investigated the cross-talk of MAPK and PPAR pathways and how δ-tocotrienol prevented inflammation in the in vitro model.

2. Results

2.1. Isolation and Purification of δ-Tocotrienol from Rice Bran

Crude rice bran oil was extracted from rice bran by supercritical carbon dioxide extraction. The rice bran oil extracts from rice bran were then identified by high performance liquid chromatography (HPLC). As Figure 1A indicates, there are 8 peaks in rice bran extracts which include α-tocopherol, β-tocopherol, γ-tocopherol, δ-tocopherol, α-tocotrienol, β-tocotrienol, γ-tocotrienol and δ-tocotrienol. The yield of δ-tocotrienol that was isolated from rice bran oil that was prepared by carbon dioxide extraction was 132.7 μg/kg. After the purification of δ-tocotrienol from the rice bran oil using the Shim-pack PREP-ODS (20.0 mm × 250 mm, 15 μm, Shimadzu Co., Ltd., Kyoto, Japan), δ-tocotrienol and related substance, which was extracted from rice bran, was finally detected by the fluorescence detector (Prominence RF-20A/Axs, Shimadzu Co., Ltd., Kyoto, Japan). The purity of δ-tocotrienol that was extracted from rice bran is 96.2% (Figure 1B).

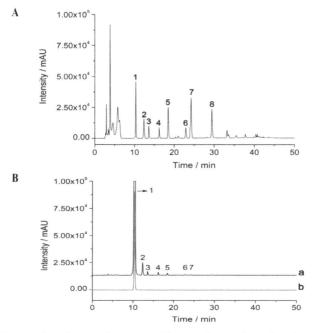

Figure 1. Isolation and purification of δ-tocotrienol from rice bran. (**A**) HPLC analyzed the different peaks of oil from the rice bran. (**B**) HPLC identified the purified δ-tocotrienol. The red color peak is the standard sample of δ-tocotrienol. HPLC: high performance liquid chromatography; "a": experiment sample; "b": standard sample. Peak 1: δ-tocotrienol; peak 2: β-tocotrienol; peak 3: γ-tocotrienol; peak 4: α-tocotrienol; peak 5: δ-tocopherol; peak 6: β-tocopherol; peak 7: γ-tocopherol; peak 8: α-tocopherol.

2.2. The Toxicity of δ-Tocotrienol on RAW264.7 Cells

To investigate the cell toxicity of δ-tocotrienol, different concentrations of δ-tocotrienol were divided into 6 groups: control, δ-tocotrienol (5 μM), δ-tocotrienol (10 μM), δ-tocotrienol (20 μM), δ-tocotrienol (40 μM), δ-tocotrienol (80 μM). The phenotype of the cells after δ-tocotrienol treatment was observed by optical microscope (Leica, Solms, Germany). The optical density (OD) value, which stands for the rate of cell survival from control group to δ-tocotrienol (80 μM), had no significant differences ($p > 0.05$). Results revealed that under each concentration of δ-tocotrienol treatment, this alone had no effect on murine macrophages RAW264.7. The cell viability of different intensities of δ-tocotrienol on RAW264.7 cells was determined by trypan blue dye exclusion or a quantitative colorimetric assay with MTS [3-(4,5-diethylthiazol-2-yl)-5-(3-carboxymethoxyphenyl)-2-(4-sulfo phenyl)-2H-etrazolium,inner salt] assay. The data showed that δ-tocotrienol exerted no obvious suppression effect on cell viability of RAW264.7 (0–40 μM), see Figure 2A,B. Although our data showed that 40 μM δ-tocotrienol did not affect cell viability, we selected 20 μM δ-tocotrienol in the next experiments to avoid any cytotoxicity of δ-tocotrienol.

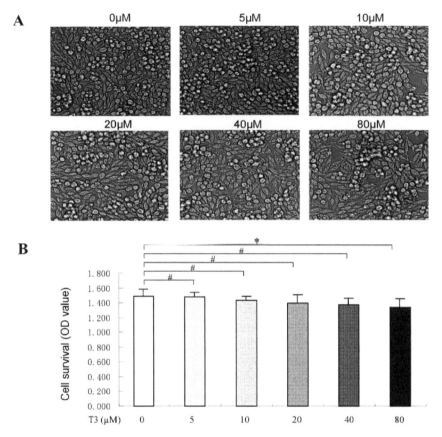

Figure 2. Effect of δ-tocotrienols on the phenotype of LPS-induced RAW264.7. (**A**) The morphologic change of LPS-induced RAW264.7 after treatment of δ-tocotrienols; (**B**) Effects of δ-tocotrienols in cell viability. LPS: liposaccharide; OD: optical density; T3: δ-tocotrienol. Data are expressed as the mean ± SD of three independent experiments. *: $p < 0.05$; #: $p > 0.05$.

2.3. δ-Tocotrienol Downregulated the Expressions of Proinflammatory Factors

During suffering inflammatory disease, the proinflammatory factors, such as TNF-α, IL-1β, IL-6, and mediators of iNOS were always overproduced [27]. In our study, the mRNA expressions of proinflammatory factors were assessed by real-time quantitative PCR (RT-qPCR). The results indicated that the upregulation expressions of pro-inflammatory cytokine mRNAs in the LPS-stimulated group were significantly higher than that of the control group (Figure 3A–D). δ-tocotrienol treatments decreased the mRNA expressions of TNF-α, IL-1β, IL-6 and iNOS in a dosage-dependant manner, as shown in Figure 3A–D. Western blotting further confirmed that δ-tocotrienol treatments (5 μM, 10 μM, 20 μM) inhibited the protein expression levels of TNF-α, IL-1β, IL-6 and iNOS in the LPS-stimulated macrophage (Figure 4A–E). Taken together, δ-tocotrienol exerts an anti-inflammatory effect via decreasing expressions of inflammatory factors.

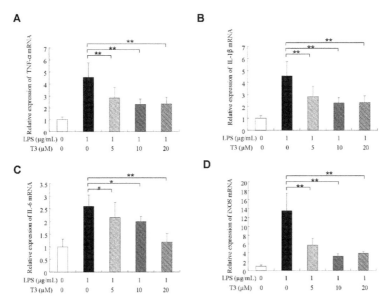

Figure 3. δ-Tocotrienols inhibit mRNA expression of inflammatory cytokines/mediator in LPS-stimulated RAW264.7 cells. (**A**) Relative expression of TNF-α mRNA; (**B**) Relative expression of IL-1β mRNA; (**C**) Relative expression of IL-6 mRNA; (**D**) Relative expression of inducible nitric oxide synthase (iNOS) mRNA. T3: δ-tocotrienol; LPS: lipopolysaccharide. The data came from three independent experiments. Comparing with LPS group, *: $p < 0.05$; **: $p < 0.01$; #: $p > 0.05$.

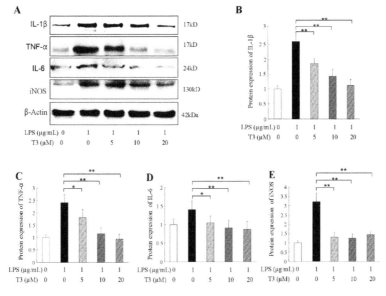

Figure 4. δ-Tocotrienols inhibit protein expression of inflammatory factors in LPS-activated RAW264.7 cells. (**A**) Representative image of Western blotting from 3 independent experiments; (**B**) Protein expression of IL-1β; (**C**) Protein expression of TNF-α; (**D**) Protein expression of IL-6; (**E**) Relative expression of iNOS mRNA. iNOS: inducible nitric oxide synthase; LPS: lipopolysaccharide T3: δ-tocotrienol. Comparing with LPS group, *: $p < 0.05$; **: $p < 0.01$.

2.4. Effect of δ-Tocotrienol on MAPKs in LPS-Stimulated RAW264.7 Cells

It has been approved that mitogen-activated protein kinases (MAPKs) are phosphorylated in the inflammatory response, and that the MAPK transduction pathway activation is the key to signaling to regulate the expression of inflammatory cytokine [28,29]. To explore the anti-inflammatory mechanism of δ-tocotrienol, the phosphorylation situation of 3 subtypes of MAPKs, including c-Jun N-terminal kinase (JNK), extracellular signal-regulated kinase 1/2 (ERK1/2), and p38 were analyzed by Western blotting in the LPS-stimulated RAW264.7 cells. As shown in Figure 5A, LPS treatment caused an obvious increase of phosphorylation of ERK1/2, JNK and p38; Adding δ-tocotrienol resulted in a reduction of phosphorylation of ERK1/2, JNK (see Figure 5B,C), however δ-tocotrienol did not inhibit the phosphorylation of p38 (see Figure 5D) in a dosage-dependent manner. Our data showed that δ-tocotrienol that was treated with 20 µM was the effective dosage for the inhibition of ERK1/2 and JNK phosphorylation, and the protein contents of p-ERK1/2 and p-JNK were reduced to 76.6% and 28.9% (Figure 5B,C), respectively. These results suggest that δ-tocotrienol exerts an anti-inflammatory effect which may be mediated by inhibiting the ERK/JNK activation (phosphorylation) in the LPS-stimulated cell inflammation model.

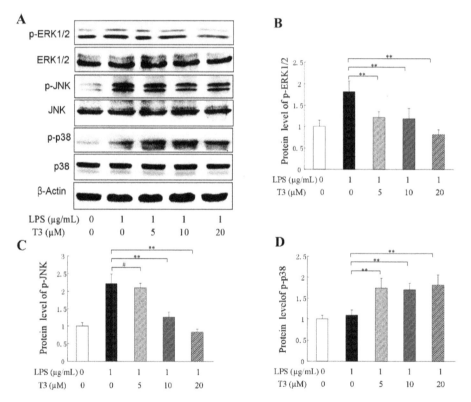

Figure 5. δ-Tocotrienol prevents MAPK pathways in LPS-stimulated RAW264.7 cells. (**A**) Representative image of Western blotting from 3 independent experiments; (**B**) Protein level of p-ERK1/2; (**C**) Protein level of p-JNK; (**D**) Protein level of p-p38. ERK1/2: extracellular regulated protein kinases; JNK: c-Jun N-terminal kinase; LPS: lipopolysaccharide; MAPK: mitogen-activated protein kinase; T3: δ-tocotrienol. The values represent the means ± SD. Comparing with LPS group, **: $p < 0.01$; #: $p > 0.05$.

2.5. Effect of δ-Tocotrienol on NF-κB /AP-1 Activities and Translocations

Transcription factors AP-1 and NF-κB are involved in many biological functions. In the inflammatory response, inflammatory cytokine, such as TNF-α, IFN-γ, IL-1β, IL-6 and iNOS have several AP-1 and NF-κB binding sites and the two transcript factors can directly bind the promoter of those genes to regulate inflammatory cytokine expressions [30,31]. After exposure to LPS alone, our data showed that the contents of p65 and c-Jun in the nuclei were increased significantly and LPS promoted the nuclear translocation of p65 and c-Jun (Figure 6A,B). After treatments of different dosages of δ-tocotrienol, the contents of p65 and c-Jun in the nuclei were obviously reduced in a dose dependent manner compared with the LPS group and, in contrast, the contents of p65 and c-Jun in the cytoplasm were increased in RAW264.7 cells. Compared with the LPS group, the relative luciferase activities of NF-κB were reduced to 57.9%, 43.6% and 43.5% by reporter gene analysis (Figure 6A,C), and the relative luciferase activities of AP-1 were reduced to 63.2%, 53.8% and 41.4% (Figure 6B,D), respectively. This suggests that δ-tocotrienol may reduce inflammatory cytokine expressions via inhibiting NF-κB and AP-1 activation in the LPS-induced RAW264.7 cells. Furthermore, pNF-κB-Luc and pAP-1-Luc reporter genes were used to detect the effect of δ-tocotrienol on the transcriptional activities of NF-κB and AP-1. Consistent with the nuclear translocation data, luciferase reporter assays found that δ-tocotrienol significantly inhibited NF-κB and AP-1 activities in a dose-dependent manner, as shown in Figure 7A,B. MAPKs are found to be close with AP-1 and NF-κB activations [29,32]. Our results suggest that δ-tocotrienol may affect inflammatory cytokine expressions via MAPK/NF-κB and MAPK/AP-1 pathways.

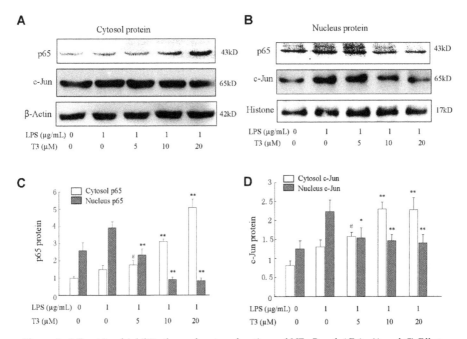

Figure 6. δ-Tocotrienol inhibits the nuclear translocations of NF-κB and AP-1. (**A and C**) Effect of δ-tocotrienol on the protein content of p65 and c-Jun by Western blotting analysis in cytosol; (**B and D**) Effect of δ-tocotrienol on the protein content of p65 and c-Jun by Western blotting analysis in nucleus. AP-1: activator protein-1; LPS: lipopolysaccharide; NF-κB: nuclear factor-kappa B; T3: δ-tocotrienol. The figure shown here are representative data from three independent experiments. The values represent the means ± SD. Comparing with LPS group, *: $p < 0.05$; **: $p < 0.01$; #: $p > 0.05$.

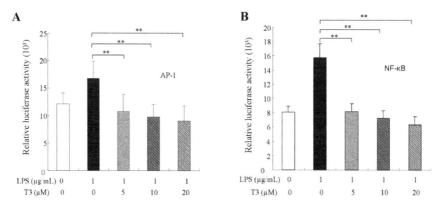

Figure 7. δ-Tocotrienol inhibits the transcriptional activities of NF-κB and AP-1. (**A**) Effect of δ-tocotrienol on the transcriptional activity of NF-κB in LPS-stimulated RAW264.7 cells; (**B**) Effect of δ-tocotrienol on the transcriptional activity of AP-1 in LPS-stimulated RAW264.7 cells. T3: δ-tocotrienol; LPS: lipopolysaccharide. The values represent the means ± SD. Comparing with LPS group, **: $p < 0.01$.

2.6. Effect of δ-Tocotrienol on the Activities of PPARα and PPARγ In Vitro Models

Peroxisome proliferator-activated receptors (PPARs) are ligand-activated nuclear receptors which have three isoforms: PPARα, PPARβ/δ, PPARγ, and each isoform has its own physiological functions. PPARα was supposed to be involved in heart failure [33,34]. Both PPARα and PPARβ/δ have overlapping functions in cardiovascular diseases [34]. PPARγ is well known for its therapeutic potency of metabolic syndrome, type 2 diabetes and obesity [12,35,36]. In this study, we estimated the effect of δ-tocotrienol on the PPAR pathway in the LPS-stimulated RAW264.7 cells. The results revealed that in LPS-induced RAW264.7, δ-tocotrienol significantly inhibited the phosphorylation of PPARα at concentration of 5 μM, 10 μM, 20 μM in a dosage-dependent manner compared with the control group, as shown in Figure 8A,B. In this study, our data also demonstrated that δ-tocotrienol significantly depressed the phosphorylation of PPARγ at concentrations of 5 μM, 10 μM, 20 μM in a dosage-dependent manner compared with the control group.

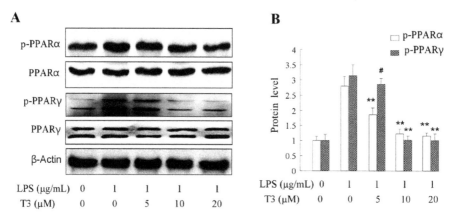

Figure 8. δ-Tocotrienols inhibit PPAR signaling in LPS-stimulated RAW264.7 cells. (**A**) Representative image of PPARs Western blotting from 3 independent experiments; (**B**) Protein level of p-PPARs. LPS: lipopolysaccharide; PPAR: peroxisome proliferator-activated receptor; T3: δ-tocotrienol. Comparing with LPS group, **: $p < 0.01$; #: $p > 0.05$.

2.7. Effect of δ-Tocotrienol on MAPKs and PPARs Signaling Models

To investigate whether the MAPK signaling pathway interacts with PPARs, which take part in the anti-inflammation of δ-tocotrienol, LPS-induced RAW264.7 cells were treated with the p38MAPK inhibitor SB203580, the JNK inhibitor SP600125 and the ERK1/2 inhibitor U0126. As shown in Figure 9A, in contrast to the δ-tocotrienol treated group, SB600125, U0126 and SP203580 treatment all suppressed the phosphorylation of PPARγ (Ser112) protein which was stimulated by LPS in the presence of δ-tocotrienol. Moreover, compared with the δ-tocotrienol treated group (Figure 9B), both SP600125 and U0126 treatment inhibited the phosphorylated of PPARα (Ser384), while SB203580 treatment did not activate the phosphorylation of PPARα (Ser384) level. These data indicated that δ-tocotrienol inhibited PPARα activation via inhibiting JNK and ERK1/2 activities; δ-tocotrienol inhibited PPARγ phosphorylation through inhibiting p38, JNK and ERK1/2 activities.

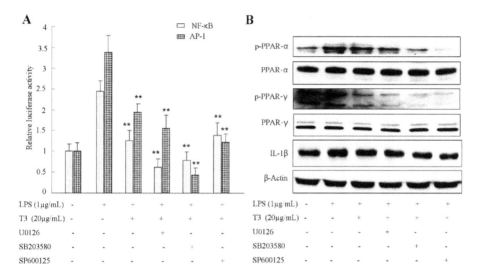

Figure 9. δ-Tocotrienols inhibit MAPK/AP-1/NFκB and MAPK-PPAR signalings in LPS-stimulated RAW264.7 cells. (**A**) RAW264.7 cells were pretreated with the p38MAPK inhibitor SB203580 with 20 μM, the JNK inhibitor SP600125 with 20 μM, and the ERK1/2 inhibitor U0126 with 10 μM for 30 min, and were then treated with/without δ-tocotrienols for 2 h, and finally treated with LPS for 12 h. The results shown here are representative data from three independent experiments. (**B**) The phosphorylated or total forms of PPARs after treatment of MAPK inhibitors were measured by Western blotting. T3: δ-tocotrienol; LPS: lipopolysaccharide.

3. Discussion

In the present study, we demonstrated the anti-inflammatory effects and molecular mechanisms of δ-tocotrienol through the MAPKs/AP-1 and PPARs/AP-1 pathways. In previous studies, it is reported that δ-tocotrienol depressed the expressions of proinflammatory genes, however the role of δ-tocotrienol in the MAPK/AP-1 and PPARs/AP-1 pathways and the interactions between these two pathways remains unclear [15]. Our results verified that δ-tocotrienol significantly depressed the productions of IL-1β, IL-6, iNOS and TNF-α, meanwhile it does not have cytotoxicity on LPS-induced RAW264.7, as confirmed by MTS assay.

Rice bran oil and rice germ oil, together with palm oil have been used traditionally as cooking oil which have a high content of tocotrienol [37]. Recent studies showed that vitamin E components, like tocotrienol-rich fraction, had already been used as dietary complements to prevent breast cancer and hypercholesterolemia and its anti-inflammatory activity is the greatest compared with that of a-tocopherol and a-tocopheryl acetate [38–40]. Vitamin E components, such as γ-tocopherol, δ-tocopherol and γ-tocotrienol, have specific anti-inflammatory and antioxidant effects which are superior to those of α-tocopherol [41]. Several studies have shown that γ-tocotrienol inhibited LPS-stimulated RAW264.7 macrophages and IL-1β-activated lung epithelial cells through NF-κB and JAK-STAT6 or JAK-STAT3 signaling pathways [42,43]. In human endothelial cells, δ-tocotrienol is the most potent isomer of tocotrienols in depressing the expression of IL-6, ICAM-1, VCAM-1 and NF-κB compared with that of α-, β-, γ-tocotrienol [35]. δ-Tocotrienol has several potential health benefits, such as prevention of certain types of cancer [44], heart diseases and other acute or chronic inflammations. Among the isoforms of tocotrienols, the antioxidant and anti-inflammation functions of γ-tocotrienol were well studied, and only few experiments showed that δ-tocotrienol can decrease the expression of inflammatory factors in macrophages, however its molecular mechanism is unknown.

In the present study, we demonstrated the anti-inflammatory effects and molecular mechanisms of δ-tocotrienol through the MAPKs/AP-1 and PPARs/AP-1 pathways. In previous studies, it is reported that δ-tocotrienol depressed the expressions of proinflammatory genes, however the role of δ-tocotrienol in the MAPK/AP-1 and PPARs/AP-1 pathways and the interactions between these two pathways remains unclear [15]. Our results verified that δ-tocotrienol significantly depressed the productions of IL-1β, IL-6, iNOS and TNF-α, meanwhile it does not have cytotoxicity on LPS-induced RAW264.7, as confirmed by MTS assay.

MAPKs signaling pathway and PPARs signaling pathway were supposed to take part in the occurrence of inflammation. Although the cellular signaling pathways and molecular mechanisms of inflammation activation are very complicated, mitogen-activated protein kinase (MAPK) is a key signaling pathway in the initiation and development of the inflammation process. MAPK can transmit the extracellular information into cytoplasm and nucleus in the end. These serine/threonine kinases include extracellular signal-regulated kinase 1/2 (ERK1/2), extracellular signal-regulated kinase 5 (ERK5) c-Jun NH2-terminal kinase (JNK) and p38 and finally to the NF-κB and AP-1 in cell nucleus. Among PPAR receptors, PPARα was the first to be identified and expressed mainly in liver, heart, kidney and adipose tissues [15,45]. PPARα upregulates the expression of IκB, which inhibits the activation and nuclear translocation of the proinflammatory transcription factor NF-κB [46]. Both PPARα and PPARγ are reported to reduce the NF-κB transcriptional activity [13]. Fatty acids and their derivatives can activate peroxisome proliferator-activated receptors (PPARs) which regulate the expression of signaling pathways genes that are involved in adipogenesis, lipid metabolism, inflammation, type 2 diabetes and the maintenance of metabolic homeostasis [47]. In this study, δ-tocotrienol was found to decrease the production of inflammatory cytokines, such as IL-6, IL-1β and TNF-α with iNOS. Meanwhile in PPARα knock-out young (4-week-old) and senescent mice (42-week old), it was reported that δ-tocotrienol can also decrease the mRNA expressions of IL-6, IL-1β and TNF-α in vivo. However, the mediation of δ-tocotrienol via PPARs and MAPKs signaling is still unclear. In our present study, we found that δ-tocotrienol inhibits inflammation by activation of both PPARα and PPARγ receptors. Indeed, overweight and obesity inflammation are related to the interaction of nutrition, the immune system and metabolic organs [48–50]. In low grade chronic inflammation, where the innate immune system and arteries, heart, and brain are involved, all the three PPAR isotypes showed anti-inflammatory effects [31,45]. Both PPARα and PPARγ are reported to reduce the NF-κB transcriptional activity [13].

In our present study, we found that δ-tocotrienol inhibited MAPKs activation and downregulated the expression of inflammatory cytokines as IL-1β, IL-6, TNF-α and iNOS in the LPS-stimulated cell inflammation model. For all of those cytokines, they have AP-1 and NF-κB binding sites in the promoters of those genes. c-Jun is a direct target of JNK, and JNK activation will result in AP-1 activation, which promotes the expressions of proinflammatory factors. Our study also confirmed that δ-tocotrienol can inhibit the phosphorylation of JNK and transcriptional activity of AP-1. This means that δ-tocotrienol can inhibit expressions of proinflammatory factors via downregulating JNK (MAPK). δ-tocotrienol inhibited activation ERK1/2 and transcriptional activity of NF-κB, and δ-tocotrienol decreased expressions of proinflammatory factors through ERK1/2/NF-κB, which belonged to another important pathway. The results suggest that both JNK (MAPK) and ERK1/2/NF-κB were involved in the inhibition of the activation of MAPKs. Meanwhile, the effect of δ-tocotrienol on PPARs signaling in LPS activated RAW264.7 cells was estimated by Western blotting. The results demonstrated that the treatment of δ-tocotrienol suppressed the phosphorylation of PPARα and PPARγ and the two different isotypes in LPS that induced murine macrophages in a dosage dependent way. It was found that PPARα and PPARγ can repress the inflammatory response by blocking the activation of NF-κB [51,52]. NF-κB was formed by p65 and p50 proteins, and the phosphorylation of translocation of NF-κB from cytoplasm to nucleus leads to overexpressions of proinflammatory factors [53]. Moreover, when MAPK inhibitors were added to δ-tocotrienol treated RAW264.7 cells, the phosphorylation of PPARγ was further downregulated. On the other hand, both JNK and ERK1/2 inhibitors treatment blocked the phosphorylation of PPARα (Ser384), while p38 inhibitor treated had a weak effect on the phosphorylation of PPARα (Ser384) level. The results indicated that δ-tocotrienol upregulated the phosphorylation of PPARα through JNK and ERK1/2 and upregulated the phosphorylation of PPARγ by JNK and ERK1/2.

In conclusion, it is well known that MAPKs signaling play a key role in inflammation; we demonstrated that δ-tocotrienol repressed the inflammatory response via the inhibition of MAPK/ERK/JNK activation. PPARs are always the target of many drugs which are therapy to metabolic syndrome, dyslipidemia, insulin resistance, hypertension, type 2 diabetes and cardiovascular diseases. This is the first study to report the fact that δ-tocotrienol reduces AP-1 activation during LPS-stimulated inflammatory response, and δ-tocotrienol inhibits inflammatory cytokine expressions via MAPK and PPARs signalings. Further investigation found that crosstalk exists between MAPKs and PPARs, which is involved in the anti-inflammatory effect of δ-tocotrienol. δ-tocotrienol can be developed as a food supplement for diseases like obesity, cardiovascular diseases, diabetes, hypertension and hyperlipidemia, which are closely related to inflammation and chronic low-grade inflammation which MAPKs and PPARs signaling pathways are involved in.

4. Materials and Methods

4.1. Materials and Reagents

The rice bran was purchased from Hunan Jinjian Cereals Industry Co., Ltd. (Changde, China). Lipopolysaccharide (LPS) from *Escherichia coli* O127:B8 was obtained from Sigma-Aldrich (St. Louis, MO, USA). Stock solutions of δ-tocotrienol were purchased from Chromadex, Inc. (Irvine, CA, USA), purity 99.4%. Stock solutions of δ-tocotrienol were dissolved in ethanol and were blended by ultrasonic concussion for 5 min. Fetal bovine serum (FBS) and Roswell Park Memorial Institute (RPMI) medium were bought from Gibco (Grand Island, NY, USA). The Nuclear and Cytoplasmic Protein Extraction Kit (P0028), Enhanced BCA protein kit (P0009) and Penicillin and streptomycin were purchased from Beyotime Biotechnology Company (Shanghai, China). Antibody to histone H3 was obtained from Beyotime Biotechnology Company (Nantong, China). Polyclonal antibody against β-Actin (Cat#12620), iNOS (Cat#13120), IL-1β (Cat#12507), IL-6 (Cat#12912), TNF-α (Cat#11948), c-Jun, Phospho-c-Jun (Ser73), ERK1/2, phospho-ERK1/2 (T202/Y204), JNK phospho-JNK (T183/Y185), p38, phospho-p38 (Thr180/Tyr182), PPAR-α, phosphor-PPAR-α, PPAR-γ and phosphor-PPAR-γ. MAPK inhibitors SP600125, U0126 and SB203580 (MAPK inhibitors) were obtained from Cell Signaling Technology (Danvers, MA, USA). Goat anti-mouse IgG HRP-conjugated antibody was purchased from Southern Biotech (Birmingham, AL, USA). Goat anti-rabbit IgG HRP-conjugated antibody was purchased from Invitrogen (Carlsbad, CA, USA). The pNF-κB-Luc, pAP-1-Luc reporter vectors and the pRL-TK internal control vector were purchased from Promega (Madison, WI, USA). Enhanced chemiluminescence (ECL) substrate was bought from Thermo Scientific (Waltham, MA, USA).

4.2. Isolation of Rice Bran Oil by Supercritical Carbon Dioxide Extraction

The bran was dried using a commercial dryer (STERIS, Worcester, MA, USA) for 3 min at 110 °C in a vacuum sealed plastic pouch and was stored at −20 °C for further use. Each rice bran sample of 100 g was accurately weighed through analytical balance and was loaded into a 200 mL high-pressure vessel equipped with a water jacket (HanYang Sci., Seoul, Korea). The CO_2 flow rate was routinely kept constant at 2.5 L/min. In every experimental design, the extracted oil was weighed with an analytical balance at set time intervals. Supercritical CO_2 extraction was carried out using HA 221-50-06-C (Huaan Company Ltd., Nantong, China). Pure CO_2 was applied by using a high pressure pump 2TB-50 (Huaan Company Ltd., Nantong, China). According to Yoon [29], the extraction temperature was set at 60 °C, and the extraction pressure was set at 27.6 MPa for 60 min. The SC-CO_2 extraction experiments at each specific combination of pressure and temperature were performed in triplicate.

4.3. High Performance Liquid Chromatography (HPLC)

The rice bran oil extracts were dissolved in methanol, were further filtered with a 0.45 μm filter and were analyzed by HPLC. δ-Tocotrienol standard sample was purchased from Sigma (Sigma Co., Ltd., St. Louis, MO, USA). HPLC analysis was performed on a Shimadzu Prominence series apparatus with a fluorescence detector (Prominence RF-20A/Axs, Shimadzu Co., Ltd., Kyoto, Japan). The excitation wavelength was 296 nm and the emission wavelength was 325 nm, which were operated on fluorescence detector. The Hypersil Gold PFP column (250 mm × 4.6 mm i.d., 5 μm, ThermoFisher Scientific, Waltham, MA, USA) was used as an analytical column. The eluents were methanol/H_2O (85:15, *vol/vol*) at a flow rate of 0.8 mL/min. All the results were recorded, and the peaks were integrated by the chromatography software Labsolution LC (Shimadzu, Kyoto, Japan). δ-Tocotrienol was purified by Shim-pack PREP-ODS (20.0 mm × 250 mm, 15 μm, Shimadzu, Kyoto, Japan). The eluents include acetonitrile, tetrahydrofuran, methanol, 1% ammonium acetate (684:220:68:28) and the flow rate was 8 mL/min. The δ-tocotrienol standard that was purchased from Chromadex, Inc. (Irvine, CA, USA) was used to determine the absorption peak of δ-tocotrienol.

4.4. Cell Culture

RAW264.7 is a mouse monocyte-macrophage cell line and was purchased from the Institute of Cell Biology, Chinese Academy of Science, Shanghai, China. RAW264.7 cells were cultured in RPMI 1640 medium that was supplemented with 10% FBS (Gibco-BRL, Carlsbad, CA, USA) at 37 °C in a humidified incubator with 5% CO_2 atmosphere. The experiment details were described in our recent publication [32]. δ-Tocotrienol that was extracted from rice bran was dissolved in ethanol.

4.5. Cell Viability Assay

Cell viability was evaluated by the CellTiter 96 Aqueous One Solution Proliferation Assay Kit (Promega). The treated cells were incubated for 24 h, and then growth medium was replaced by a solution of 100 μL of fresh growth medium and 20 μL of MTS. The plate was incubated for another 2 h at 37 °C and the absorbance was measured at 490 nm. The percentage of cell viability relative to ethanol (solvent control) was calculated.

4.6. Observation of Morphological Changes

The morphological change of murine macrophages RAW264.7 is considered one of the remarkable characteristics of the toxicological effect. To determine whether δ-tocotrienol was toxicant to RAW264.7 cells, an optical microscopy (DM2500, Leica, Solms, Germany) was used to detect the toxicity of δ-tocotrienol and was compared with the control group. After 72 h of δ-tocotrienol (0 μM, 5 μM, 10 μM, 20 μM, 40 μM, 80 μM) treatment on RAW264.7 cells, the morphological changes, including cell floating and shrinkage and nucleic blebbing, were observed.

4.7. RNA Isolation and RT-qPCR

Total RNA from murine macrophages RAW 264.7 cells was extracted by the Trizol reagent kit (Transgen, Beijing, China) and was then reverse transcribed by using high-Capacity cDNA Reverse Transcription Kits (Applied Biosystems, Foster City, CA, USA). Consistent with Liu et al. [28] and Guo et al. [32], the relative mRNA expression levels of pro-inflammatory factors and iNOS were analyzed by real-time quantitative PCR (RT-qPCR). Cells were treated with δ-tocotrienol (5 μM, 10 μM, 20 μM) for 2 h followed by adding LPS (1 μg/mL) for 6 h. According to the manufacturer's protocol, 1 μg total RNA extracted from RAW264.7 cells was used in reverse transcription reaction with the One Step RT-PCR kit (Gibco-BRL). PCR amplifications were carried out for 32 cycles and each cycle consisted of a denaturing step for 3 min at 94 °C, a further denaturing at 94 °C for 30 s, an annealing step for 30 s at 60 °C and a polymerization step for 1 min at 72 °C. The PCR primer was according to Guo's publication [32].

4.8. Extraction of Nuclear and Cytosolic Proteins

RAW264.7 cells were cultured in a 100 mm dish at a density of 1×10^6 cells/mL for 24 h. After incubation, the cells were treated with various concentrations of δ-tocotrienol (0.5 μM, 10 μM and 20 μM) for 2 h and 1 μg/mL of LPS was then added for 60 min. Total protein from the cells was extracted with radio immunoprecipitation assay (RIPA) buffer (2 mM PMSF, 2 mM EDTA and 2 mM orthovanadate, 1% Triton X-100, 0.5% SDS, 0.1% deoxycholate) that was supplemented with a cocktail of protease and phosphatase inhibitors. RAW264.7 cells were harvested, and nuclear and cytosolic fractions were prepared using a Nuclear Extraction Kit (Sigma-Aldrich, St. Louis, MO, USA) according to the manufacturer's instructions.

4.9. Western Blot Analysis

RAW264.7 cells (1×10^6) were lysed in Tris buffered saline Tween (TBST) buffer (50 mM Tris, pH 7.6, 150 mM NaCl, and 0.05% Tween-20) and protease and phosphates inhibitors were added. Nuclear and cytoplasmic extraction kits were used to collect nuclear and cytoplasmic proteins. Equal amounts of nuclear, cytoplasm or whole cell extracts were separated by 13% SDS-PAGE, were transferred to nitrocellulose filters and blocked for 1 h and were then incubated with the corresponding antibodies to β-Actin (1:1000), IL-1β (1:1000), TNF-α (1:1000), IL-6 (1:1000), iNOS (1:500), IκB-α (1:500), c-Jun (1:1000), Phospho-c-Jun (1:500), phospho-ERK1/2 (1:1000), phospho-JNK (1:500) and phospho-p38 (1:500) at 4 °C overnight. The membrane was washed three times with Tris-bufffered saline, containing 0.05% Tween 20 (TBST) for 10 min and was incubated with anti-rabbit or anti-mouse IgG-horseradish peroxidase (1:5000, Pierce, Waltham, MA, USA) at room temperature for 1 h. The protein bands were visualized using an ECL system following the manufacturer's instructions.

4.10. Luciferase Reporter Assay

RAW264.7 cells were seeded in 24 well plates (Falcon Plastics, Oxnard, CA, USA) and were then transiently transfected at 80% confluency, with either 1.0 μg NF-κB-luc or AP-1-luc reporter plasmid DNA along with 0.5 μg SV40-β-galactosidase expression construct DNA (pSV β-gal) as an internal control, and 1.0 μg of the empty vector phRL-TK, using Lipofectamine 2000 (Invitrogen Life Technologies, Carlsbad, CA, USA) following the manufacturer's protocol.

4.11. Statistical Analysis

For statistical analysis, SPSS17.0 software (Chicago, IL, USA) was employed. One-way ANOVA or student's *t*-test was used for determining the statistically significant differences between the values of various experimental and control groups. Data was expressed as means ± SD, and a *p* value of 0.05 was considered statistically significant and of 0.01 was considered statistically very significant.

Author Contributions: Conceptualization, J.S., Q.L. and F.L.; Writing—Original Draft Preparation, J.S., T.Y., Y.X., Y.L., X.Z., T.H., T.G., Y.N., J.S., S.L. and F.L.; Writing—Review & Editing, J.S., Q.L. and F.L.; Supervision, Q.L. and F.L.; Funding Acquisition, Q.L. and F.L.

Funding: This study was supported by the Project "2011 Collaborative Innovation Center of Hunan province" (2013, No. 448), Natural Science Foundation of Hunan Province (No.2018JJ2672, No.2017JJ3528), the Key Project of the Education Department of Hunan province (No. 16A228), the Special Fund for Agro-scientific Research in the Public Interest of China (No.201303071-2-1), The Key Research and Develop Plan Project of Hunan Province (2017SK2190) and Science and Technology Innovation Platform and Talent Project of Hunan Province (2017TP1021).

Conflicts of Interest: The authors declare no conflict of interest. The funders had no role in the design of the study; in the collection, analyses, or interpretation of the data; in the writing of the manuscript, or in the decision to publish the results.

References

1. Shao, J.; Li, Y.; Wang, Z.; Xiao, M.; Yin, P.; Lu, Y.; Qian, X.; Xu, Y.; Liu, J. 7b, a novel naphthalimide derivative, exhibited anti-inflammatory effects via targeted-inhibiting TAK1 following down-regulation of ERK1/2-and p38 MAPK-mediated activation of NF-κB in LPS-stimulated RAW264.7 macrophages. *Int. Immunopharmacol.* **2013**, *17*, 216–228. [CrossRef] [PubMed]

2. Nahar, P.P.; Driscoll, M.V.; Li, L.; Slitt, A.L.; Seeram, N.P. Phenolic mediated anti-inflammatory properties of a maple syrup extract in RAW 264.7 murine macrophages. *J. Funct. Foods* **2014**, *6*, 126–136. [CrossRef]

3. Kim, K.S.; Lee, D.S.; Bae, G.S.; Park, S.J.; Kang, D.G.; Lee, H.S.; Oh, H.; Kim, Y.C. The inhibition of JNK MAPK and NF-κB signaling by tenuifoliside A isolated from Polygala tenuifolia in lipopolysaccharide-induced macrophages is associated with its anti-inflammatory effect. *Eur. J. Pharmacol.* **2013**, *721*, 267–276. [CrossRef] [PubMed]

4. Oh, Y.C.; Cho, W.K.; Jeong, Y.H.; Im, G.Y.; Lee, K.J.; Yang, H.J.; Ma, J.Y. Anti-inflammatory effect of Sosihotang via inhibition of nuclear factor-κB and mitogen-activated protein kinases signaling pathways in lipopolysaccharide- stimulated RAW264.7 macrophage cells. *Food Chem. Toxicol.* **2013**, *53*, 343–351. [CrossRef] [PubMed]

5. An, H.J.; Kim, I.T.; Park, H.J.; Kim, H.M.; Choi, J.H.; Lee, K.T. Tormentic acid, a triterpenoid saponin, isolated from Rosa rugosa, inhibited LPS-induced iNOS, COX-2, and TNF-α expression through inactivation of the nuclear factor-κB pathway in RAW 264.7 macrophages. *Int. Immunopharmacol.* **2011**, *11*, 504–510. [CrossRef] [PubMed]

6. Calder, P.C. n-3 polyunsaturated fatty acids, inflammation, and inflammatory diseases. *Am. J. Clin. Nutr.* **2006**, *83*, 77–109. [CrossRef] [PubMed]

7. Desvergne, B.; Wahli, W. Peroxisome proliferator-activated receptors: Nuclear control of metabolism. *Endocr. Rev.* **1999**, *20*, 649–688. [CrossRef] [PubMed]

8. Utreras, E.; Futatsugi, A.; Rudrabhatla, P.; Keller, J.; Iadarola, M.J.; Pant, H.C.; Kulkarni, A.B. Tumor necrosis factor-α regulates cyclin-dependent kinase 5 activity during pain signaling through transcriptional activation of p35. *J. Biol. Chem.* **2009**, *284*, 2275–2284. [CrossRef] [PubMed]

9. Qiang, L.; Wang, L. Brown remodeling of white adipose tissue by SirT1-dependent deacetylation of Pparγ. *Cell* **2012**, *150*, 620–632. [CrossRef] [PubMed]

10. Barish, G.D.; Narkar, V.A.; Evans, R.M. PPARδ: A dagger in the heart of the metabolic syndrome. *J. Clin. Investig.* **2006**, *116*, 590–597. [CrossRef] [PubMed]

11. Fang, F.; Kang, Z.; Wong, C. Vitamin E tocotrienols improve insulin sensitivity through activating peroxisome proliferator-activated receptors. *Mol. Nutr. Food Res.* **2010**, *54*, 345–352. [CrossRef] [PubMed]

12. Forman, B.M.; Chen, J.; Evans, R.M. Hypolipidemic drugs, polyunsaturated fatty acids, and eicosanoids are ligands for peroxisome proliferator-activated receptors α and δ. *Proc. Natl. Acad. Sci. USA* **1997**, *94*, 4312–4317. [CrossRef] [PubMed]

13. Poulsen, L.; Siersbaek, M.; Mandrup, S. PPARs: Fatty acid sensors controlling metabolism. *Semin. Cell Dev. Biol.* **2012**, *23*, 631–639. [CrossRef] [PubMed]

14. Soccio, R.E.; Chen, E.R.; Lazar, M.A. Thiazolidinediones and the promise of insulin sensitization in type 2 diabetes. *Cell Metab.* **2014**, *20*, 573–591. [CrossRef] [PubMed]

15. Qureshi, A.A.; Reis, J.C.; Papasian, C.J.; Morrison, D.C.; Qureshi, N. Tocotrienols inhibit lipopolysaccharide-induced pro-inflammatory cytokines in macrophages of female mice. *Lipids Health Dis.* **2010**, *9*, 143–157. [CrossRef] [PubMed]

16. Qureshi, A.A.; Tan, X.; Reis, J.C.; Badr, M.Z.; Papasian, C.J. Inhibition of nitric oxide in LPS-stimulated macrophages of young and senescent mice by δ-tocotrienol and quercetin. *Lipids Health Dis.* **2011**, *10*, 239–250. [CrossRef] [PubMed]

17. Laborte, A.G.; Gutierrez, M.A.; Balanza, J.G.; Saito, K.; Zwart, S.J.; Boschetti, M.; Murty, M.V.R.; Villano, L.; Aunario, J.K.; Reinke, R.; et al. RiceAtlas, a spatial database of global rice calendars and production. *Sci. Data* **2017**, *4*, 170074–170083. [CrossRef] [PubMed]

18. Park, H.Y.; Lee, K.W.; Choi, H. Rice bran constituents: Immunomodulatory and therapeutic activities. *Food Funct.* **2017**, *8*, 935–943. [CrossRef] [PubMed]

19. Chang, T.T. Rice: Origin, Domestication, and Diversification. 1. In *Rice: Origin, History, Technology, and Production*; Smith, C.W., Dilday, R., Eds.; Horboken: Chichester, NJ, USA, 2003; pp. 3–25.

20. Evans, H.M.; Bishop, K.S. On the existence of a hitherto unrecognized dietary factor essential for reproduction. *Science* **1922**, *56*, 650–651. [CrossRef] [PubMed]

21. Qureshi, A.A.; Mo, H.; Packer, L.; Peterson, D.M. Isolation and identification of novel tocotrienol from rice bran with hypocholesterolemic, antioxidant, and antitumor properties. *J. Agric. Food Chem.* **2000**, *48*, 3130–3140. [CrossRef] [PubMed]

22. Tuncel, N.B.; Yılmaz, N. δ-Tocotrienol content, phenolic acid profiles and antioxidant activity of rice milling fractions. *Eur. Food Res. Technol.* **2011**, *233*, 577–585. [CrossRef]

23. Xu, W.L.; Liu, J.R.; Liu, H.K.; Qi, G.Y.; Sun, X.R.; Sun, W.G.; Chen, B.Q. Inhibition of proliferation and induction of apoptosis by γ-tocotrienol in human colon carcinoma HT-29 cells. *Nutrition* **2009**, *25*, 555–566. [CrossRef] [PubMed]

24. Tan, B.; Brzuskiewicz, L. Separation of tocopherol and tocotrienol isomers using normal- and reverse-phase liquid chromatography. *Anal. Biochem.* **1989**, *180*, 368–373. [CrossRef]

25. Mustacich, D.J.; Leonard, S.W.; Patel, N.K.; Traber, M.G. α-Tocopherol β-oxidation localized to rat liver mitochondria. *Free Radic. Biol. Med.* **2010**, *48*, 73–81. [CrossRef] [PubMed]

26. Ahsan, H.; Ahad, A.; Iqbal, J.; Siddiqui, W.A. Pharmacological potential of tocotrienols: A review. *Nutr. Metab.* **2014**, *11*, 52–73. [CrossRef] [PubMed]

27. Nguyen, A.; Tao, H.; Metrione, M.; Hajri, T. Very low density lipoprotein receptor expression is a determinant factor in adipose tissue inflammation and adipocyte-macrophage interaction. *J. Biol. Chem.* **2013**, *289*, 1688–1703. [CrossRef] [PubMed]

28. Liu, B.; Lin, Q.; Yang, T.; Zeng, L.; Shi, L.; Chen, Y.; Luo, F. Oat β-glucan prevents DSS induced colitis in mice by (or through) decreasing the expression of inflammatory cytokines TNF-α, IL-1β, IL-6 and iNOS. *Food Funct.* **2015**, *11*, 3454–3463. [CrossRef] [PubMed]

29. Yoon, S.W.; Pyo, Y.G.; Lee, J.; Lee, J.S.; Kim, B.H.; Kim, I.H. Concentrations of tocols and γ-oryzanol compounds in rice bran oil obtained by fractional extraction with supercritical carbon dioxide. *J. Oleo Sci.* **2014**, *63*, 47–53. [CrossRef] [PubMed]

30. Guha, M.; Mackman, N. LPS induction of gene expression in human monocytes. *Cell Signal.* **2001**, *13*, 85–94. [CrossRef]

31. Dali-Youcef, N.; Ricci, R. Signalling networks governing metabolic inflammation. *Handb. Exp. Pharmacol.* **2016**, *233*, 195–220. [PubMed]

32. Guo, T.; Lin, Q.; Li, X.; Nie, Y.; Wang, L.; Shi, L.; Xu, W.; Hu, T.; Guo, T.; Luo, F. Octacosanol attenuates inflammation in both RAW264.7 macrophages and a mouse model of colitis. *J. Agric. Food Chem.* **2017**, *65*, 3647–3658. [CrossRef] [PubMed]

33. Kaimoto, S.; Hoshino, A.; Ariyoshi, M. Activation of PPARα in the early stage of heart failure maintained myocardial function and energetics in pressure overload heart failure. *Am. J. Physiol. Heart Circ. Physiol.* **2016**, *312*, H305–H313. [CrossRef] [PubMed]

34. Ajith, T.A.; Jayakumar, T.G. Peroxisome proliferator-activated receptors in cardiac energy metabolism and cardiovascular disease. *Clin. Exp. Pharmacol. Physiol.* **2016**, *43*, 649–658. [CrossRef] [PubMed]

35. Vacca, M.; Degirolamo, C.; Mariani-Costantini, R.; Palasciano, G.; Moschetta, A. Lipid-sensing nuclear receptors in the pathophysiology and treatment of the metabolic syndrome. *Wiley Interdisc. Rev. Syst. Biol. Med.* **2011**, *5*, 562–587. [CrossRef] [PubMed]

36. Kung, J.; Henry, R.R. Thiazolidinedione safety. *Expert Opin. Drug Saf.* **2012**, *11*, 565–579. [PubMed]
37. Aggarwal, B.B.; Sundaram, C.; Prasad, S.; Kannappan, R. Tocotrienols, the vitamin E of the 21st century: Its potential against cancer and other chronic diseases. *Biochem. Pharmacol.* **2010**, *80*, 1613–1631. [CrossRef] [PubMed]
38. Nesaretnam, K.; Devasagayam, T.P.A.; Singh, B.B.; Basiron, Y. Influence of palm oil or its tocotrienol-rich fraction on the lipid peroxidation potential of rat liver mitochondria and microsomes. *Biochem. Mol. Biol. Int.* **1993**, *30*, 159–167. [PubMed]
39. Serbinova, B.; Kagan, Y.; Han, D.; Packer, L. Free radical recycling and intramembrane mobility in the antioxidant properties of α-tocopherol and α-tocotrienol. *Free Radic. Biol. Med.* **1991**, *10*, 263–275. [CrossRef]
40. Ng, L.T.; Ko, HJ. Comparative effects of tocotrienol-rich fraction, α-tocopherol and α-tocopheryl acetate on inflammatory mediators and nuclear factor κB expression in mouse peritoneal macrophages. *Food Chem.* **2012**, *134*, 920–925. [CrossRef] [PubMed]
41. Jiang, Q. Natural forms of vitamin E: Metabolism, antioxidant, and anti-inflammatory activities and their role in disease prevention and therapy. *Free Radic. Biol. Med.* **2014**, *72*, 76–90. [CrossRef] [PubMed]
42. Jiang, Q.; Elson-Schwab, I.; Courtemanche, C.; Ames, B.N. γ-Tocopherol and its major metabolite, in contrast to α-tocopherol, inhibit cycloox-ygenase activity in macrophages and epithelial cells. *Proc. Natl. Acad. Sci. USA* **2000**, *97*, 11494–11499. [CrossRef] [PubMed]
43. Jiang, Q.; Yin, X.; Lill, M.A.; Danielson, M.L.; Freiser, H.; Huang, J. Long-chain carboxychromanols metabolites of vitamin E are potent inhibitors of cyclooxygenases. *Proc. Natl. Acad. Sci. USA* **2008**, *105*, 20464–20469. [CrossRef] [PubMed]
44. Montagnani, M.; Marzagalli, M.; Moretti, R.M. δ-Tocotrienol triggers endoplasmic reticulum stress mediated apoptosis in human melanoma cells. *Sci. Rep.* **2016**, *6*, 30502–30515. [CrossRef] [PubMed]
45. Michalik, L.; Auwerx, J.; Berger, J.P.; Chatterjee, V.K.; Glass, C.K.; Gonzalez, F.J.; Grimaldi, P.A.; Kadowaki, T.; Lazar, M.A.; O'Rahilly, S.; et al. International Union of Pharmacology. LXI. Peroxisome proliferator-activated receptors. *Pharmacol. Rev.* **2006**, *58*, 726–741. [CrossRef] [PubMed]
46. Delerive, P.; De Bosscher, K.; Vanden Berghe, W.; Fruchart, J.C.; Haegeman, G.; Staels, B. DNA binding-independent induction of IκBα gene transcription by PPARα. *Mol. Endocrinol.* **2002**, *16*, 1029–1039. [CrossRef] [PubMed]
47. Ahmadian, M.; Suh, J.M.; Hah, N. PPARγ signaling and metabolism: The good, the bad and the future. *Nat. Med.* **2013**, *19*, 557–566. [CrossRef] [PubMed]
48. Odegaard, J.I.; Ricardo-Gonzalez, R.R.; Goforth, M.H.; Morel, C.R.; Subramanian, V.; Mukundan, L.; Red Eagle, A.; Vats, D.; Brombacher, F.; Ferrante, A.W.; et al. Macrophage-specific PPARγ controls alternative activation and improves insulin resistance. *Nature* **2007**, *447*, 1116–1120. [CrossRef] [PubMed]
49. Hevener, A.L.; Olefsky, J.M.; Reichart, D.; Nguyen, M.T.; Bandyopadyhay, G.; Leung, H.Y.; Watt, M.J.; Benner, C.; Febbraio, M.A.; Nguyen, A.K.; Folian, B.; Subramaniam, S.; et al. Macrophage PPARα is required for normal skeletal muscle and hepatic insulin sensitivity and full antidiabetic effects of thiazolidinediones. *J. Clin. Investig.* **2007**, *117*, 1658–1669. [CrossRef] [PubMed]
50. Kersten, S. Regulation of nutrient metabolism and inflammation. *Results Probl. Cell Differ.* **2010**, *52*, 13–25. [PubMed]
51. Necela, B.M.; Su, W.; Thompson, E.A. Toll-like receptor 4 mediates cross-talk between peroxisome proliferator-activated receptor α and nuclear factor-κB in macrophages. *Immunology* **2008**, *125*, 344–358. [CrossRef] [PubMed]
52. Neve, B.P.; Fruchart, J.C.; Staels, B. Role of the peroxisome proliferator-activated receptors (PPAR) in atherosclerosis. *Biochem. Pharmacol.* **2000**, *60*, 1245–1250. [CrossRef]
53. Tornatore, L.; Thotakura, A.K.; Bennett, J.; Moretti, M.; Franzoso, G. The nuclear factor κB signaling pathway: Integrating metabolism with inflammation. *Trends Cell Biol.* **2012**, *22*, 557–566. [CrossRef] [PubMed]

International Journal of
Molecular Sciences

Article

Citrus aurantium L. and Its Flavonoids Regulate TNBS-Induced Inflammatory Bowel Disease through Anti-Inflammation and Suppressing Isolated Jejunum Contraction

Wei He [1,2], Yongmin Li [2], Mengyang Liu [1], Haiyang Yu [3], Qian Chen [1], Yue Chen [1], Jingya Ruan [3], Zhijuan Ding [3], Yi Zhang [3,*] and Tao Wang [1,*]

1   Institute of Traditional Chinese Medicine, Tianjin University of Traditional Chinese Medicine,
    Tianjin 300193, China; WeiHe850227@gmail.com (W.H.); liumengyang0212@tjutcm.edu.cn (M.L.);
    qianchen6688@gmail.com (Q.C.); YueChen17208@gmail.com (Y.C.)
2   College of Traditional Chinese Medicine, Hebei North University, Zhangjiakou 075000, China;
    yongminli1020@gmail.com
3   Tianjin Key Laboratory of TCM Chemistry and Analysis, Institute of Traditional Chinese Medicine,
    Tianjin University of Traditional Chinese Medicine, Tianjin 300193, China; hyyu@tjutcm.edu.cn (H.Y.);
    ruanjingya123@gmail.com (J.R.); zding2772@gmail.com (Z.D.)
*   Correspondence: zhwwxzh@263.net (Y.Z.); wangtao@tjutcm.edu.cn (T.W.);
    Tel./Fax: +86-22-5959-6163 (Y.Z.); +86-22-59596168 (T.W.)

Received: 4 September 2018; Accepted: 4 October 2018; Published: 7 October 2018

Abstract: Inflammatory bowel disease (IBD) is a serious digestive system disease, for which the clinical therapeutic choices remain limited. Dried fruits of *Citrus aurantium* L. (CAL) are a traditional medicine used for regulation of the digestive system. The aim of this study was to identify the regulatory effects of CAL on IBD and to clarify the mechanism of the active compounds. In trinitrobenzene sulfonic acid-induced IBD rats, 125 to 500 mg/kg of oral CAL significantly alleviated weight loss and diarrhea, decreased colitis inflammatory cell infiltration, and inhibited pro-inflammatory cytokine production. The mechanisms of characteristic flavonoids in CAL were evaluated involving inflammation and intestine contraction aspects. Naringenin, nobiletin, and hesperetin showed anti-inflammatory effects on lipopolysaccharide-induced RAW cells. The mechanism may be related to the inhibition of the tumor necrosis factor-α (TNF-α)-induced nuclear factor kappa-light-chain-enhancer of activated B cells (NF-κB) pathway to suppress cyclooxygenase-2 (COX-2) and inducible nitric oxide synthase (iNOS) expressions. Naringenin and nobiletin showed inhibitory effects on isolated jejunum contraction. The mechanism of naringenin is partly related to COX, NOS, inositol triphosphate (IP$_3$), and finally, to decreased jejunum motility. This study demonstrated that CAL, and its flavonoids' regulatory effects on IBD through anti-inflammation and inhibition of intestine muscle contraction, can provide basic information on developing new drugs or supplements against IBD based on CAL.

Keywords: *Citrus aurantium* L.; naringenin; nobiletin; hesperetin; inflammatory; jejunum contraction

1. Introduction

Inflammatory bowel disease (IBD) is a serious digestive system disease, characterized as a chronic and relapsing inflammation of the gastrointestinal tract [1]. Epidemiological studies showed a large variation in the prevalence of IBD in different regions in the world. The highest incidence is noted in the United States of America (USA), where approximately 2.5 million inhabitants have IBD, ranging from the age of six to over 60 [2–4]. Although IBD is a rare disease in Asia, population-based studies reported the annual incidence of IBD increased fivefold from 1990 to 2016 with a continuous long-term increasing tendency [5–7]. The rising prevalence is likely to become a substantial challenge to Asian countries.

Patients with IBD may have symptoms of abdominal cramping, bloody diarrhea, and bloating with a change in stool frequency and form. These symptoms are embarrassing and uncomfortable, and they seriously affect the quality of life. Gut luminal factors, such as food, microbiota, and bile acids, together with their internal interactions might be important for the generation of symptoms in IBD patients. The etiology of IBD is related to various factors, including physical factors (diet, medication, and natural course of illness), psychological factors (anxiety, depression, trauma, and loss), and social factors (financial, vocational, and residential). The pathogenesis of IBD is yet to be fully elucidated [8].

Pathological characteristics of IBD include a reduction in mucus layer thickness, inflammatory cell infiltration in the tunica mucosa and tunica submucosa, an ablated mucosa layer, the presence of ulcers in the muscular layer, a dropout of crypt epithelial cells, and the destruction of epithelia and lamina propria in the intestine lumen.

Until now, there is no appropriate drug for IBD treatment. Clinically, some medication was used to relieve symptoms. Salicylazosulfapyridine was used to relieve IBD inflammation [9]. Azathoprine, an immunosuppressive medication, was used for the inhibition of the immune response [10]. However, the above drugs are not enough for clinical IBD therapeutic requirements.

The fruit of *Citrus aurantium* L. (CAL), commonly named bitter orange, a member of genus *Citrus* (Rutaceae), is widely used as an edible and medicinal resource in China. CAL contains essential oils (limonene, linalool, and citral), flavonoids (naringenin, hesperetin, and apigenin), triterpenoids (limonin and limonexin), coumarins (marmin, meranzin, and scopoletin), and alkaloids (synephrine and *N*-methyltyramine) [11]. Previous studies demonstrated that CAL extracts and its main components had anti-cancer, anti-inflammatory, anti-oxidant, and vasodilatory effects [12–16].

In traditional Chinese medicine (TCM), CAL is used as a qi regulatory component in digestive formula. Our research group reported the effects of CAL on gastric emptying and gastro-protection [17]. As a further study, in this paper, we found that CAL 70% ethanol (EtOH) extract had an amelioratory effect on 2,4,6-trinitrobenzene sulfonic acid (TNBS)-induced IBD rats. The molecular underlying mechanisms of anti-inflammation and jejunum contraction inhibition were elucidated, which indicated that CAL may be beneficial for treating IBD.

2. Results

2.1. CAL Improves Symptoms of TNBS-Induced IBD Colitis in Rats

To define whether CAL had a positive effect on TNBS-induced rats, a series of indices were measured in the experiment, such as body weight, diarrhea and bloody-stool incidence, colon length, etc. In this study, compared to the normal group, significant reductions in body weight (Figure 1A) and colon length (Figure 1B), along with obvious increases in colon weight (Figure 1C), the ratio of weight/length (Figure 1D), disease activity index (DAI; Figure 1E), and macroscopic injury score (Figure 1F), were found in the TNBS-treated group. Furthermore, the results showed that CAL alleviated TNBS-induced weight loss, diarrhea, and bloody stool, and significantly reduced DAI and macroscopic injury score. Moreover, we found that pre-treatment with CAL significantly alleviated TNBS-induced colon shortening, and decreased colon weight and the ratio of weight/length. Taken together, these results indicated that CAL reduced TNBS-induced acute colitis.

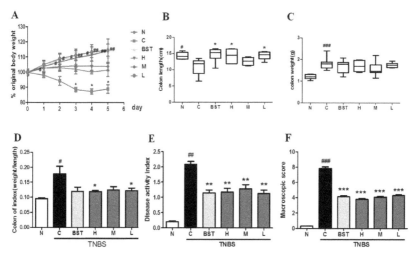

Figure 1. *Citrus aurantium* L. (CAL) alleviates 2,4,6-trinitrobenzene sulfonic acid (TNBS)-induced colitis in rats. The time-course of changes on day 4 after TNBS-induced inflammatory bowel disease (IBD) in (**A**) body weight; (**B**) colon length; (**C**) colon weight; (**D**) the ratio of weight/length; (**E**) disease activity index (DAI) score; and (**F**) macroscopic injury score. N: normal group; C: control (TNBS only) group; BST: balsalazide 1 g/kg + TNBS group; H (high): CAL 500 mg/kg + TNBS group; M (medium): CAL 250 mg/kg + TNBS group; L (low): CAL 125 mg/kg + TNBS group; $n = 8$, # $p < 0.05$, ## $p < 0.01$, ### $p < 0.001$ vs. normal group; * $p < 0.05$, ** $p < 0.01$, *** $p < 0.001$ vs. control group.

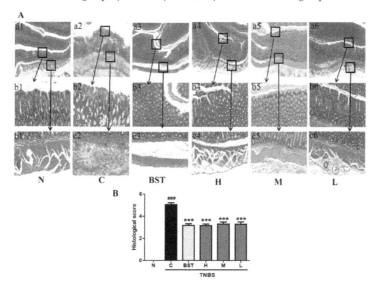

Figure 2. CAL suppresses histological injury in TNBS-induced colitis in rats. (**A**) Representative images of hematoxylin and eosin (H&E) staining of colon tissue from different groups (a1–a6). Scale bar = 100 μm. The area within the rectangle in each picture is enlarged and presented below, correspondingly, displaying the mucosa (b1–b6) and submucosa (c1–c6) in each group. Scale bar = 10 μm. (**B**) Colonic histological score. N: normal group; C: TNBS only group; BST: balsalazide 1 g/kg + TNBS group; H: CAL 500 mg/kg + TNBS group; M: CAL 250 mg/kg + TNBS group; L: CAL 125 mg/kg + TNBS group; $n = 8$, ### $p < 0.001$ vs. normal group; *** $p < 0.001$ vs. TNBS group. Data (mean ± standard error of the mean (SEM)) were analyzed by ANOVA.

Next, we measured the effects of CAL on colorectal histology in rats with TNBS-induced colitis. As shown in Figure 2A, unlike the normal group, TNBS treatment caused serious inflammation with a scattered infiltration of monocytes. However, CAL treatment demonstrated a lower level of inflammation with scattered infiltration of monocytes in TNBS-treated rats and a decrease in the morphological alteration. This result indicated CAL has protective effects on intestinal cytoarchitecture in colonic layers and inhibitory effects on inflammation (Figure 2B).

2.2. CAL Suppresses Inflammation in TNBS-Induced Colitis

An increase in myeloperoxidase (MPO) and nitric oxide (NO) levels represents an aggravated inflammatory reaction. In order to clarify the anti-inflammatory effects of CAL, the levels of MPO and NO were detected. As shown in Figure 3A, compared with the normal group, there was an obvious increase in the model group. CAL treatment significantly inhibited TNBS-induced MPO activity in both colon tissues and sera. Furthermore, CAL dramatically decreased TNBS-stimulated NO production. Tumor necrosis factor-α (TNF-α), cyclooxygenase-2 (COX-2), inducible nitric oxide synthase (iNOS), and nuclear factor kappa-light-chain-enhancer of activated B cells (NF-κB) are the major inflammatory cytokines in IBD. The RT-PCR and Western blot results show that TNBS significantly induced pro-inflammatory cytokine messenger RNA (mRNA) and protein levels of TNF-α, COX-2, iNOS, and NF-κB in colon tissues, while CAL downregulated their expressions in different levels (Figure 3B,C).

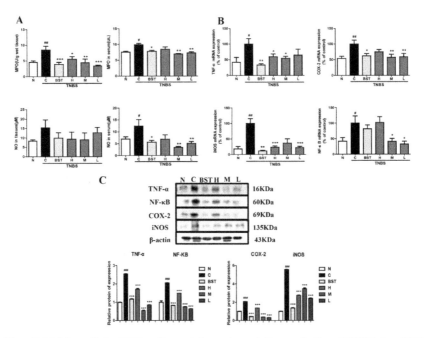

Figure 3. Inhibitory effects of CAL on the pro-inflammatory cytokine production of TNBS-induced IBD rats. (**A**) Nitric oxide (NO) and myeloperoxidase (MPO) content in serum and colon tissue. (**B**) The mRNA expressions of pro-inflammatory cytokines in colon tissue. (**C**) The protein expressions of pro-inflammatory cytokines in colon tissue. N: normal group; C: TNBS alone group; BST: balsalazide 1 g/kg + TNBS group; H: CAL 500 mg/kg + TNBS group; M: CAL 250 mg/kg + TNBS group; L: CAL 125 mg/kg + TNBS group; $n = 8$, # $p < 0.05$, ## $p < 0.01$, ### $p < 0.001$ vs. normal group; * $p < 0.05$, ** $p < 0.01$, *** $p < 0.001$ vs. TNBS group. Data (mean ± SEM) were analyzed by ANOVA.

2.3. The Effects of CAL, Naringenin, Nobiletin, and Hesperetin on Mouse-Isolated Jejunum Contractility

Although hesperidin and naringine are the major flavonoids in CAL, as literature reports, after oral administration, both of these flavonoids are enzymatically hydrolyzed by intestinal microbiota, yielding their aglycons, hesperetin and naringenin, respectively [18]. Nobiletin is a characteristic citrus flavonoid with a polymethoxylated structure, whose structure is resistant to modification by intestinal microbiota [19].

To clarify the amelioratory effect of CAL on TNBS-induced colitis, firstly, we investigated the effects of CAL and hesperetin, naringenin, and nobiletin on mouse jejunum contractility. As shown in Figure 4, CAL extraction (from 100–200 μg/mL), as well as naringenin and nobiletin (100 μM), dramatically inhibited the active tension on spontaneous contractions of intestine smooth muscle. However, at the same concentration, hesperetin showed no significant changes on isolated jejunum movement.

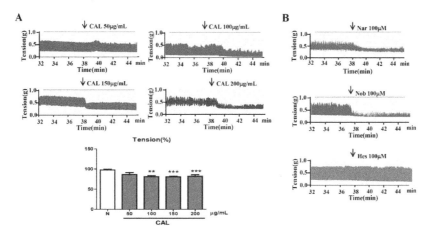

Figure 4. Effect of CAL, naringenin, nobiletin, and hesperetin on isolated jejunum contraction. (**A**) Effect of CAL extraction on isolated jejunum contraction. (**B**) Effects of naringenin, nobiletin, and hesperetin on isolated jejunum contraction. Nar: naringenin; Nob: nobiletin; Hes: hesperetin; $n = 6$, ** $p < 0.01$, *** $p < 0.001$ vs. normal group. Data (mean ± SEM) were analyzed by ANOVA.

2.4. Mechanism Studies of Naringenin and Nobiletin on Jejunum Contractility

Indomethacin (blocker of prostaglandin I2 (PGI2)), N(ω)-nitro-l-arginine methyl ester (L-NAME; the inhibitor of NOS), acetylcholine (ACh; activator of inositol triphosphate (IP3), was used to clarify the mechanism of flavonoids of CAL on jejunum contractility, As shown in Figure 5, indomethacin (10μM), L-NAME (100μM) and Ach (0.1μM) could completely antagonist the inhibition effect of naringenin on mouse jejunum contractility, but have no significant effect on nobiletin.

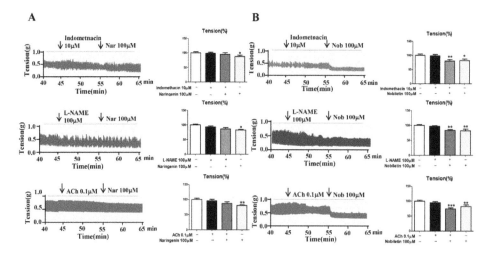

Figure 5. Inhibition mechanisms of (**A**) naringenin and (**B**) nobiletin on isolated jejunum contraction. Nar: naringenin; Nob: nobiletin; $n = 6$, * $p < 0.05$, ** $p < 0.01$, *** $p < 0.001$ vs. normal group. Data (mean ± SEM) were analyzed by ANOVA.

2.5. Anti-Inflammatory Effect of Naringenin, Nobiletin, and Hesperetin in Lipopolysaccharide (LPS)-Induced RAW264.7 Cells

We also investigated whether naringenin, nobiletin, and hesperetin inhibited LPS-induced pro-inflammatory cytokines. As shown in Figure 6A, compared with the normal group, LPS caused a significant increase in NO production in Raw264.7 cells, while naringenin, nobiletin, and hesperetin treatment dramatically inhibit LPS-stimulated NO production. Furthermore, compared to the normal group, LPS led an obvious upregulation in the protein expressions of TNF-α, NF-κB, COX-2, and iNOS. Naringenin, nobiletin, and hesperetin also strongly inhibited the protein expressions of TNF-α, NF-κB, COX-2, and iNOS in LPS-induced RAW264.7 cells (Figure 6B). Taken together, our results suggest that naringenin, nobiletin, and hesperetin have beneficial anti-inflammatory effects in LPS-induced RAW264.7 cells.

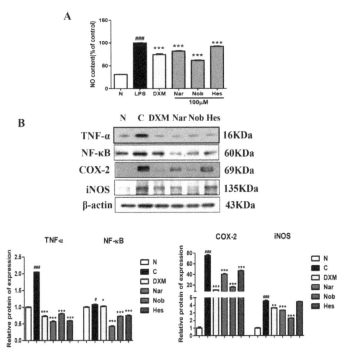

Figure 6. Inhibitory effects of naringenin, nobiletin, and hesperetin on pro-inflammatory cytokine production in lipopolysaccharide (LPS)-induced RAW264.7 cells. (**A**) NO content in the supernatant of RAW264.7 cells. (**B**) The protein expressions of pro-inflammatory cytokines in LPS-induced RAW264.7 cells. N: normal group; C: LPS only group (0.5 μg/mL); DXM: dexamethasone 1 μg/mL + LPS (0.5 μg/mL); Nar: naringenin (100 μM) + LPS (0.5 μg/mL); Nob: nobiletin (100 μM) + LPS (0.5 μg/mL); Hes: hesperetin (100 μM) + LPS (0.5 μg/mL); $n = 6$, # $p < 0.05$, ### $p < 0.001$ vs. normal group; * $p < 0.05$, ** $p < 0.01$, *** $p < 0.001$ vs. LPS group. Data (mean ± SEM) were analyzed by ANOVA.

3. Discussion

IBD is a gastrointestinal tract disease, which is characterized by chronic, relapsing inflammation and abnormal intestinal contraction. Current medications can help treat IBD, but direct therapeutic medicine for IBD does not yet exist. In this paper, we firstly reported that CAL, a kind of fruit, had regulatory effects on IBD. We partially clarified the mechanism of CAL's major flavonoids, naringenin and nobiletin, on the suppression of inflammation and regulation of jejunum motility.

In the present study, pre-treatment with CAL in a TNBS-induced colitis model showed an improvement in weight loss, diarrhea, and bloody stool, ameliorated colon weight, colon DAI, and macroscopic scores, and increased colon length and decreased the ratio of weight/length. This result indicated that CAL showed benefits for symptomatic relief in IBD abdominal discomfort. Intestine spasm is the key factor in abdominal pain and diarrhea or loose stool. Previous studies demonstrated that decreased intestinal contractility led to a reduction in gastrointestinal motility, which in turn alleviated abdominal pain and diarrhea in IBD patients [20,21]. CAL significantly reduced isolated jejunum contraction, revealing the potential therapeutic use in the treatment of IBD abdominal discomfort.

Overloading inflammatory response is a basic pathological process through the occurrence and development of IBD [22–24]. Colon tissue pathological examination results showed that CAL treatment significantly improved the intact mucosal layer and intestinal glands, and decreased the infiltration and erosion of inflammatory cells. The inflammation suppressing effect of CAL was further confirmed by a reduction in NO and MPO levels in both serum and colon tissue. The mechanism may be related to the TNF-α-induced NF-κB activation pathway for reducing the expressions of COX-2 and iNOS.

Naringenin, nobiletin, and hesperetin are the characteristic flavonoids in CAL [11,25]. In this paper, preliminary screening showed that naringenin and nobiletin had stronger inhibitory effects on isolated jejunum contraction, but hesperetin had no significant effect. From a chemical structure perspective, the only difference between naringenin and hesperetin is the hydroxy substitution in the B cycle, which is 4′-hydroxy in naringenin and 3′-hydroxy-4′-methoxy in hesperetin. This result indicated that 4′-hydroxy is the essential group for inhibitory effects on jejunum contraction; however, evaluations involving numbers should be carried out to validate the structure–activity relationship.

In IBD patients, the intestinal tract motility index and high-amplitude propagating contractions were significantly greater than in healthy volunteers. Abnormal intestinal tract contraction is one of the causes of abdominal pain or discomfort. In smooth-muscle contraction, calcium triggers a contraction via a reaction with regulatory factors. The mechanism for jejunum contraction is carried out via the release of calcium ions. The inhibitory effect of naringenin was blocked by indomethacin (the inhibitor of COX, blocks the generation of PGI2, leading to an increase in intracellular Ca^{2+}, and has an anti-relaxation effect on smooth muscle) [26], L-NAME (the inhibitor of NOS, increases intracellular Ca^{2+}, leading to an anti-relaxation effect) [27], ACh (activates IP_3), causes increased intracellular Ca^{2+}, and promotes the contractile activity of the intestinal smooth muscle) [28], indicating that the effect is at least partly related to COX, NOS, and IP_3, and finally, the decrease in intracellular Ca^{2+}. However, there were no significant changes between nobiletin with or without the above inhibitors; thus, the mechanism needs to be further explored.

According to the anti-inflammatory effects, naringenin, nobiletin, and hesperetin showed important protective roles on LPS-induced RAW264.7 cells, and significantly decreased the level of NO in the cell supernatant. The mechanism was related to the inhibition of the TNF-α-induced NF-κB pathway responsible for suppressing the expressions of COX-2 and iNOS, in accordance with CAL extract in TNBS-induced rats.

In summary, on the basis of in vitro and in vivo studies, our study demonstrated that CAL, as an edible fruit, and its flavonoids showed significant regulatory effects on TNBS-induced IBD rats through anti-inflammation and the inhibition of jejunum muscle contraction. These results provide molecular information for further investigation of the mechanisms via which CAL moderates IBD. The intestine barrier is a key factor in IBD, and the contribution of CAL to mucosal barrier function needs further investigation.

4. Materials and Methods

4.1. Materials

CAL was provided by Tianjin Zhongxin Pharmaceutical Group Co., Ltd (Tianjin, China), for which the content of Naringin was 3.8%, as determined using HPLC/ultraviolet (UV) detection [29]. Naringenin (purity >98%, HPLC), nobiletin (purity >98%, HPLC), and hesperetin (purity >98%, HPLC) were purchased from Shanghai Yuanye Bio-Technology Co., Ltd. (Shanghai, China). Balsalazide (H20041706) was purchased from Shanxi Zhendong Ante Biopharmaceutical Co., Ltd. (Shanxi, China). Cell culture reagents and supplies were purchased from Hyclone Laboratories, Inc. (Logan, UT, USA). Rabbit anti-TNF-α, COX-2, NF-κB, iNOS, and β-actin were purchased from Abcam plc. (Cambridge, MA, USA). Horseradish peroxidase-conjugated anti-rabbit immunoglobulin G (IgG) were purchased from Zhongshan Goldbridge Biotechnology (Beijing, China). TNBS, ACh, L-NAME, indomethacin, dimethyl sulfoxide (DMSO), dexamethasone, and LPS were obtained from Sigma Chemical Co., (St. Louis, MO, USA). NO and MPO detection kits were purchased from Nanjing Jiancheng Bioengineering Institute (Nanjing, China).

4.2. Animals

Healthy male adult Sprague/Dawley (SD) rats weighting 180–200 g were received from Beijing HFK Bioscience Co. Ltd. (Beijing, China; Certificate of Conformity: No. 11401300071030). All animal experiments were approved by the Science and Technological Committee and the Animal Use and Care Committee of TUTCM (No. 201712003). Animals were housed in cages in a room with controlled temperature (22 ± 2 °C), relative humidity (40–60%), and a 12-h light/dark cycle throughout the study. The animals were acclimated to their environment for one week and had ad libitum access to tap water and a rodent standard diet (crude protein 16%, crude fat 4%, crude fiber 12%, and ash 8%).

4.3. TNBS-Induced Experimental Colitis

After one week of adaption, 48 rats were randomly divided into six groups, each consisting of eight rats. The groups were as follows: normal group (N), control group (C), positive control group (PC), and CAL groups. CAL was suspended in 5% acacia (Sigma-Aldrich Inc., St. Louis, MO, USA) solution, and oral administration volumes were 10 mL/kg body weight; the final doses were 500, 250, and 125 mg/kg. The normal and control groups received 5% acacia water solution with the same volume, while the positive control group received balsalazide 5% acacia water solution. The same treatments were conducted once every day for three consecutive days.

Experimental colitis was induced according to previously established protocols with slight modifications [30,31]. On the fourth day, rats were fasted for 24 h and they had free access to drinking water. On the fifth day, rats were anesthetized with diethyl ether and a catheter was inserted through the anus so that its terminus reached approximately to the level of the splenic flexure (8 cm proximal to the anal verge). Subsequently, 1 mL of TNBS dissolved in ethanol (50% v/v) was infused at a dose of 100 mg/kg. Throughout the TNBS challenge period, all groups received the same treatment as the pretreatment. During the experiment, body movement, body weight, diarrhea incidence, and bloody stool were recorded daily.

4.4. Colon Damage Assay

On the ninth day, the blood of rats was collected from orbit, and then, rats were sacrificed under ether anesthesia by cervical dislocation for the assessment of colon damage. The colon length and weight were measured. The colon macroscopically visible damage was scored based on the literature-reported method [32,33] (Table 1). DAI score was determined as previously reported [34] (Table 2). Routine hematoxylin and eosin (H&E)-stained colon sections according to previously described morphological criteria and the damages were both assessed blindly by two investigators according to a modified histological grading scale, which takes both inflammatory cell infiltration and tissue damage into consideration [35] (Table 3).

Table 1. Evaluation of macroscopic scores.

Colon Damage	Score
No damage	0
Hyperemia with ulcers	1
Hyperemia and wall thickening without ulcers	2
One ulceration site without wall thickening	3
Two or more ulceration sites	4
0.5-cm extension of inflammation or major damage	5
1-cm extension of inflammation or severe damage	6–10

Table 2. Evaluation of disease activity index (DAI) scores.

DAI Score	Weight Loss (%)	Stool Consistency	Occult/gross Bleeding
0	None	None	None
1	1–5		
2	5–10	Loose	Hem occult positive
3	10–15		
4	>15	Diarrhea	Gross bleeding

Table 3. Evaluation of histological scores.

Inflammatory Cell Infiltration		Tissue Damage	
No infiltration	0	No mucosal damage	0
Increased number of inflammatory cells in the lamina propria	1	Discrete epithelial lesions	1
Inflammatory cells extending into the submucosa	2	Erosions or focal ulcerations	2
Transmural inflammatory cell infiltration	3	Severe mucosal damage with extensive ulceration extending into the bowel wall	3

4.5. Detection of Inflammatory Cytokines and Mediators in Colon and Serum

Colon samples (40–50 mg) were homogenized with saline (1:9 w/v) in a digital homogenizer. After centrifugation at $3500 \times g$ for 10 min, the supernatant was collected for further detection. Blood samples were centrifuged at $3500 \times g$ for 10 min, and the serum was transferred into new Eppendorf tubes. All the above experiments were kept under 10 °C.

The levels of NO and MPO in both serum and colon tissue were measured using commercial kits. Inflammatory-related cytokines and mediators such as COX-2, iNOS, TNF-α, and NF-κB were analyzed using the methods of RT-PCR and Western blot as described below.

4.6. Effects of CAL and Its Flavonoids on Mice Jejunum Contraction

After fasting for 24 h, mice were sacrificed, and about 1 cm of the jejunum was cut down. The preparations were mounted longitudinally to an isometric force transducer with a silk-braided non-absorbable suture (Johnson & Johnson Medical China Ltd., Beijing, China), and were allowed to equilibrate in an organ bath with 10 mL of Tyrode's buffer (1 L contains NaCl 8.0 g, $CaCl_2$ 0.2 g, KCl 0.2 g, $MgCl_2$ 0.1 g, $NaHCO_3$ 1.0 g, KH_2PO_4 0.05 g, and glucose 1.0 g; pH 7.4) for 30 min to achieve a stable state. The organ bath was maintained at a constant temperature (37.0 $\pm$ 0.5 °C), and bubbled with 95% O_2 and 5% CO_2 gas. Intestine contractions were recorded using the Power Lab system and the Chart 7 software (AD instrument Ltd., New South Wales, Australia). Indomethacin (10 μM), L-NAME (100 μM), and Ach (0.1 μM) were used for mechanism researches.

4.7. Inflammatory Response Induced by LPS on RAW264.7

RAW264.7 cells were obtained from the cell center at the Chinese Academy of Medical Science and Peking Union Medical College (Beijing, China). The RAW264.7cells were cultured in Dulbecco's modified Eagle medium (DMEM), supplemented with 10% fetal bovine serum (FBS), penicillin (100 units/mL), streptomycin (100 mg/mL), L-glutamine (4.5 mg/mL), and glucose (4.5 mg/mL), and incubated at 37 °C in a humidified atmosphere containing 5% CO_2 and 95% air. The media were refreshed every two days.

Initially, 2×10^6 cells/mL RAW264.7 cells were seeded on a 24-well plate and incubated overnight. The next day, the media were changed, which contained LPS (0.5 μg/mL) with or without naringenin (100 μM), hesperetin (100 μM), nobiletin (100 μM), and the positive drug dexamethasone (1 μg/mL), and then, the cells were incubated for 24 h. The cell supernatant was collected to detect NO levels, and cells were harvested for protein and RT-PCR analysis.

4.8. RT-PCR Analysis

Total RNA was extracted from colon tissues and RAW264.7 cells using TRIzol reagent (Sigma, USA) and complementary DNA (cDNA) was generated using RT-PCR reagent (Thermo Fisher Sci. Inc., Vilnius, Lithuania). RT-PCR was performed using the SYBR Green Quantity Tech RT-PCR kit (Thermo Fisher Sci. Inc., St. Austin, TX, USA) through PCR 7500. The housekeeping gene, glyceraldehyde 3-phosphate dehydrogenase GAPDH), served as an internal control. The comparative Ct method ($2^{-\triangle\triangle Ct}$) was used to analyze differences in the levels of detective mRNA between groups. The sequences of the primers used in this investigation are shown in Table 4.

Table 4. Primers used for RT-PCR analysis. COX-2—cyclooxygenase 2; TNF-α—tumor necrosis factor alpha; iNOS—inducible nitric oxide synthase; NF-κB—nuclear factor kappa-light-chain-enhancer of activated B cells; GAPDH—glyceraldehyde 3-phosphate dehydrogenase; F—forward; R—reverse.

Species	Gene	Primer Sequence	
	COX-2	F: TCGGAGGAGAAGTGGGTTTTAG	R: TTGATGGTGGCTGTCTTGGTAGG
	TNF-α	F: GATGTGGAACTGGCAGAGGAG	R: CACGAGCAGGAATGAGAAGAG
Rat	iNOS	F: TTGGAGCGAGTTGTGGATTGTT	R: TAGGTGAGGGCTTGCCTGAGTG
	NF-κB	F: AACACTGCCGACCTCAAGAT	R: CATCGGCTTGAGAAAAGGAG
	GAPDH	F: TGAGGCCGGTGCTGAGTATGT	R: CAGTCTTCTGGGTGGCAGTGA

4.9. Western Blot Analysis

As described previously [36], the rats' colon segments and the RAW264.7 cells treated with LPS were analyzed by Western blot. The protein concentrations in the supernatants and tissues were quantified using a bicinchoninic acid protein assay kit (Thermo Fisher Sci. Inc., Rockford, IL, USA). Firstly, 60 μg of protein was mixed with 4× loading dye (Laemmli Buffer) and 2-mercapto ethanol, before being heated at 95 °C for 5 min. The protein was resolved by 8–12% sodium dodecyl sulfate polyacrylamide gel electrophoresis and transferred to immunoblot polyvinylidene difluoride (PVDF) membranes (Merck Millipore Ltd., Darmstadt, Germany). The membranes were incubated at 4 °C overnight with primary antibodies against TNF-α (1:1000) (ab6671, Abcam), COX-2 (1:1000) (ab52237, Abcam), NF-κB (1:1000) (ab16502, Abcam), iNOS (1:800) (ab3523, Abcam), and β-actin (1:1000) (ab8227, Abcam). Then, the membranes were washed three times with Tris-buffered saline/Tween 20 (TBS-T; 10 min each time) and incubated with a horseradish peroxidase-labeled secondary goat anti-rabbit (1:10,000) antibody for 1 h at room temperature. Next, the blots were again washed three times with TBS-T (10 min each time).

Finally, protein bands were visualized with an enhanced chemiluminescence system (Millipore, Billerica, MA, USA). The relative optical densities of protein bands were analyzed with the Amersham imager 600 luminescent image analyzer (GE healthcare Japan Co., Tokyo, Japan).

4.10. Statistic Analysis

Values were expressed as means ± SD. All the grouped data were statistically analyzed with the SPSS 11.0 software. Significant differences between the normal group or control group were evaluated by one-way analysis of variance (ANOVA), and Tukey's studentized range test was used for post hoc evaluations. A p-value <0.05 was considered to indicate statistical significance.

Author Contributions: M.L., Y.Z., and T.W. contributed to experimental design. W.H., Y.L., Y.C., J.R., and Z.D. contributed to the acquisition and analysis of data. H.Y., Q.C., Y.Z., and T.W. reviewed the manuscript. T.W. acquired the funding. W.H. and T.W. wrote the manuscript.

Acknowledgments: This research was supported by the National Natural Science Foundation of China (81173524; 81673688), and the Important Drug Development Fund, Ministry of Science and Technology of China (2018ZX09735-002).

Conflicts of Interest: The authors declare no conflicts of interest.

Abbreviations

IBD	inflammatory bowel disease
TNBS	2,4,6-trinitrobenzene sulfonic acid
NO	nitric oxide
MPO	myeloperoxidase
H&E	hematoxylin and eosin
DAI	disease activity index
TNF-α	tumor necrosis factor-α
COX-2	cyclooxygenase-2
iNOS	inducible nitric oxide synthase
NF-κB	nuclear factor kappa-light-chain-enhancer of activated B cells
LPS	lipopolysaccharide
ACh	acetylcholine
L-NAME	N(ω)-nitro-L-arginine methylester hydrochloride
NOS	nitric oxide synthase
IP$_3$	inositol triphosphate

References

1. Chachu, K.; Osterman, M. How to Diagnose and Treat IBD Mimics in the Refractory IBD Patient Who Does Not Have IBD. *Inflamm. Bowel Dis.* **2016**, *22*, 1262–1274. [CrossRef] [PubMed]
2. Stapersma, L.; Van den brink, G.; Szigethy, E.M.; Escher, J.C.; Utens, E.M.W.J. Systematic review with meta-analysis: anxiety and depression in children and adolescents with inflammatory bowel disease. *Aliment Pharmacol. Ther.* **2018**. [CrossRef] [PubMed]
3. Gisbert, J.; Chaparro, M. Systematic review with meta-analysis: inflammatory bowel disease in the elderly. *Aliment Pharmacol. Ther.* **2014**, *39*, 459–477. [CrossRef] [PubMed]
4. Wang, H.J.; Gu, J.F.; Hou, X.F.; Chen, J.; Yang, N.; Liu, Y.; Wang, G.; Du, M.; Qiu, H.H.; Luo, Y.; Jiang, Z.Y.; Feng, L. Anti-inflammatory effect of miltirone on inflammatory bowel disease via TLR4/NF-κB/IQGAP2 signaling pathway. *Biomed. Pharmacother.* **2017**, *85*, 531–540. [CrossRef] [PubMed]
5. Kim, E.S.; Chen, M.; Lee, J.; Lee, C.K.; Kim, Y.S. Diagnosis of inflammatory bowel disease in Asia: the results of a multinational web-based survey in the 2(nd) Asian Organization for Crohn's and Colitis (AOCC) meeting in Seoul. *Intest. Res.* **2016**, *14*, 224–230. [CrossRef] [PubMed]
6. Thia, K.T.; Loftus, E.V., Jr.; Sandborn, W.J.; Yang, S.K. An update on the epidemiology of inflammatory bowel disease in Asia. *Am. J. Gastroenterol.* **2008**, *103*, 3167–3182. [CrossRef] [PubMed]
7. Zeng, Z.R.; Zhu, Z.H.; Yang, Y.Y.; Ruan, W.S.; Peng, X.B.; Su, Y.H.; Peng, L.; Chen, J.Q.; Yin, Q.; Zhao, C.; et al. Incidence and clinical characteristics of inflammatory bowel disease in a developed region of Guangdong Province, China: A prospective population-based study. *J. Gastroenterol. Hepatol.* **2013**, *28*, 1148–1153. [PubMed]
8. Tang, Z.H.; Li, T.; Tong, Y.G.; Chen, X.J.; Chen, X.P.; Wang, Y.T.; Lu, J.J. A Systematic Review of the Anticancer Properties of Compounds Isolated from Licorice (Gancao). *Planta Med.* **2015**, *81*, 1670–1687. [CrossRef] [PubMed]
9. Zheng, H.H.; Chen, M.Y.; Li, Y.; Wang, Y.Y.; Wei, L.; Liao, Z.Q.; Wang, M.X.; Ma, F.L.; Liao, Q.F.; Xie, Z.Y. Modulation of Gut Microbiome Composition and Function in Experimental Colitis Treated with Sulfasalazine. *Front. Microbiol.* **2017**, *8*, 1703–1717. [CrossRef] [PubMed]
10. Hommel, K.A.; Baldassano, R.N. Brief report: Barriers to treatment adherence in pediatric inflammatory bowel disease. *J. Pediatr. Psychol.* **2010**, *35*, 1005–1010. [CrossRef] [PubMed]
11. Lu, Y.H.; Zhang, C.W.; Bucheli, P.; Wei, D.Z. Citrus flavonoids in fruit and traditional Chinese medicinal food ingredients in China. *Plant Foods Hum. Nutr.* **2006**, *61*, 57–65. [CrossRef] [PubMed]
12. Rani, N.; Bharti, S.; Krishnamurthy, B.; Bhatia, J.; Sharma, C.; Kamal, M.A.; Ojha, S.; Arya, D.S. Pharmacological Properties and Therapeutic Potential of Naringenin: A Citrus Flavonoid of Pharmaceutical Promise. *Curr. Pharm. Des.* **2016**, *22*, 4341–4359. [CrossRef] [PubMed]

13. Wang, Y.; Qian, J.; Cao, J.P.; Wang, D.L.; Liu, C.R.; Yang, R.X.; Li, X.; Sun, C.D. Antioxidant Capacity, Anticancer Ability and Flavonoids Composition of 35 Citrus (Citrus reticulata Blanco) Varieties. *Molecules* **2017**, *22*, 1114. [CrossRef] [PubMed]

14. Pepe, G.; Pagano, F.; Adesso, S.; Sommella, E.; Ostacolo, C.; Manfra, M.; Chieppa, M.; Sala, M.; Russo, M.; Marzocco, S.; et al. Bioavailable Citrus sinensis Extract: Polyphenolic Composition and Biological Activity. *Molecules* **2017**, *22*, 623. [CrossRef] [PubMed]

15. Cheng, L.P.; Ren, Y.J.; Lin, D.B.; Peng, S.; Zhong, B.; Ma, Z.C. The Anti-Inflammatory Properties of Citrus wilsonii Tanaka Extract in LPS-Induced RAW 264.7 and Primary Mouse Bone Marrow-Derived Dendritic Cells. *Molecules* **2017**, *22*, 1213. [CrossRef] [PubMed]

16. Rodrigues, M.; Alves, G.; Falcão, A. Investigating herb-drug interactions: the effect of Citrus aurantium fruit extract on the pharmacokinetics of amiodarone in rats. *Food Chem. Toxicol.* **2013**, *60*, 153–159. [CrossRef] [PubMed]

17. He, W.; Zhang, Y.; Wang, X.R.; Guo, L.L.; Han, L.F.; Liu, E.W.; Wang, T. Zhizhu decoction promotes gastric emptying and protects the gastric mucosa. *J. Med. Food.* **2013**, *16*, 306–311. [CrossRef] [PubMed]

18. Xuan, Z.; Wei, W.S.; Yang, B.; Tao, B.C.; Zeng, H.Y.; Jia, W.W.; Min, M.S.; Yu, Y.Z.; Wei, P.; Hong, L.Y. Urinary metabolite profiling of flavonoids in Chinese volunteers after consumption of orange juice by UFLC -Q-TOF-MS/MS. *J. Chromatogr. B.* **2017**, *1061–1062*.

19. Li, S.; Sang, S.; Pan, M.H.; Lai, C.S.; Lo, C.Y.; Yang, C.S. Anti-inflammatory property of the urinary metabolites of nobiletin in mouse. *Bioorg. Med. Chem. Lett.* **2007**, *17*, 5177–5181.

20. Lundberg, S.; Holst, M.; Hellström, P.M. Expression of iNOS mRNA associated with suppression of colonic contraction in rat colitis. *Acta Physiol. (Oxf).* **2006**, *187*, 489–494. [CrossRef] [PubMed]

21. Ohama, T.; Hori, M.; Sato, K.; Ozaki, H.; Karaki, H. Chronic treatment with interleukin-1beta attenuates contractions by decreasing the activities of CPI-17 and MYPT-1 in intestinal smooth muscle. *J. Biol. Chem.* **2003**, *278*, 48794–48804. [CrossRef] [PubMed]

22. Park, J.H.; Peyrin-Biroulet, L.; Eisenhut, M.; Shin, J.I. IBD immunopathogenesis: A comprehensive review of inflammatory molecules. *Autoimmun Rev.* **2017**, *16*, 416–426. [CrossRef] [PubMed]

23. Wang, W.H.; Li, Z.; Meng, Q.J.; Zhang, P.; Yan, P.C.; Zhang, Z.B.; Zhang, H.; Pan, J.R.; Zhai, Y.J.; Liu, Y.G.; Wang, X.K.; Li, W.W.; Zhao, Y.P. Chronic Calcium Channel Inhibitor Verapamil Antagonizes TNF-α-Mediated Inflammatory Reaction and Protects Against Inflammatory Arthritis in Mice. *Inflammation* **2016**, *39*, 1624–1634. [CrossRef] [PubMed]

24. Lee, S.B.; Lee, W.S.; Shin, J.S.; Jang, D.S.; Lee, K.T. Xanthotoxin suppresses LPS-induced expression of iNOS, COX-2, TNF-α, and IL-6 via AP-1, NF-κB, and JAK-STAT inactivation in RAW 264.7 macrophages. *Int. Immunopharmacol.* **2017**, *49*, 21–29. [CrossRef] [PubMed]

25. Sun, Y.S.; Wang, J.H.; Gu, S.B.; Liu, Z.B.; Zhang, Y.J.; Zhang, X.X. Simultaneous determination of flavonoids in different parts of Citrus reticulata "Chachi" fruit by high performance liquid chromatography -photodiode array detection. *Molecules* **2010**, *15*, 5378–5388. [CrossRef] [PubMed]

26. Guo, Y.C.; Chang, C.M.; Hsu, W.L.; Chiu, S.J.; Tsai, Y.T.; Chou, Y.H.; Hou, M.F.; Wang, J.Y.; Lee, M.H.; Tsai, K.L.; Chang, W.C. Indomethacin inhibits cancer cell migration via attenuation of cellular calcium mobilization. *Molecules* **2013**, *18*, 6584–6596. [CrossRef] [PubMed]

27. Godo, S.; Sawada, A.; Saito, H.; Ikeda, S.; Enkhjargal, B.; Suzuki, K.; Tanaka, S.; Shimokawa, H. Disruption of Physiological Balance Between Nitric Oxide and Endothelium-Dependent Hyperpolarization Impairs Cardiovascular Homeostasis in Mice. *Arterioscler. Thromb. Vasc. Biol.* **2016**, *36*, 97–107. [CrossRef] [PubMed]

28. Cancela, J.M. Specific Ca^{2+} signaling evoked by cholecystokinin and acetylcholine: the roles of NAADP, cADPR, and IP_3. *Annu. Rev. Physiol.* **2001**, *63*, 99–117. [CrossRef] [PubMed]

29. Zhan, Z.B.; Deng, K.Z.; Xiong, Y.; Ding, Y.Q.; Deng, M.Z. Stimultaneous determination of six ingredients in Aurantii Fructus Immaturus by HPLC. *Chin. Hosp. Pharm. J.* **2015**, *35*, 1080–1082.

30. Kim, H.; Berstad, A. Experimental colitis in animal models. *Scand. J. Gastroenterol.* **1992**, *27*, 529–537. [CrossRef] [PubMed]

31. Algieri, F.; Rodriguez-Nogales, A.; Garrido-Mesa, J.; Camuesco, D.; Vezza, T.; Garrido-Mesa, N.; Utrilla, P.; Rodriguez-Cabezas, M.E.; Pischel, I.; Galvez, J. Intestinal anti-inflammatory activity of calcium pyruvate in the TNBS model of rat colitis: Comparison with ethyl pyruvate. *Biochem. Pharmacol.* **2016**, *103*, 53–63. [CrossRef] [PubMed]

32. Rashidian, A.; Muhammadnejad, A.; Dehpour, A.R.; Mehr, S.E.; Akhavan, M.M.; Shirkoohi, R.; Chamanara, M.; Mousavi, S.E.; Rezayat, S.M. Atorvastatin attenuates TNBS-induced rat colitis: The involvement of the TLR4/NF-kB signaling pathway. *Inflammopharmacology* **2016**, *24*, 109–118. [CrossRef] [PubMed]

33. Takagi, T.; Naito, Y.; Mizushima, K.; Akagiri, S.; Suzuki, T.; Hirata, I.; Omatsu, T.; Handa, O.; Kokura, S.; Ichikawa, H.; Yoshikawa, T. Inhalation of carbon monoxide ameliorates TNBS-induced colitis in mice through the inhibition of TNF-α expression. *Dig. Dis. Sci.* **2010**, *55*, 2797–2804. [CrossRef] [PubMed]

34. Chen, T.; Hu, S.H.; Zhang, H.W.; Guan, Q.F.; Yang, Y.H.; Wang, X.M. Anti-inflammatory effects of Dioscorea alata L. anthocyanins in a TNBS-induced colitis model. *Food Funct.* **2017**, *8*, 659–669. [CrossRef] [PubMed]

35. Novak, G.; Parker, C.E.; Pai, R.K.; MacDonald, J.K.; Feagan, B.G.; Sandborn, W.J.; D'Haens, G.; Jairath, V.; Khanna, R. Histologic scoring indices for evaluation of disease activity in Crohn's disease. *Cochrane DB Syst. Rev.* **2017**, *7*, 1–69.

36. Jian, L.; Meng, Y.L.; Hai, Y.Y.; Wei, W.; Li, F.H.; Qian, C.; Jing, Y.R.; Shao, S.W.; Yi, Z.; Tao, W. Mangiferin Improves Hepatic Lipid Metabolism Mainly Through Its Metabolite-Norathyriol by Modulating SIRT-1/ AMPK/SREBP-1c Signaling. *Front Pharmacol.* **2018**, *9*. [CrossRef]

Article

Topical Spilanthol Inhibits MAPK Signaling and Ameliorates Allergic Inflammation in DNCB-Induced Atopic Dermatitis in Mice

Wen-Chung Huang [1,2,†], Chun-Hsun Huang [3,4,†], Sindy Hu [3,4], Hui-Ling Peng [1] and Shu-Ju Wu [4,5,*]

1   Graduate Institute of Health Industry Technology, Research Center for Food and Cosmetic Safety, College of Human Ecology, Chang Gung University of Science and Technology, Taoyuan City 33303, Taiwan; wchuang@mail.cgust.edu.tw (W.-C.H.); hlpeng@mail.cgust.edu.tw (H.-L.P.)
2   Division of Allergy, Asthma, and Rheumatology, Department of Pediatrics, Chang Gung Memorial Hospital, Linkou, Taoyuan City 33303, Taiwan
3   Department of Cosmetic Science, Research Center for Food and Cosmetic Safety, and Research Center for Chinese Herbal Medicine, College of Human Ecology, Chang Gung University of Science and Technology, Guishan Dist., Taoyuan City 33303, Taiwan; chuang@mail.cgust.edu.tw (C.-H.H.); sindyhu@hotmail.com (S.H.)
4   Department of Dermatology, Aesthetic Medical Center, Chang Gung Memorial Hospital, Taoyuan City 33303, Taiwan
5   Department of Nutrition and Health Sciences, Research Center for Chinese Herbal Medicine, College of Human Ecology, Chang Gung University of Science and Technology, Taoyuan City 33303, Taiwan
*   Correspondence: sjwu@mail.cgust.edu.tw; Tel.: +886-3-2118999 (ext. 5493)
†   These authors contributed equally to this work.

Received: 24 April 2019; Accepted: 18 May 2019; Published: 20 May 2019

Abstract: Atopic dermatitis (AD) is a recurrent allergic skin disease caused by genetic and environmental factors. Patients with AD may experience immune imbalance, increased levels of mast cells, immunoglobulin (Ig) E and pro-inflammatory factors (Cyclooxygenase, COX-2 and inducible NO synthase, iNOS). While spilanthol (SP) has anti-inflammatory and analgesic activities, its effect on AD remains to be explored. To develop a new means of SP, inflammation-related symptoms of AD were alleviated, and 2,4-dinitrochlorobenzene (DNCB) was used to induce AD-like skin lesions in BALB/c mice. Histopathological analysis was used to examine mast cells and eosinophils infiltration in AD-like skin lesions. The levels of IgE, IgG1 and IgG2a were measured by enzyme-linked immunosorbent assay (ELISA) kits. Western blot was used for analysis of the mitogen-activated protein kinase (MAPK) pathways and COX-2 and iNOS protein expression. Topical SP treatment reduced serum IgE and IgG2a levels and suppressed COX-2 and iNOS expression via blocked mitogen-activated protein kinase (MAPK) pathways in DNCB-induced AD-like lesions. Histopathological examination revealed that SP reduced epidermal thickness and collagen accumulation and inhibited mast cells and eosinophils infiltration into the AD-like lesions skin. These results indicate that SP may protect against AD skin lesions through inhibited MAPK signaling pathways and may diminish the infiltration of inflammatory cells to block allergic inflammation.

Keywords: spilanthol; IgE; allergic inflammation; MAPK; atopic dermatitis

---

1. Introduction

Common symptoms of atopic dermatitis (also known as atopic eczema) include itching, redness, and cracking skin. Pathological characteristics include dry, fragile skin as a result of epidermal defense dysfunction. Due to abnormal immune function, a variety of allergens are able to penetrate the skin, making it more prone to allergic reaction or inflammation [1]. In addition, atopic dermatitis (AD) is the product of a series of complex interactions of innate and adaptive immune responses and IgE-mediated allergies to various exogenous antigens [2]. Serious inflammation is a hallmark of acute AD lesions, and chronic AD lesions are characterized by lichenified fibrosis and epidermal thickening [3].

Studies have found that allergic reactions activate T helper (Th) cells, and that an imbalance between Th1 and Th2 cells causes AD [4]. Activation of Th2 cells leads to an allergic response producing IgE and IgG1, which in turn strengthen the immune response [5,6]. IgE has a high affinity for the IgE receptor expressed on the surface of mast cells; if IgE adheres to the mast cells, they are called sensitized cells. Mast cells are Th2-activated regulatory cells that release a lot of inflammatory-related cytokines, which can cause inflammation and allergic reaction [7,8]. Th2-activated cells also enable the aggregation of eosinophils, causing localized severe inflammation. IgG2a production is dependent on Th1 cells, which can regulate the activity of Th2 cells. However, Th2 cells will inhibit the activity of Th1 cells, creating an imbalance in which Th2 cell activity is much higher than Th1 cell activity, which in turn can cause an allergic reaction. Th1 and Th2 immune response, AD, tend to Th2 and have allergic constitution [7,9,10]. Therefore, decreasing the activity of Th2 cells may improve skin symptoms of AD. In addition, MAPKs pathway, which include the extracellular signal-regulated kinase (ERK), c jun N-terminal kinase (JNK), and p38 MAPK, have also been implicated in inflammatory signaling cascades. Phosphorylation of MAPKs causes the inflammatory mediators' production and promotes an allergic inflammatory response. MAPKs are important pathways in the inhibition of allergic inflammation. Therefore, inactivation of MAPKs subsequently decreases the allergic inflammatory response [11–13].

Spilanthes acmella Murr. is used as traditional folk medicine to treat toothache in the East Asia area. It has demonstrated a variety of biological effects, including anesthesia, analgesia, diuretic, and antibacterial effects [14–17]. Interestingly, research has supported the use of *Spilanthes* plant extract as a nutritional supplement and sweetener [18]. Alkamides are the most abundant phytochemicals present in *S. acmella*. Spilanthol (SP): ((2E,6Z,8E)-N-isobutylamide-2,6,8- decatrienamide) is a high-value bioactive compound and belongs to alkamides from *S. acmella* [19]. In addition, SP is also found in genus *Spilanthes*, including *Acmella brachyglossa*, *Acmella ciliate*, etc. [20,21]. SP reportedly has antibacterial, analgesic, and anti-wrinkle properties [22,23]. Previous studies showed that extract of *A. olerecea* is used in treatment of skin diseases including scabies and psoriasis, and used in anti-age applications (antiwrinkle cream) [20]. In a previous study, we found that SP exerts its anti-inflammatory activity by suppressing intercellular adhesion molecule 1 (ICAM-1) and COX-2 expression, and blocking the phosphorylated JNK signaling pathway [24]. However, it is not yet known about SP used in treatment of AD.

Therefore, in this study we evaluated the effects of SP on AD and sought to understand the mechanisms through which SP regulates allergic inflammation. Our findings indicate that SP reduces Th2-mediated infiltration by mast cells and eosinophils and decreases ear and dorsal skin thickness, and SP also inhibits COX-2 and iNOS expression by blocking MAPK pathways in mice with DNCB-induced AD.

2. Results

2.1. Spilanthol Attenuates Ear Swelling in BALB/c Mice with DNCB-Induced AD

To investigate the effect of SP on AD, we used DNCB-induced ear and dorsal skin inflammation of BALB/c mice (Figure 1A). DNCB-induced AD-like symptoms included ear swelling, scarring, and excoriation of the skin and ear compared with normal mice (Figure 1B). We measured ear thickness on day 30 of DNCB-induced experimental model ear swelling. Topical administration of SP significantly reduced ear swelling compared with DNCB-sensitized mice (Figure 1C) (SP-5: 0.461 ± 0.25 mm, $p < 0.05$; SP-10: 0.44 ± 0.18 mm, $p < 0.05$, vs. the DNCB group: 0.69 ± 0.24 mm).

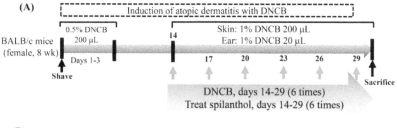

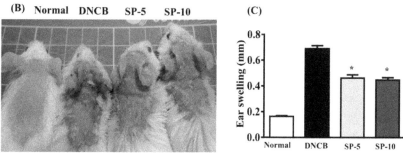

Figure 1. DNCB (2,4-dinitrochlorobenzene) induces atopic dermatitis (AD)-like lesions. (**A**) BALB/C mice were treated with 0.5% DNCB in acetone/olive oil (3:1) on days 1–3. Then, mice were challenged with 1% DNCB on days 14, 17, 20, 23, 26, and 29. AD-like lesions were treated with spilanthol (SP) (5 mg/kg or 10 mg/kg) or vehicle on days 14–27. Mice were sacrificed on day 30. (**B**) Clinical features of AD-like skin lesions treated topically with SP. (**C**) SP attenuates ear swelling by day 30 in DNCB-induced AD-like ear lesions. Data are presented as mean ± SEM (n = 8 mice/group). *$p < 0.05$, versus DNCB mice.

2.2. Spilanthol Attenuates Collagen Deposition and Reduces Epidermal and Dermal Thickness in BALB/c Mice with DNCB-Induced AD

Masson's Trichrome staining was used to evaluate collagen deposition and tissue fibrosis in DNCB-induced AD-like lesions. The main object of Masson's Trichrome staining is collagen; collagen fibers were stained blue and the background was stained red. Hence, we used this staining to evaluate the improvement of collagen deposition after SP administration. Treatment with SP-5 or SP-10 significantly reduced ear thickness and hardening of the dorsal skin surface caused by inflammation; the remodeling on day 30 compared with the DNCB-sensitized group is shown in an image map (Figure 2A,C). Masson's Trichrome stain revealed that at day 30, collagen deposition in AD-like skin lesions was significantly lower in the ear (Figure 2B) and dorsal skin (Figure 2D) of the SP-5 and SP-10 groups than in the DNCB-sensitized group. Thicknesses of both the epidermis and dermis were also significantly reduced in the ear (Figure 2E) and dorsal skin (Figure 2F) of SP-treated groups compared with the DNCB-sensitized group at day 30. Collectively, these results support that SP administration modulates the recovery of AD-like lesions by reducing epidermal and dermal hyperplasia, down-regulating collagen over-build.

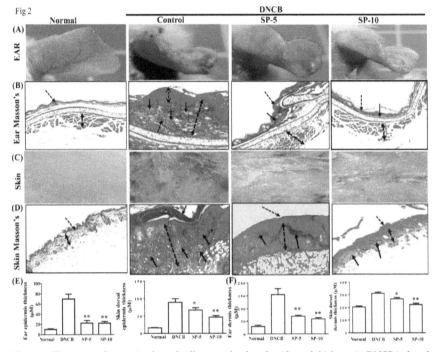

Figure 2. SP attenuated excessive dermal collagen and reduced epidermal thickness in DNCB-induced AD-like skin and ear lesions. (**A**) Ear lesions, (**B**) collagen deposition, (**C**) dorsal skin lesions, and (**D**) collagen deposition determined by Masson's Trichrome staining, day 30. Black arrows: Collagen deposition; dashed arrows: Dermal hyperplasia. (**E**) Epidermal and (**F**) dermal thickness of ear and skin. Data presented as mean ± SEM (*n* = 8 mice/group). *$p < 0.05$, **$p < 0.01$ versus DNCB mice.

2.3. Spilanthol Inhibits Mast Cell Infiltration and Affects Serum Cytokines in BALB/c Mice with DNCB-Induced AD

Exposure to allergens stimulates IgE production in tissue and activates mast cells, then IgE and mast cells can induce complex immune responses and allergic symptoms [25]. Activated mast cells release inflammatory mediators, causing allergic inflammation in AD. To control activated mast cell release, inflammatory mediators can reduce allergic inflammation in AD [26,27]. Therefore, we focused on determining local infiltration by mast cells and assessing the inhibitory effect of SP on mast cell infiltration in mice with DNCB-induced AD. Toluidine blue staining of the ear and dorsal skin of DNCB-treated mice was performed to observe mast cell features. Topical administration of SP suppressed mast cell infiltration in the ears and dorsal skin compared with the DNCB-sensitized group (Figure 3A,B). The number of mast cells significantly decreased after SP administration compared with the DNCB-sensitized group (ear: SP-5: 61.5 ± 8.7, $p < 0.01$, SP-10: 47.2 ± 7.2, $p < 0.01$, vs. the DNCB-sensitized group: 137.4 ± 5.5; skin: SP-5: 54.6 ± 2.1, $p < 0.01$, SP-10: 53.2 ± 2.4, $p < 0.01$, vs. the DNCB-sensitized group: 87.8.0 ± 3.1) (Figure 3B,D). We also measured antibody levels to determine whether SP was able to modulate the allergic response in serum. Increasing serum IgE level is a major characteristic of AD, and we found that topical administration of SP significantly suppressed serum IgE and IgG1 levels in SP-10 mice, whereas serum IgG2a levels were significantly increased in SP-treated mice compared with the DNCB-sensitized group (Figure 3E). This suggests that SP can suppress the infiltration of mast cells and modulate the immune response.

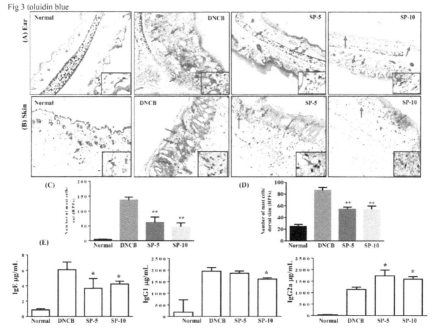

Figure 3. SP inhibits mast cell infiltration and modulates cytokine levels in DNCB-induced AD-like skin and ear lesions. Mast cell infiltration (red arrows) stained with toluidine blue in (**A**) ear and (**B**) dorsal skin sections. (**C**) Mast cells measured under 10–15 high-power fields (HPFs) in ear and (**D**) dorsal skin. (**E**) Serum levels of IgE, IgG1, and IgG2 measured using ELISA. Data presented as mean ± SEM (*n* = 8 mice/group). * *p* < 0.05, ** *p* < 0.01 versus DNCB mice.

2.4. Spilanthol Suppresses Eosinophil Infiltration and Inhibits Protein Expression of MAPK Signaling Pathways in BALB/c Mice with DNCB-Induced AD

To investigate the effect of SP on ear and dorsal skin, sections were stained with hematoxylin and eosin (H&E) to examine eosinophil infiltration in AD-like skin lesions. DNCB-sensitized mice exhibited more eosinophil infiltration than non-sensitized control mice. Increasing the permeability of blood vessels allows eosinophils to infiltrate into tissue. Topical administration of SP significantly decreased eosinophil infiltration compared with DNCB-sensitized mice (Figure 4A,B). The number of eosinophils decreased significantly after administration of SP compared with DNCB-sensitized mice (ear: SP-5: 74.5 ± 8.1, *p* < 0.01, SP-10: 40.7 ± 2.1, *p* < 0.01, vs. the DNCB group: 196.8.0 ± 4.8; dorsal skin: SP-5: 90.8 ± 4.3, *p* < 0.01, SP-10: 118.1 ± 2.6, *p* < 0.01, vs. the DNCB group: 403.5 ± 8.3) (Figure 4C,D).

The production of inflammation mediators by activated MAPK signaling pathways is also related to allergic inflammation. Therefore, we also investigated the effect of SP on the expression of ERK1/2, p38, and JNK proteins (Figure 4E). Results showed that levels of phosphorylated MAPK proteins (p-p38, p-JNK, and p-ERK) were increased significantly more in DNCB mice than in non-sensitized control mice, and topical administration of SP significantly decreased phosphorylation of ERK1/2, p38, and JNK in SP-treated mice compared with DNCB-sensitized mice (Figure 4F). These results indicated that SP suppressed allergic inflammation by blocking MAPK signaling pathways.

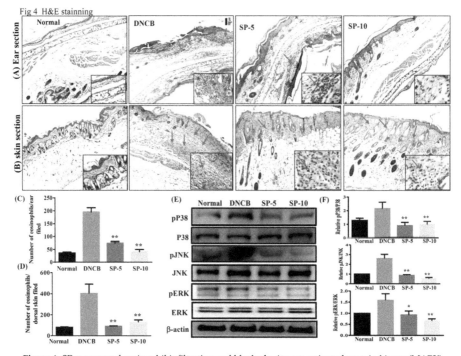

Figure 4. SP suppressed eosinophil infiltration and blocked mitogen-activated protein kinase (MAPK) signaling in DNCB-induced AD-like skin and ear lesions. Eosinophil infiltration (red arrows) in (**A**) ear and (**B**) dorsal skin lesions, determined by hematoxylin and eosin (H&E) stain. The number of eosinophils infiltrating the (**C**) ear and (**D**) dorsal skin measured under 10–15 high-power fields (HPFs). (**E**) Western blotting assays of p-extracellular signal-regulated kinase (p-ERK), p-p38, and p-c-jun N-terminal kinase (p-JNK) (*n* = 6/group), and (**F**) expression of p-ERK, p-p38, and p-JNK relative to ERK, p38, and JNK. The proteins were normalized to total JNK, ERK, and p38 protein levels, the total MAPK levels were used as internal controls. The relative intensity was calculated as the ratio of the intensities of the pP38, p-JNK, and p-ERK bands to the intensity of the total P38, JNK, and ERK bands, respectively. Data presented as mean ± SEM; *$p < 0.05$, **$p < 0.01$ versus DNCB mice. 100x magnification; amplified graph is 200x; *n* = 8 mice/group. Data presented as mean ± SEM. *$p < 0.05$, **$p < 0.01$ versus sensitized control mice.

2.5. Spilanthol Inhibits the Expression of Pro-Inflammatory Factors COX-2 and iNOS in BALB/c Mice with DNCB-Induced AD

Studies have indicated that increases in pro-inflammatory factors COX-2 and iNOS are observed in patients with AD [28]. Next, we investigated the effect of SP on DNCB-induced COX-2 and iNOS expression in AD-like mice. Immunohistochemistry showed that expression of COX-2 was lower in paraffin sections of ear biopsies (Figure 5A). Immunoblot analysis revealed that the levels of COX-2 and iNOS were significantly lower in SP-treated groups than in DNCB-sensitized mice (Figure 5B,C). Immunoblot analysis of COX-2 expression was consistent with the results of the immunohistochemical analysis. These results demonstrate that SP can reduce the inflammatory response by down-regulating the expression of inflammatory mediators COX-2 and iNOS in AD-like mice. We also evaluated the effects of SP on liver and kidney toxicity, as demonstrated by the drastic elevation of serum glutamate-oxaloacetic transaminase (GOT), glutamate-pyruvate transaminase (GPT), creatinine, and blood urea nitrogen (BUN). We found that serum GOT and GPT in the four groups of mice were within the normal range, although SP significantly decreased serum GOT and GPT levels in

SP-treated mice compared with DNCB-sensitized mice (Figure 5D). In addition, serum creatinine and BUN levels were statistically similar among all experimental groups (Figure 5E). In brief, SP does not injure the liver or kidneys of AD-like mice.

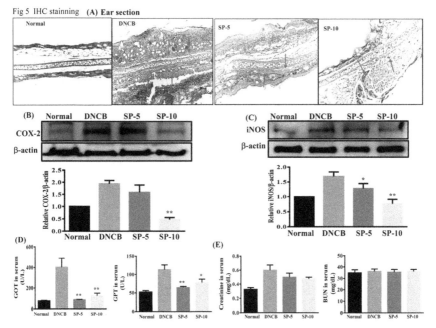

Figure 5. Effects of SP on cyclooxygenase-2 (COX-2) and inducible NO synthase (iNOS) in DNCB-induced AD-like skin lesions. (**A**) Immunohistochemical staining of COX-2 in ear (red arrows). (**B**) COX-2 level assayed by Western blot, and COX-2 protein expression relative to β-actin. (**C**) iNOS level assayed by Western blot, and iNOS protein expression relative to β-actin. Quantification of β-actin, iNOS, and COX-2 expression. β-actin expression was used as an internal control, the relative intensity was calculated as the ratio of the intensities of the COX-2 and iNOS bands to the intensity of the β-actin. Effects of spilanthol on (**D**) serum GOT and GPT, and (**E**) serum creatinine and BUN. Serum was centrifuged, collected, and evaluated by ELISA. Data presented as mean ± SEM; *$p < 0.05$, **$p < 0.01$ versus DNCB mice. 100x magnification; amplified graph is 200x; $n = 8$ mice/group. Data presented as mean ± SEM. * $p < 0.05$, ** $p < 0.01$ versus sensitized control mice.

3. Discussion

In this study, we investigated the anti-AD activity of SP in BALB/c mice with DNCB-induced AD. DNCB is an allergenic chemical commonly used to induce AD in animal models [27,29]. Environmental or allergic AD is known as extrinsic type AD, and genetic or non-allergic AD is known as intrinsic type AD [30]. Extrinsic or environmental factors induce severe AD through stimulation, triggering IgE-mediated forms of skin inflammation and allergic reaction [31]. AD is one of the most common chronic inflammatory skin diseases, and is characterized by erythema, dry skin, pruritus, and abnormal immune responses [27]. Repeated triggering of the allergic-inflammatory response leads to remodeling and hardening of the skin surface, leading the epidermis to thicken and break, resulting in infiltration of eosinophils and mast cells in AD skin lesions [32]. We found that topical treatment with SP ameliorated DNCB-induced AD-like skin lesions and improved skin lesion severity, ear swelling, and epidermal thickness in DNCB-treated BALB/c mice (Figures 1 and 2). Moreover, SP reduced DNCB-induced collagen hyperplasia in AD-like skin lesions, as determined by Masson's stain

(Figure 2B,D). These results suggest that SP may be useful for the treatment of AD by reducing hyperkeratosis and fibrotic remodeling of the skin.

In the pathogenesis of AD, epidermal barrier function is impaired and the infiltration of environmental allergens into the skin increases, which in turn causes the allergic reactions and inflammation that are major characteristics of IgE-mediated hypersensitivity reactions [33]. Studies have shown that excessive IgE levels are closely related to imbalances of Th1 and Th2 cells in AD patients [30]. Th2-related cytokines, including of IL-4, are stimulators of IgE synthesis; excessive levels of IgE will activate mast cells and IL-5 induces eosinophil differentiation and infiltration into AD skin lesions, causing allergic inflammation. Excessive secretion of cytokines by activated Th2 cells will contribute to AD symptoms; therefore, down-regulation of Th2 cytokines may decrease production of IgE and improve AD [27,34]. Studies have indicated that increased secretion of Th1-related cytokines and decreased Th2-related cytokine levels may prevent excessive IgE production [35]. Reportedly, the IgG1 immune complex is responsible for class-switching to Th2 cytokines, and IgG2a is oriented toward Th1 cytokine immune deviation [36]. In addition, adjusting the balance of Th1/Th2 cytokines to inhibit mast cell activation, then decreasing the levels of IgG1 and increasing IgG2a has a significant anti-allergic inflammatory effect [37]. We found that topical treatment with SP reduced IgE levels and regulated IgG1 and IgG2a levels in DNCB-treated BALB/c mice (Figure 3E). In addition, SP also improved the infiltration of mast cells and eosinophils into AD skin lesions (Figure 3A,B and Figure 4A,B). These findings suggest that SP has a significant anti-allergic effect in AD. The SP may suppress eosinophil infiltration and down-regulate IgE expression to reduce mast cell infiltration into AD skin lesions.

Skin epidermal barrier dysfunction causing hardening and fragility of the skin surface is one of the main causes of AD, and inflammation can be modulated to reduce skin barrier function, thus aggravating lesions [29,30]. In addition, studies have indicated that constituents of MAPK pathways, including ERK, JNK, and p38, are involved in the pathogenesis of AD; in other words, AD is a chronic allergic inflammatory skin disease [38]. MAPK pathway activation promotes a number of inflammatory mediators, including COX-2 and iNOS [39]. COX-2 catalyzes arachidonic acid into prostaglandin, the levels of prostaglandin and COX-2 activity are related to promote inflammatory pain [40]. iNOS is produced by cytokines in inflammatory cells, which generate the free radical NO from L-arginine. iNOS and NO are related to cellular oxidative stress and the host cellular immune response [41] Several reports have shown that SP exhibits anti-inflammatory efficacy in vitro and in vivo [18,20–22]. However, it has been unknown whether SP exhibits anti-inflammatory activity in AD skin lesions. DNCB is a potential allergen that can induce skin sensitivity and inflammation [42]. Therefore, we identified SP as a possible suppressor of MAPK signal pathways triggered by DNCB in mice with DNCB-induced AD. In this work, we found that the anti-allergic effects of SP seem to occur through the blocked phosphorylation of ERK1/2, JNK, and p38 MAPK signaling pathways, and suppress COX-2 and iNOS expression in DNCB-induced AD skin lesions (Figures 4 and 5). Based on these results, we suggest that SP may be useful as a treatment for allergic inflammation in AD.

We found that SP not only inhibited the levels of IgE and IgG2a, but also increased IgG1 level. SP may therefore be associated with mast cell-related allergic effects. Furthermore, SP significantly decreased eosinophil infiltration and reduced the expression of pro-inflammatory factors COX-2 and iNOS by suppressing MAPK pathways. SP may be associated with the improvement of eosinophil-related allergic inflammation in AD-like skin lesions. In addition, we found evidence that SP decreased collagen over-deposition in the dermis and reduced epidermal thickness in AD-like lesions. Collectively, we propose a model to explain the anti-allergic effects of SP in AD-like mice (Figure 6).

In summary, we present the first study demonstrating that SP has anti-AD potential. Results of this study demonstrate that SP can improve AD symptoms. SP-regulated Th1/Th2 balance, inhibited mast cell hyperplasia, and suppressed MAPK pathways ameliorated DNCB-induced AD-like skin inflammation in mice.

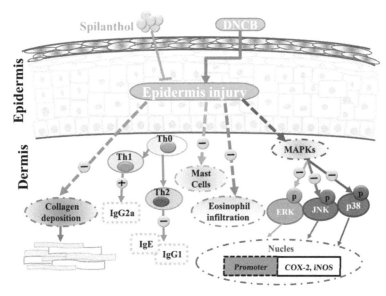

Figure 6. Topical spilanthol improves mast cell infiltration, modulates Th1/Th2 cytokine levels, and inhibits MAPK signaling, ameliorating allergic inflammation in DNCB-induced atopic.

4. Materials and Methods

4.1. Animals

Eight-week-old female BALB/c mice were purchased from the National Laboratory Animal Center (Taiwan) and housed at the Animal Center of Chang Gung University in an air-conditioned room at a consistent temperature (23 ± 2 °C) and 55 ± 15% humidity, with a 12 h light–dark cycle. All procedures involving animals were approved in accordance with the guidelines and regulations of the Laboratory Animal Care Committee of Chang Gung University of Science and Technology and Chang Gung University (IACUC approval number: 2015-020; 29 December 2015).

4.2. DNCB Induction of AD-Like Skin Lesions and Spilanthol Treatment

Spilanthol was purchased from ChromaDex, Irvine, CA, USA. Mice were randomly divided into four groups (*n* = 8 per group): A mock-sensitized control group were sensitized and challenged with normal saline; a sensitized control group were treated with DNCB in a 3:1 ratio of acetone:olive oil; an SP-5 group were challenged with DNCB and treated topically with SP 5 g/kg; and an SP-10 group were challenged with DNCB and treated topically with SP 10 g/kg. The dorsal skin was shaved, and then sensitized using DNCB (Sigma-Aldrich, St. Louis, MO, USA) as described in a previous study [25]. To sensitize the skin, 200 μL 0.5% DNCB in acetone:olive oil (3:1) was applied to the shaved area on experimental days 1–3. Next, for the challenge process, 100 μL of 1% DNCB was applied to each ear and the dorsal skin on experimental days 14, 17, 20, 23, 26, and 29. All SP treatments were applied to the ears and backs of the mice daily on experimental days 14 to 29. The experimental design is described in Figure 1A.

4.3. Measurement of Ear and Epidermal Thickness

Images were captured weekly with a digital camera (Coolpix, Nikon Inc., Tokyo, Japan) to record clinical symptoms on the ear and dorsal skin. Ear thickness was measured using a dial gauge (Olympus, Tokyo, Japan) on day 30. Ear and skin epidermal thickness were measured using Masson's stain and the aid of a microscope with Image-Pro Plus software (version 6.0 for Windows).

4.4. Histopathological Analysis

The ear and dorsal skin of each mouse were obtained on day 30 and fixed in 10% formalin. These tissues were cut into 6-μm thick sections and stained with Masson's, hematoxylin and eosin (H&E), toluidine blue, and immunohistochemical stain, as previously described [25,39]. The sections were under 10–15 high-power fields (HPFs) using a light microscope at 100–200× magnification to measure mast cells and eosinophils. Mast cells and eosinophils were stained with toluidine blue and H&E, respectively. Collagen accumulation was assessed by Masson's stain and using COX-2 antibody; immunohistochemical stain was used to observe positive COX-2 staining. Then, sections were examined using light microscopy to observe histological changes in all stained sections.

4.5. Measurement of Serum IgE and Cytokines

Blood samples were collected from BALB/c mice on day 30 and centrifuged at 3000 g for 10 min at 4 °C to obtain serum. The levels of serum IgE, IgG1, and IgG2a were measured using enzyme-linked immunosorbent assay (ELISA) kits (BD Biosciences, San Diego, CA, USA) according to the manufacturer's instructions. Optical density was measured using a microplate reader (Multiskan FC, Thermo, Waltham, MA, USA). In addition, liver function indices (GPT and GOT) and kidney function indices (BUN and creatinine) were analyzed enzymatically using commercially available assay kits (Wako Pure Chemical, Osaka, Japan).

4.6. Western Blot Analysis

Dorsal skin samples were harvested on day 30 and stored at −80 °C. To investigate protein expression, protein lysates were prepared using protein lysis buffer (Sigma, St. Louis, MO, USA). The protein amounts were quantitated using the BCA protein assay kit (Pierce). Then, equal amounts of protein were separated on 10% SDS-PAGE gels and electrotransferred to polyvinylidene fluoride membranes (PVDF; Millipore, Billerica, MA, United States). The PVDF membranes were probed with primary antibodies raised against COX-2 and iNOS (Santa Cruz, CA, USA); ERK1/2, p38, JNK, phospho-ERK 1/2, phospho-p38, and phospho-JNK (Millipore); and β-actin (Sigma) overnight at 4 °C. Next, membranes were washed 3 times in Tris-buffered saline with Tween 20 (TBST) buffer (150 mM NaCl, 10 mM Tris-HCl pH 8.0, 0.1% Tween 20), then incubated in secondary antibodies at room temperature for 1 h, followed by incubation with HRP-conjugated secondary antibodies at room temperature for 1 h. Finally, the membranes were washed using TBST and incubated with Luminol/Enhancer Solution (Millipore). Protein bands were quantitated using the BioSpectrum 600 system (UVP, Upland, CA, United States).

4.7. Statistical Analysis

Data are reported as the mean ± standard error of the mean (SEM). All statistical significance was assessed using one-way analysis of variance (ANOVA) and Tukey's test. Differences were considered statistically significant at $p < 0.05$.

Author Contributions: W.-C.H. and H.-L.P. designed the study and performed the experiments. C.-H.H. and S.H. searched the literature and performed the experiments. S.-J.W. interpreted the data and drafted the manuscript.

Funding: This study was supported in part by grants from Chang Gung Memorial Hospital (CMRPF1G0202, CMRPF1H0111) and the Ministry of Science and Technology in Taiwan (MOST 105-2320-B-255-004).

Conflicts of Interest: The authors declare that they have no conflict of interest.

Abbreviations

AD	Atopic dermatitis
SP	Spilanthol
IgE	Immunoglobulin (Ig) E
IgG2a	Immunoglobulin (Ig) G2a
IgG1	Immunoglobulin (Ig) G1
COX-2	Cyclooxygenase-2
iNOS	Inducible NO synthase
DNCB	2,4-dinitrochlorobenzene
MAPK	Mitogen-activated protein kinase
ERK	Extracellular signal-regulated kinase
JNK	c-jun N-terminal kinase

References

1. Boguniewicz, M.; Leung, D.Y. Atopic dermatitis: A disease of altered skin barrier and immune dysregulation. *Immunol. Rev.* **2011**, *242*, 233–246. [CrossRef]
2. Kim, Y.J.; Choi, M.J.; Bak, D.H. Topical administration of EGF suppresses immune response and protects skin barrier in DNCB-induced atopic dermatitis in NC/Nga mice. *Sci. Rep.* **2018**, *8*, 11895. [CrossRef]
3. Lan, C.C.; Fang, A.H.; Wu, P.H.; Wu, C.S. Tacrolimus abrogates TGF-β1-induced type I collagen production in normal human fibroblasts through suppressing p38MAPK signalling pathway: Implications on treatment of chronic atopic dermatitis lesions. *J. Eur. Acad. Dermatol.* **2014**, *28*, 204–215. [CrossRef]
4. Brandt, E.B.; Sivaprasad, U. Th2 cytokines and atopic dermatitis. *J. Clin. Cell. Immuno.* **2011**, *2*, 110. [CrossRef]
5. Turner, M.J.; Travers, J.B.; Kaplan, M.H. T helper cell subsets in the development of atopic dermatitis. *J. Drugs. Dermatol.* **2012**, *11*, 1174–1178.
6. Lefeber, D.J.; Benaissa-Trouw, B.; Vliegenthart, J.F. Th1-Directing Adjuvants Increase the Immunogenicity of Oligosaccharide-Protein Conjugate Vaccines Related to Streptococcus pneumoniae Type 3. *Infect. Immun.* **2003**, *12*, 6915–6920. [CrossRef] [PubMed]
7. Yosipovitch, G.; Papoiu, A.D.P. What causes itch in atopic dermatitis? *Curr. Allergy. Asthm. R.* **2008**, *8*, 306–311. [CrossRef]
8. Holgate, S.T. The role of mast cells and basophils in inflammation. *Clin. Exp. Allergy.* **2000**, *30*, 28–32. [CrossRef]
9. Rostamian, M.; Sohrabi, S.; Kavosifard, H. Lower levels of IgG1 in comparison with IgG2a are associated with protective immunity against Leishmania tropica infection in BALB/c mice. *J. Microbiol. Immunol. Infect.* **2017**, *50*, 160e166. [CrossRef] [PubMed]
10. Yoshihara, S.; Yamada, Y.; Abe, T. Association of epithelial damage and signs of neutrophil mobilization in the airways during acute exacerbations of paediatric asthma. *Clin. Exp. Immunol.* **2006**, *144*, 212–216. [CrossRef] [PubMed]
11. Hommes, D.W.; Peppelenbosc, M.P.; van Deventer, S.J. Mitogen activated protein (MAP) kinase signal transduction pathways and novel anti-inflammatory targets. *Gut* **2003**, *52*, 144–151. [CrossRef] [PubMed]
12. Arthur, J.S.; Ley, S.C. Mitogen-activated protein kinases in innate immunity. *Nat. Rev. Immunol.* **2013**, *13*, 679–692. [CrossRef] [PubMed]
13. Barnes, P.J. Pathophysiology of allergic inflammation. *Immunol. Rev.* **2011**, *242*, 31–50. [CrossRef] [PubMed]
14. Wu, L.C.; Fan, N.C.; Lin, M.H. Anti-inflammatory effect of spilanthol from Spilanthes acmella on murine macrophage by down-regulating LPS-induced inflammatory mediators. *J. Agr. Food. Chem.* **2008**, *9*, 2341–2349. [CrossRef] [PubMed]
15. Chakraborty, A.; Devi, B.R.; Sanjebam, R. Preliminary studies on local anesthetic and antipyretic activities of Spilanthes acmella Murr. in experimental animal models. *Indian. J. Pharmacol.* **2010**, *42*, 277–279. [CrossRef]
16. Gerbino, A.; Schena, G.; Milano, S. Spilanthol from Acmella Oleracea Lowers the Intracellular Levels of cAMP Impairing NKCC2 Phosphorylation and Water Channel AQP2 Membrane Expression in Mouse Kidney. *PLoS ONE* **2016**, *11*, e0156021. [CrossRef]

17. Cheng, Y.-B.; Liu, R.H.; Ho, M.-C.; Wu, T.-Y.; Chen, C.-Y.; Lo, I.-W.; Hou, M.-F.; Yuan, S.-S.; Wu, Y.-C.; Chang, F.-R. Alkylamides of Acmella oleracea. *Molecules* **2015**, *20*, 6970–6977. [CrossRef]

18. Singh, M.; Pradhan, S. In vitro production of spilanthol from Spilanthes acmella Murr.: State of the art and future prospect. *Int. J. Adv. Res.* **2015**, *3*, 1559–1567.

19. Joseph, B.; George, J.; Jeevitha, M.V. Tohle of Acmella Olerecea in Medicine—A review. *World J. Pharm. Res.* **2017**, *2*, 2781–2792.

20. Barbosaa, A.F.; de Carvalhoa, M.G.; Smithb, R.E. Spilanthol: Occurrence, extraction, chemistry and biological activities. *Rev. Bras. Farmacogn.* **2016**, *26*, 128–133. [CrossRef]

21. Prachayasittukal, V.; Prachayasittukal, S.; Ruchiwarat, S.; Prachayasittukal, V. High therapeutic potential of Spilanthes acmella: A review. *Excli. J.* **2013**, *12*, 291–312.

22. Dubey, S.; Maity, S.; Singh, M. Phytochemistry, pharmacol-ogy and toxicology of Spilanthes acmella: A review. *Adv. Pharmacol. Sci.* **2013**, *2013*, 423750. [PubMed]

23. Prachayasittikul, S.; Suphapong, S.; Worachartcheewan, A. Bioactive metabolites from Spilanthes acmella Murr. *Molecules* **2009**, *14*, 850–886. [CrossRef]

24. Huang, C.H.; Chang, L.C.; Hu, S. Spilanthol inhibits TNF α induced ICAM 1 expression and pro inflammatory responses by inducing heme oxygenase 1 expression and suppressing pJNK in HaCaT keratinocytes. *Mol. Med. Rep.* **2018**, *18*, 2987–2994. [CrossRef]

25. Leung, D.Y.; Soter, N.A. Cellular and immunologic mechanisms in atopic dermatitis. *J. Am. Acad.Dermatol.* **2001**, *44*, S1–S12. [CrossRef]

26. Galli, S.J.; Tsai, M. IgE and mast cells in allergic disease. *Nat. Med.* **2015**, *18*, 693–704. [CrossRef] [PubMed]

27. Fang, L.W.; Cheng, C.C.; Hwang, T.S. Danggui Buxue Tang Inhibits 2,4-Dinitrochlorobenzene: Induced Atopic Dermatitis in Mice. *Evid.-Based Complementary Altern. Med.* **2015**, *2015*, 672891.

28. Ahn, J.Y.; Choi, S.E.; Jeong, M.S.; Park, K.H.; Moon, N.J.; Joo, S.S.; Lee, C.S.; Choi, Y.W.; Li, K.; Lee, M.K.; et al. Effect of taxifolin glycoside on atopic dermatitis-like skin lesions in NC/Nga mice. *Phytother. Res.* **2010**, *24*, 1071–1077. [CrossRef] [PubMed]

29. Ku, J.M.; Hong, S.H.; Kim, S.R. The prevention of 2,4-dinitrochlorobenzene-induced inflammation in atopic dermatitis-like skin lesions in BALB/c mice by Jawoongo. *BMC. Complem. Altern. Med.* **2018**, *18*, 215. [CrossRef]

30. Jegal, J.; Park, N.J.; Bong, S.K. Dioscorea quinqueloba Ameliorates Oxazolone- and 2,4-Dinitrochlorobenzene-induced Atopic Dermatitis Symptoms in Murine Models. *Nutrients* **2017**, *9*, 1324. [CrossRef]

31. Darlenski, R.; Kazandjieva, J.; Hristakieva, E.; Fluhr, J.W. Atopic dermatitis as a systemic disease. *Clin. Dermatol.* **2014**, *32*, 409–413. [CrossRef] [PubMed]

32. Lee, K.S. A novel model for human atopic dermatitis: Application of repeated DNCB patch in BALB/c mice, in comparison with NC/Nga mice. *Lab. Anim. Res.* **2010**, *26*, 95–102. [CrossRef]

33. Danso, M.O. TNF-α and Th2 cytokines induce atopic dermatitis–like features on epidermal differentiation proteins and stratum corneum lipids in human skin equivalents. *J. Invest. Dermatol.* **2014**, *134*, 1941–1950. [CrossRef]

34. Deo, S.S.; Mistry, K.J.; Kakade, A.M. Role played by Th2 type cytokines in IgE mediated allergy and asthma. *Lung. India.* **2010**, *27*, 66–71. [CrossRef] [PubMed]

35. Baumann, U.; Chouchakova, N.; Gewecke, B. Distinct Tissue Site-Specific Requirements of Mast Cells and Complement Components C3/C5a Receptor in IgG Immune Complex-Induced Injury of Skin and Lung. *J. Immunol.* **2001**, *167*, 1022–1027. [CrossRef] [PubMed]

36. Govindaraj, D.; Sharma, S.; Singh, N.; Arora, N. T cell epitopes of Per a 10 modulate local-systemic immune responses and airway inflammation by augmenting Th1 and T regulatory cell functions in murine model. *Immunobiology* **2019**, *18*. [CrossRef]

37. Piaoa, C.H.; Kim, T.G.; Buic, T.T. Ethanol extract of Dryopteris crassirhizoma alleviates allergic inflammation via inhibition of Th2 response and mast cell activation in a murine model of allergic rhinitis. *J. Ethnopharmacol.* **2019**, *232*, 21–29. [CrossRef]

38. Johansen, C.; Kragballe, K.; Westergaard, M. The mitogen-activated protein kinases p38 and ERK1/2 are increased in lesional psoriatic skin. *Brit. J. Dermatol.* **2005**, *152*, 37–42. [CrossRef]

39. Senthil, K.J.; Hsieh, H.W.; Wang, S.Y. Anti-inflammatory effect of lucidone in mice via inhibition of NF-κB/MAP kinase pathway. *Int. Immunopharmacol.* **2010**, *10*, 385–392. [CrossRef]

40. Giuliano, F.; Warner, T.D. Origins of prostaglandin E2: Involvements of cyclooxygenase (COX)-1 and COX-2 in human and rat systems. *J. Pharmacol. Exp. Ther.* **2002**, *303*, 1001. [CrossRef]
41. Shah, G.; Zhang, G.; Chen, F. iNOS expression and NO production contribute to the direct effects of BCG on urothelial carcinoma cell biology. *Urol. Oncol.* **2014**, *32*, 45e1–45e9. [CrossRef] [PubMed]
42. Chan, C.C.; Liou, C.J.; Xu, P.Y. Effect of dehydroepiandrosterone on atopic dermatitis-like skin lesions induced by 1-chloro-2,4-dinitrobenzene in mouse. *J. Dermatol. Sci.* **2013**, *72*, 149–157. [CrossRef] [PubMed]

Article

Effects of *Sapindus mukorossi* Seed Oil on Skin Wound Healing: In Vivo and in Vitro Testing

Chang-Chih Chen [1,2], Chia-Jen Nien [3], Lih-Geeng Chen [4], Kuen-Yu Huang [3], Wei-Jen Chang [5] and Haw-Ming Huang [3,5,*]

[1] Emergency Department, Mackay Momorial Hospital, Taipei 110, Taiwan; longus4280@gmail.com
[2] Medical School, Mackay Medical College, New Taipei City 252, Taiwan
[3] Graduate Institute of Biomedical Optomechatronics, College of Biomedical Engineering, Taipei Medical University, Taipei 110, Taiwan; yz26796029@hotmail.com (C.-J.N.); alvin199223@gmail.com (K.-Y.H.)
[4] Department of Microbiology, Immunology and Biopharmaceuticals, College of Life Sciences, National Chiayi University, Chiayi 600, Taiwan; lgchen@mail.ncyu.edu.tw
[5] School of Dentistry, College of Oral Medicine, Taipei Medical University, Taipei 110, Taiwan; m8404006@tmu.edu.tw
* Correspondence: hhm@tmu.edu.tw; Tel.: +886-2-2736-1661 (ext. 5128)

Received: 1 May 2019; Accepted: 23 May 2019; Published: 26 May 2019

Abstract: *Sapindus mukorossi* seed oil is commonly used as a source for biodiesel fuel. Its phytochemical composition is similar to the extracted oil from *Sapindus trifoliatus* seeds, which exhibit beneficial effects for skin wound healing. Since *S. mukorossi* seed shows no cyanogenic property, it could be a potential candidate for the treatment of skin wounds. Thus, we evaluated the effectiveness of *S. mukorossi* seed oil in the treatment of skin wounds. We characterized and quantified the fatty acids and unsaponifiable fractions (including β-sitosterol and δ-tocopherol) contained in *S. mukorossi* seed-extracted oil by GC-MS and HPLC, respectively. Cell proliferation and migratory ability were evaluated by cell viability and scratch experiments using CCD-966SK cells treated with *S. mukorossi* oil. The anti-inflammatory effects of the oil were evaluated by measuring the nitric oxide (NO) production in lipopolysaccharide-treated RAW 264.7 cells. Antimicrobial activity tests were performed with *Propionibacterium acnes*, *Staphylococcus aureus*, and *Candida albicans* using a modified Japanese Industrial Standard procedure. Uniform artificial wounds were created on the dorsum of rats. The wounds were treated with a carboxymethyl cellulose (CMC)/hyaluronic acid (HA)/sodium alginate (SA) hydrogel for releasing the *S. mukorossi* seed oil. The wound sizes were measured photographically for 12 days and were compared to wounds covered with analogous membranes containing a saline solution. Our results showed that the *S. mukorossi* seed oil used in this study contains abundant monounsaturated fatty acids, β-sitosterol, and δ-tocopherol. In the in vitro tests, *S. mukorossi* seed oil prompted cell proliferation and migration capability. Additionally, the oil had significant anti-inflammatory and anti-microbial activities. In the in vivo animal experiments, *S. mukorossi* seed oil-treated wounds revealed acceleration of sequential skin wound healing events after two days of healing. The size of oil-treated wound decreased to half the size of the untreated control after eight days of healing. The results suggest that *S. mukorossi* seed oil could be a potential source for promoting skin wound healing.

Keywords: wound healing; *Sapindus mukorossi*; β-sitosterol; anti-inflammatory

1. Introduction

The soapnut tree, which belongs to the family Sapindaceae, is one of the most economically important trees found in tropical and subtropical climates from Japan to India in Asia [1–3]. Soapnut is known for its fruit, which contains triterpenoid saponins (10.1%) in the pericarp [3]. Saponin is a natural detergent for washing the body, hair, and clothes, and it is used as a natural surfactant [1,2,4–6].

There are more than 40 wild species in the genus *Sapindus* (family Sapindaceae) [6]. Among these species, *Sapindus mukorossi* (*S. mukorossi*) and *Sapindus trifoliatus* (*S. trifoliatus*) are the two main varieties. Recently, the use of saponins from *S. mukorossi* has gained the attention of investigators because of their various biological and pharmacological applications. It is reported that saponins exhibit properties that inhibit tumor cell growth [2]. These saponins also have anti-microbial activity [7] and reportedly can be used to treat eczema and psoriasis [3,8].

S. mukorossi is composed of about 56% pericarp [3], with the balance being the hard, black, smooth seed that contains the kernel inside [5,9] (Figure 1). The seed kernel of *S. mukorossi* contains 23% oil in the pulp, of which almost 90% are triglycerides [2]. Most of the reports of *S. mukorossi* are mainly about the nature and application of saponins in the pericarp part of the fruit. This situation is because the oil in the *S. mukorossi* seed kernel is inedible, and thus, the seed is usually treated as waste [1,10,11]. Recently, to achieve the goals of a "waste-to-energy" scheme, *S. mukorossi* seed oil was investigated as a potential source for the production of biodiesel fuel [10,12,13].

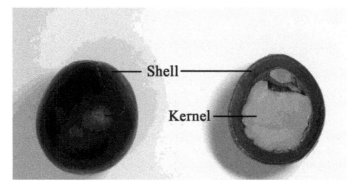

Figure 1. Pictures of the intact seed, seed shell and the kernel of the *Sapindus mukorossi* seed.

It is well known that many seed oils have therapeutic anti-inflammatory and antioxidant effects on the skin and promote wound healing and repair of skin [14–16]. In 2014, Pai et al. tested the n-hexane and ethyl acetate extracts of *S. trifoliatus* seeds and found that the seed extracts exhibited significant antibacterial, antifungal, and antioxidant activities, and revealed benefits for skin wound healing [17]. However, because *S. trifoliatus* seed extract contains cyanolipids, which is irritating or toxic to human skin [18], the pharmacological benefits are limited. Since the composition of *S. mukorossi* oil is very similar to that of *S. trifoliatus* oil [19] but without the toxic cyanolipids [20], it is reasonable to hypothesize that the oil extract of *S. mukorossi* seed kernel could provide similar pharmaceutical effects without the adverse effect of cyanolipid.

The application of *S. mukorossi* (Wu Huan Zi in Chinese) seed kernel for antimicrobial and skin care is recorded in China's traditional pharmaceutical book, Compendium of Materia Medica (Bencao Gangmu in Mandarin) some 500 years ago. In 2015, Srinivasarao et al. found that the extract of *S. mukorossi* exhibited antimicrobial and antioxidant activity and suggested that *S. mukorossi* could be used as a potential source of natural antimicrobial treatment because it possessed strong antioxidant potential [21]. However, in their report, the extract was from whole *S. mukorossi* fruit; thus, it is difficult to know whether the antimicrobial and antioxidant effects were from the pericarp or the seed kernel. Recent studies indicate that *S. mukorossi* oil has abundant phytosterols and arachidonic acid (23.85%) [1,19]. It is reported that phytosterols have an anti-inflammatory effect on skin and are capable of reducing swelling and erythema [22]. Additionally, arachidonic acid is not only an essential polyunsaturated fatty acid in the skin [19] but also plays an important role in reducing skin inflammation [23]. Since *S. mukorossi* seed extract contains anti-inflammatory, antimicrobial, and antioxidant compounds, it could serve as a potential treatment for skin and soft-tissue infections

(SSTIs) [24]. However, the direct topical application of *S. mukorossi* seed oil on the skin has not yet been well investigated. Accordingly, the purpose of this study was to test the pharmacological effects of *S. mukorossi* seed oil on skin wound healing in both in vivo and in vitro experiments.

2. Results

2.1. GC-MS Analysis

The fatty acid composition of the *S. mukorossi* seed-extracted oil was determined by gas chromatography-mass spectrometry (GC-MS) analysis. A representative chromatogram is shown in Figure 2a. The identity of the peak was analyzed using fatty acid standards and the MS database. The percentages of fatty acid esters were obtained by calculating the peak area ratios, which are listed in Table 1. The results show that *S. mukorossi* seeds contain 5.35% of palmitic acid (C16:0), 0.9% stearic acid (C18:0), 52.46% oleic acid (C18:1), 7.19% linoleic acid (C18:2), 1.61% linolenic acid (C18:3), 6.84% arachidic acid (C20:0), 23.71% eicosenic acid (C20:1), 1.24% bechenic acid, and 0.68% erucic acid (C22:1).

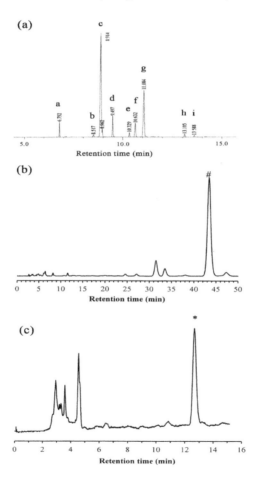

Figure 2. (a) Total ion chromatograms of *S. mukorossi* seed oil tested in this study. (b) δ-tocopherol and (c) β-sitosterol fractions from high-pressure liquid chromatography. # and * indicated the detected peaks of δ-tocopherol and β-sitosterol, respectively.

Table 1. Fatty acid composition of *Sapindus mukorossi* seed-extracted oil by gas chromatography-mass spectrometry.

Peak	Retention Time (min)	Percentage	Fatty Acid
a	6.792	5.35	Palmitic acid (16:0)
b	8.317	0.90	Stearic acid (18:0)
c	8.914	52.46	Oleic acid (18:1)
d	9.497	7.19	Linoleic acid (18:2)
e	10.329	1.61	Linolenic acid (18:3)
f	10.632	6.84	Arachidic acid (20:0)
g	11.084	23.71	Eicosenic acid (20:1)
h	13.105	1.24	Behenic acid (22:0)
i	13.588	0.68	Erucic acid (22:1)

2.2. HPLC Analysis

High-pressure liquid chromatography (HPLC) was performed to determine the quantities of δ-tocopherol and β-sitosterol. Table 2 provides the linear calibration curves for the standard solutions of the two analytes. As shown in Figure 2b,c, the retention times for δ-tocopherol and β-sitosterol were 12.67 min and 43.40 min, respectively. The total amount of δ-tocopherol and β-sitosterol in the *S. mukorossi* seed oil was 73.9 ± 23.6 µg/mL (in 1% oil) and 232.64 ± 4.5 µg/mL, respectively.

Table 2. Linearity of the standard curves of δ-tocopherol and β-sitosterol.

Compound	Calibration Equation [a]	Retention Time (t_r)	Correlation Coefficient (r^2)
δ-Tocopherol	$Y = 4903.9X \pm 27882$	12.67	0.9908
β-Sitosterol	$Y = 3480.3X \pm 7887.6$	43.40	0.9996

[a] The variable X is the concentration of the standard (mg/mL), and the variable Y is the peak area.

2.3. Antimicrobial Activity Testing

The antimicrobial activity of *S. mukorossi* seed oil is shown in Table 3. After treatment with 1% *S. mukorossi* seed oil for 24 h, the inhibition rates for *Propionibacterium acnes*, *Staphylococcus aureus*, and *Candida albicans* reached 99%.

Table 3. Antimicrobial activity of *Sapindus mukorossi* seed oil extract.

Microorganism	Inactivation Rate [a] (%)
Propionibacterium acnes	>99.99
Staphylococcus aureus	>99.99
Candida albicans	99.9

[a] The inactivation rate (%) = $[1 - (CFU_{sample}/CFU_{control})] \times 100$.

2.4. Anti-Inflammatory Testing

As shown in Figure 3, *S. mukorossi* seed oil significantly affected nitric oxide (NO) release in the lipopolysaccharide (LPS)-treated cells. The NO release of the samples was normalized by comparing the measured data to the untreated samples. When the cells were treated with *N*-nitro-L-arginine-methyl ester (L-NAME), 21% NO release was noted compared to the control. When the cells were pretreated with 25 µg/mL *S. mukorossi* seed oil, NO release by the lipopolysaccharide (LPS)-treated RAW 264.7 cells was 92%. This value dramatically decreased to 46% when 500 µg/mL oil was used for pretreatment.

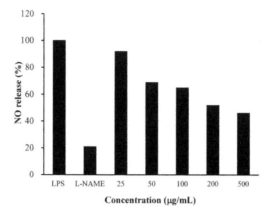

Figure 3. Nitric oxide (NO) release from the lipopolysaccharide (LPS)-treated RAW 264.7 cells decreased when the cells were pretreated with *S. mukorossi* seed oil. Data are from four independent experiments. The mean value of each group was normalized with LPS-only sample.

2.5. Cell Proliferation Assay

The in vitro cell experiments demonstrated that the cells treated with *S. mukorossi* oil exhibited a traditional growth curve. The seed oil-extract significantly enhanced the viability of the tested CCD-966SK cells on day 2 (Figure 4) ($p < 0.05$). After three days of culture, *S. mukorossi* seed oil showed no proliferation or cytotoxicity effect on the cultured cells. The scratch assay results showed that treatment with *S. mukorossi* seed oil enhanced the CCD-966SK cell migration toward the scratched area (Figure 5). The microscopic images revealed that the leading cells at the wound edge oriented towards the wound area 6 h after the scratch trauma was inflicted (Figure 5b,f). Additionally, the quantitative analysis of wound closure (Figure 6) showed that wound closure rate for the oil-treated cells was 24.73%, which is higher than that of the control cells (6.45%) at 6 h. After a 12-hour culture period, the border of the wound became unclear. In addition, a greater number of migrating cells were noted at the scratch edge in the oil-treated sample than in the control group (Figure 5c,g). The oil-treated cells demonstrated a 3.36-fold higher percentage of scratch-width closure than the control cells. At 24 h, the migrating cells had moved to the center of the scratch wound (Figure 5d,h). The oil-treated CCD-966SK cells (Figure 5h) displayed significantly increased healing ability compared to the controls (Figure 5d). The wound width closure of the oil-treated group after 24 h of culture was 82.79%, which was 1.88-fold greater than that of the controls (44.08%) (Figure 6).

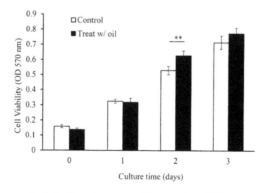

Figure 4. *S. mukorossi* seed oil significantly increased the viability of CCD-966SK cells by day 2. Data are presented as the mean ± SD. ** $p < 0.01$.

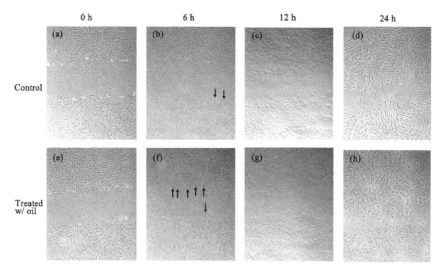

Figure 5. The control CCD-966SK cultured with *S. mukorossi* seed oil free medium at 0, 6, 12, and 24 h (**a–d**). *S. mukorossi* seed oil exhibits obvious effect on migration at 0, 6, 12, and 24 h (**e–h**) after incubation. The leading cells at the wound edge oriented toward the wound area 6 h after the scratch trauma was inflicted (black arrows).

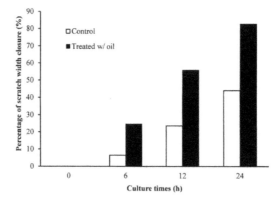

Figure 6. The percentage of scratch-width closure measured by quantifying the images of the scratch assay at 0, 6, 12, and 24 h after incubation. Data are from four independent experiments. The mean value of each group was normalized with LPS-only sample.

2.6. In Vivo Wound Healing Experiment

The in vivo skin wound healing activity of *S. mukorossi* seed oil extract is shown in Figure 7. Two days after the skin excision, the typical healing responses inside the epidermis of the wound were obviously better in the group treated with *S. mukorossi* seed oil. During the initial two days of healing, the wounds of both the oil-treated and control groups developed hyperemic areas with well-defined borders that preserved the rectangular shape of the wound. In the oil-treated group, the wounds underwent accelerated healing with the growth of granulation tissue, absence of edema, and lower secretions than in the untreated control group. In addition, a quantitative assessment demonstrated that the in vivo experimental wounds treated with *S. mukorossi* seed oil (74.14 ± 1.64%) showed a statistically significant reduction ($p < 0.05$) in the wound area compared to that of the control wounds (91.02% ± 7.44%) (Figure 8). This statistically significant reduction in wound size was observed at all the experimental time points.

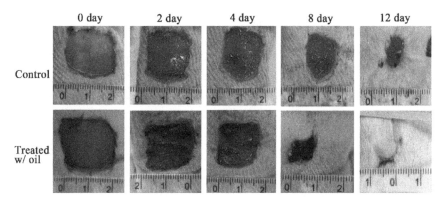

Figure 7. Photomicrographs of the wounds in rats after topical treatment with and without *S. mukorossi* seed oil on days 0, 2, 4, 6, 8, 10, and 12.

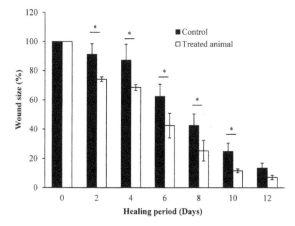

Figure 8. Quantification of the wound size in the rats treated with and without *S. mukorossi* seed oil. Data are presented as the mean ± SD. * $p < 0.05$.

On day 8, the wounds had lost their geometrical shape whether or not they had been treated with *S. mukorossi* seed oil. However, compared to the control group, rats treated with *S. mukorossi* seed oil demonstrated no secretion in the wound bed. In addition, the wound became dark brown, dry, and smaller than those in the control group. The wound size of the oil-treated rats decreased significantly to 25.30% ± 6.98% (Figure 8), which is almost half that of the untreated control wounds (42.45% ± 7.95%) ($p < 0.05$).

On the 12th day, the untreated wounds also demonstrated wound beds without secretions and hyperemia (Figure 7). The brown color and dryness of the untreated wounds on day 12 were similar to the oil-treated wounds on the 8th day. However, the treated wounds showed complete resurfacing of the epithelial layer, and the wound was almost entirely covered by hair. At this healing stage, the average percentage wound size for the control and oil-treated wounds was 13.55% ± 3.40% and 7.20% ± 1.52%, respectively (Figure 8).

3. Discussion

Wound healing is a series of processes that involves control of inflammation, proliferation, and new tissue remodeling [16,25,26]. Among these processes, inflammation is the first step in the healing response after tissue injury. In addition, cell proliferation and migration are essential responses for re-epithelialization and skin remodeling during the healing process [26]. Our results showed an improvement in CCD-966SK cell proliferation (Figure 4) and migration (Figures 5 and 6) induced by *S. mukorossi* seed oil. Similar healing effects were also observed in the artificial wound in the rat model (Figures 7 and 8). These phenomena are similar to those reported by de Moura Sperotto et al. who tested the wound healing effects of a *Plantago australis* extract and concluded that such plant extracts have an action at the end of the proliferative phase or in maturation phase that promotes the normalization of the tissue [26].

The phytochemical characteristics of the *S. mukorossi* seed oil used in this study were determined by a series of tests. The GC-MS results show that the fatty acid contained in the *S. mukorossi* seeds oil was similar to that of previous reports [9,19,20]. The most significant phytochemical finding of the tested *S. mukorossi* seed oil is that it contains a substantial amount of unsaturated fatty acids, which account for 85.65% of all the fatty acids in the seed oil. Among these unsaturated fatty acids, 76.85% were monounsaturated fatty acids. It is reported that monounsaturated fatty acids may cover the skin barrier and act as permeability enhancers [16]. Accordingly, these fatty acids have been wildly used not only in cosmetology for daily care of the face and body but also in the acceleration of skin wound healing [27].

Interestingly, Table 1 shows that the main components of the monounsaturated fatty acids in *S. mukorossi* seed oil were oleic acid (52.46%) and eicosenic acid (23.71%). Since oleic acid strongly inhibited the production of NO at the wound site [16] and were positive for wounding healing, it is not a surprise that the tested *S. mukorossi* seed oil strongly promoted the skin wound healing process as shown in Figures 7 and 8. Except for monounsaturated FAs, linoleic acid also plays a role in maintaining the integrity of the skin barrier for maintaining water permeability. In Table 1, we show that the extracted *S. mukorossi* seed oil contains 7.2% linoleic acid and 23.71% eicosenic acid. Since both linoleic acid and eicosenic acid directly play a role as activators that enhance skin cell proliferation [16,27], they may also play a role in CCD-966SK cell proliferation and migration as shown in Figures 4 and 5.

The results of in vitro cell migration (Figures 5 and 6) and in vivo animal skin wound healing (Figures 7 and 8) showed that *S. mukorossi* seed oil enhanced skin wound healing. In 2018, Lin et al. reviewed the pharmacological and medical effects of several plant oils and concluded that the therapeutic benefits for skin wound healing of plant oils are provided by their antibacterial, anti-inflammatory, and antioxidant effects. We found that *S. mukorossi* seed oil is rich in β-sitosterol and δ-tocopherol (vitamin E) (Figure 2b,c). The total amount of β-sitosterol and δ-tocopherol in the *S. mukorossi* seed oil are 0.73% and 0.023%, respectively. These values are much higher than the analogous quantities in shea butter (0.5% for total sterols and 0.08% for total tocopherols) [28]. Since Shea butter is a famous anti-inflammatory and antioxidant plant seed extract used in the cosmetic industry because of its high percentage of unsaponifiable compounds (including phytosterols and tocopherol) [16,29], *S. mukorossi* seed oil could also have potential use in skin care.

β-Sitosterol is the major phytosterol in plant oils. It provides a biological function like cholesterol and provides pharmacological and biological activities useful for the treatment of various skin illnesses, such as swelling and erythema [22,30] because of its structural similarity to cholesterol [31,32]. It was reported as a safe chemical without undesirable side effects [32,33]. Several studies tested the effects of phytosterols as anti-inflammatory, angiogenic, and cell migration stimulators and have confirmed its positive effects on skin barrier recovery and skin wound repair [14,16,31,32,34,35]. Since the *S. mukorossi* seed oil contains abundant β-sitosterol, it also showed the potential to be a skin wound healing enhancer.

Bioactive plant oil extracted from fruit pulp always contains not only β-sitosterol but also vitamin E [16,27]. The primary role of vitamin E in plants is to provide antioxidant activity [16]. It is well known that the production of reactive oxygen species (ROS) during skin injuries inhibits the healing process by various biological mechanisms [14,36]. The topical use of vitamin E is to attenuate oxidative stress by inhibiting the production of oxidase and NO.

In this study, δ-tocopherol was also detected in considerable amounts in the extracted *S. mukorossi* seed oil extracts. Thus, in Figure 4, the addition of *S. mukorossi* seed oil significantly decreased the NO release in LPS-treated RAW 264.7 macrophage cells in a dose-dependent manner. Since β-sitosterol also stimulates antioxidant enzymes and plays a role in ROS scavenging, it is not surprising that *S. mukorossi* seed oil exhibits promising beneficial effects and improved skin wound healing (Figures 7 and 8). Rekik et al. also reported that the beneficial effect on skin wound healing and collagen synthesis of vitamin E and phytosterols is because these compounds prevent the damaging effects of free radicals and ensure the stability and integrity of biological membranes [14].

The mechanism of the antimicrobial activity of S. *mukorossi* seed oil shown in Table 3 is not fully understood. The most likely mechanism of the antimicrobial action of *S. mukorossi* seed oil is the β-sitosterol content because it is a potent antimicrobial agent at low concentrations [33]. In addition, it is reported that acidic plant oils are not conducive to the growth of bacteria, which require a neutral pH environment for growth [14,32]. Such an acidic environment also leads to the promotion of cell proliferation (Figure 4) and cell migration (Figures 5 and 6). These effects construct an ideal environment for fibroblast activity and collagen reorganization, with resulting acceleration of wound healing [14,37]. Since fibroblast proliferation and migration are vital steps in skin wound healing [12] when this phenomenon is considered in combination with the efficiency of skin wound healing shown in Figures 7 and 8, we suggest that S. *mukorossi* seed oil is a candidate agent for development as a skin treatment agent.

4. Materials and Methods

4.1. Chemicals and Reagents

The reference standards of the fatty acids β-sitosterol, δ-tocopherol, lipopolysaccharide (LPS), $CDCl_3$, Griess reagent (N5751) and N-nitro-L-arginine-methyl ester (L-NAME) were purchased from Sigma-Aldrich (St. Louis, MO, USA). Methanol, tetrahydrofuran acetonitrile, sodium hydroxide, and boron trifluoride/methanol were obtained from Fisher Scientific (Pittsburgh, PA, USA). DMEM (Dulbecco's modified Eagle medium), FBS (fetal bovine serum), trypsin-EDTA, L-glutamine, penicillin/streptomycin were obtained from HyClone (South Logan, UT, USA). The tetrazolium salt (MTT) kit was purchased from Roche Applied Science (Mannheim, Germany). Isoflurane was purchased from DS Pharma Animal Health Co. (Osaka, Japan).

4.2. Plant Material

The *S. mukorossi* seeds were purchased from He He Co. Ltd. (Taipei, Taiwan). Before the oil extraction, the seeds were cleaned under running tap water followed by rinsing with sterile distilled water and then dried in an oven at 40 °C for 72 h. The seeds were then crushed using a grinder, and the kernels were separated from their hard shells. As previously reported, the oil was extracted using a cold press method and was followed by filtering (0.45 μm pore size) [19]. The oil recovery rate from the kernels was about 30%.

4.3. Phytochemical Analysis of Kernel Oil

4.3.1. GC-MS Analysis

For the GC-MS analysis, the *S. mukorossi* seed-extracted oil was transesterified to produce fatty acid methyl esters (FAME). Briefly, 20 mg of extracted oil was mixed with 1 mL of 1 N sodium hydroxide to act as a catalyst. The mixture was then stirred vigorously using a magnetic stirrer at room temperature for 30 s. Then, for saponification, the mix was maintained at 80 °C for 15 min. Then, 1 mL of boron trifluoride in a methanol solution was added to the sample, and the mixture was shaken for 30 s. The mixture was then placed in a 110 °C dry bath for 15 min. After the sample had returned to room temperature, 1 mL of n-hexane was added to the solution. The polar layer was separated and used to inject into the GC-MS system (GCMS-QP2010, Shimadzu, Tokyo, Japan).

A BPX70 capillary column with a dimension of 30 m × 0.25 mm i.d. (0.25 μm film thickness) was used for oil composition separation. Helium was used as carrier gas at a pressure of 75 kPa. The sample was injected at a temperature set at 250 °C. The programmed temperature of the oven started at 120 °C and was held for 0.5 min for solvent delay, then increased at a rate of 10 °C/min to 180 °C, and then increased at a rate of 3 °C/min to 220 °C, followed by an increase of 30 °C/min to 260 °C and then, held for 5 min. The mass spectrometer was operated in the electron impact (EI) mode at 70 eV. The temperature of the ionization chamber was set at 200 °C. For identification of the analyzed constituents with various retention times, a library search of mass spectra was performed using NIST/EPA/NIH Mass Spectral Library.

4.3.2. HPLC Analysis

HPLC was performed to determine the content of β-sitosterol and δ-tocopherol in the *S. mukorossi* seed oil. The HPLC was equipped with a low-pressure mixing pump (L2130, Hitachi, Tokyo, Japan), controlled by a CBM-20A interface module (Shimadzu Technology, Kyoto, Japan), and had a UV detector (Waters 486, Waters Corporation, Milford, MA, US). The separation was achieved using a Mightysil RP-18 GP (250 mm × 4.6 mm i.d., Mightysil RP 18 GP Cica, Tokyo, Japan) at 30 °C. For the β-sitosterol analysis, the mobile phase consisted of 96% methanol, 3% tetrahydrofuran, and 1% deionized water. For δ-tocopherol detection, pure methanol was used as the mobile phase. For testing the two molecules, 20 μL of *S. mukorossi* seed oil were injected. The flow rates for the detection of β-sitosterol and δ-tocopherol were 0.5 mL/min and 0.5 mL/min, respectively. All the samples were monitored at a wavelength of 280 nm. The compounds were identified by comparing their retention times to those of authentic standards. The quantification was achieved using linear regression analysis.

4.4. Antimicrobial Assay

The antimicrobial effects of *S. mukorossi* seed oil were tested in this study. The procedure was modified from the Japanese Industrial Standard JIS Z 2801:2000. Several microorganisms (Bioresource Collection and Research Center, BCRC, Hsinchu, Taiwan) including two bacteria (*P. acnes*; ATCC 11827 and *S. aureus*; ATCC 6538P) and a fungus (*C. albicans*; ATCC 10231) that cause skin diseases. All selected microbes were cultured in their standard culture medium. For testing the antimicrobial activity of the oil, 0.1 mL oil was mixed and inoculated with 10 mL of each microorganism culture to a concentration of 10^7 colony-forming units (CFU)/mL at 25 °C for 24 h. After serial dilution, the three bacteria were swabbed uniformly across the agar surface of Petri plates. After 48 h incubation at 23 °C for *C. albicans* or 37 °C for the bacteria, the number of colonies on each plate was counted.

$$\text{Inactivation rate (\%)} = [1 - (\text{CFU}_{\text{sample}}/\text{CFU}_{\text{control}})] \times 100 \tag{1}$$

where $\text{CFU}_{\text{sample}}$ and $\text{CFU}_{\text{control}}$ are the colony numbers of the tested and control samples, respectively.

4.5. Anti-Inflammatory Test

To test the in vitro anti-inflammatory activity of *S. mukorossi* seed oil, we assessed the oil in LPS-induced RAW 264.7 cells. RAW 264.7 macrophage cells were seeded into a 96-well plate at a concentration of 4×10^5 cells/mL. The cells were maintained in Dulbecco's modified Eagle medium (DMEM) supplemented with 10% fetal bovine serum (FBS), and 1% penicillin/streptomycin and were cultured in an incubator at 37 °C and 5% CO_2. After pre-incubation of the cells for 24 h, cells were pretreated with the *S. mukorossi* seed oil with a series of concentrations ranging from 25 to 500 μg/mL for 1 h and were further stimulated with LPS (1 μg/mL) from *Escherichia coli* strain 055:B5 for 24 h.

N-nitro-L-arginine-methyl ester (L-NAME) at a concentration 1 mM was used as a positive control. The NO concentration produced by the RAW 264.7 cells was determined through the Griess assay. Briefly, an equal volume of Griess reagent was mixed with the culture supernatant, and color development was measured at 530 nm using a microplate reader (EZ Read 400, Biochrom, Holliston, MA, USA). Anti-inflammatory activity was presented in terms of NO production percentage.

4.6. In Vitro Skin Cell Analysis

4.6.1. Cell Proliferation Assay

For testing the proliferation effect of the *S. mukorossi* seed oil on skin cells, a cell viability assay was performed according to a previous study [36]. The human skin fibroblast cell line CCD-966SK (ATCC CRL-1881) was used for this in vitro cell analysis. The cells were seeded in 24-well plates at a concentration of 2×10^4 cells/mL and were maintained in DMEM supplemented with 10% FBS and 1% penicillin/streptomycin. The cells were then incubated in an environment of 5% CO_2 at 37 °C and 100% humidity. The viability of the CCD-966SK cells exposed to *S. mukorossi* seed oil at a concentration of 200 µg/mL was evaluated after three days of incubation. The cell viability was assessed using the tetrazolium salt (MTT) method. After the cells were incubated with the tetrazolium salt for 4 h, 500 µL of DMSO were added to solubilize the formazan dye overnight. Since no toxic effects were observed on the cells, the emulsifier polyoxyethylene sorbitan mono-oleate (Tween 80) was employed as the delivery vehicle [38]. The optical density was determined using a microplate reader (EZ Read 400, Biochrom, Holliston, MA, USA) at 570 and 690 nm.

4.6.2. Scratch Wound Healing Test

The effect of *S. mukorossi* seed oil on cell migration behavior and wounded healing activity was assessed using scratch tests. Before the test, 2×10^4 cells/mL CCD-966SK cells were cultured in 6-well Petri dishes and incubated in 5% CO_2 at 37 °C and 100% humidity. When the cells reached confluence, they were starved overnight. A 1000-µL pipette tip was used to create a wound across the center of the culture dish. The scratched cells were washed with fresh medium to remove any loose or dead cells followed by exposure to 25 µg/mL *S. mukorossi* seed oil. Cells cultured with fresh medium but without oil served as a control group. For both groups, cell migration photographs were taken at 4× magnification using a bright-field illumination microscope (Eclipse TS100, Nikon Corporation, Tokyo, Japan). The images were captured by a digital camera (SPOT Idea, Diagnostic Instruments, Inc., Sterling Heights, MI, USA). The images were taken immediately (0 h) and after 6 and 12 h at five different sites from each wound area (gap). The captured images were analyzed using ImageJ software (National Institutes of Health, Bethesda, MD, USA) to evaluate the percentage of scratch closure, the percentage of gap closure was measured and compared with the results obtained before treatment (day 0) using the following formula [39]:

$$[(A_{0h} - A_{\Delta h})/A_{0h}] \times 100\% \qquad (2)$$

where A_{0h} is the scratch area at the beginning of the culture period, and $A_{\Delta h}$ is the scratch area after a certain culture period. The increase in the percentage of the closed area reflects the migration of cells.

4.7. Wound Healing Activity Test

Healthy male Sprague-Dawley (SD) rats weighing 210–290 g were used to assess the effects of *S. mukorossi* seed oil on skin wound healing. The rats were obtained from the Laboratory Animal Center at the National Applied Research Laboratories (Hsinchu, Taiwan). The animals were kept in hygienic cages during the experimental period. The environment was maintained with a 12-hour light/dark cycle, a temperature at 21 °C, and a humidity of 60% to 70%. The study protocol and procedures were reviewed and approved by the Institution Animal Care and Use Committee or Panel (IACUC

Approval No. L10708, 16 October 2018, and all efforts were made to minimize animal number and suffering to produce reliable scientific data.

The wound healing experimental procedure was performed according to a previous study [10,40]. A carboxymethyl cellulose (CMC)/hyaluronic acid (HA)/sodium alginate (SA) hydrogel [41,42] was prepared on one side of a non-woven fabric for releasing the extracted *S. mukorossi* seed oil. The ratio of the CMC, HA, and SA in the hydrogels was 1:3:12. Before the study, the rats' backs were one-way clipped (5 × 5 cm) with an electric animal shaver and the disinfected with 75% alcohol. Then, the rats were anesthetized with 5% isoflurane in an induction chamber. Before the experiment, one linear wound with an area of 2 × 2 cm was made by excising the skin on the back of the rat using sterile scissors.

Eight SD rats were randomly divided into two groups. For the tested group, the wound sites of the rats were covered with the prepared oil-hydrogel and were wrapped with porous bandages. The oil-free hydrogel was applied to the wounds of the control animals. The covered hydrogel was replaced every two days during the 12-day experiment. The rats were housed individually after wounding. For the evaluation of the progressive change in the wounded area, the wounds were photographed every two days with a digital camera. The wound area was measured using ImageJ software (National Institutes of Health, Bethesda, MD, USA). The wound area was determined by measuring the mass of the transparent paper cut to the shape of the wound. The wound contraction was expressed as a percentage reduction of the original cut size. The percentages of wound size were determined by calculating the ratio between the measured wound area and the original wound area.

4.8. Statistical Analysis

The results are presented as mean ± standard deviation (SD), and the comparison between groups was analyzed using the Student t-test. A p value less than 0.05 was considered statistically significant.

5. Conclusions

Although various medicinal plant oils are used to treat different kinds of wounds, the scientific evidence about whether *S. mukorossi* seed oil also provides benefits for skin wound healing is incomplete. The present investigation, for the first time, indicates that *S. mukorossi* seed oil extract shows remarkable antibacterial, anti-inflammatory, antioxidant, cell proliferation, cell migration stimulation, and skin wound healing. The total amount of δ-tocopherol and β-sitosterol in the *S. mukorossi* seed oil was 73.9 ± 23.6 μg/mL (in 1% oil) and 232.64 ± 4.5 μg/mL, respectively. The inhibition effect of 1% *S. mukorossi* seed oil on *P. acnes*, *S. aureus*, and *C. albicans* was 99%. Addition of 500 μg/mL *S. mukorossi* seed oil resulted in a reduction of NO release by the lipopolysaccharide (LPS)-treated RAW 264.7 cells to 46%. The wound size of the oil-treated rats decreased significantly to almost 50% when *S. mukorossi* seed oil rich membrane was used as a dressing material. In accordance with our results, we suggest that *S. mukorossi* seed oil has the potential for development to promote skin wound healing. Since the use of *S. mukorossi* seed oil involves a strategy of using a waste as source of bioactive compounds, it can conduct a cost benefit for skin care applications.

Author Contributions: C.-C.C., H.-M.H. designed the experiments; K.-Y.H., C.-J.N., L.-G.C. performed the experiments; W.-J.C., H.-M.H. analyzed the data; C.-C.C., H.-M.H. contributed reagents/materials/analysis tools; C.-C.C., H.-M.H. wrote the paper.

Funding: This research received no external funding.

Conflicts of Interest: The authors declare no conflict of interest.

Abbreviations

GC-MS	gas chromatography-mass spectrometry
HPLC	high-pressure liquid chromatography
CMC	carboxymethyl cellulose
HA	hyaluronic acid
SA	sodium alginate
NO	nitric oxide
LPS	lipopolysaccharide
L-NAME	N(ω)-nitro-L-arginine methylester hydrochloride
NOS	nitric oxide synthase
FAME	fatty acid methyl esters
MTT	tetrazolium salt
DMEM	Dulbecco's modified Eagle medium
FBS	fetal bovine serum
NIST	National Institute of Standards and Technology
EPA	Environmental Protection Agency
NIH	National Institutes of Health

References

1. Chhetri, A.B.; Tango, M.S.; Budge, S.M.; Watts, K.H.; Islam, M.R. Non-edible plant oils as new sources for biodiesel production. *Int. J. Mol. Sci.* **2008**, *9*, 169–180. [CrossRef]
2. Sonawane, S.M.; Sonawane, H. A review of recent and current research studies on the biological and pharmalogical activities of *Sapindus mukorossi*. *Int.J. Interdiscip. Res. Innov.* **2015**, *3*, 85–95.
3. Anjali, R.S.; Divya, J. *Sapindus mukorossi*: A review article. *Pharm. Innov.* **2018**, *7*, 470–472.
4. Kuo, Y.H.; Huang, H.C.; Kuo, L.M.Y.; Hsu, Y.W.; Lee, K.H.; Chang, F.R.; Wu, Y.C. New dammarane-type saponins from the galls of *Sapindus mukorossi*. *J. Agric. Food Chem.* **2005**, *53*, 4722–4727. [CrossRef]
5. Yin, S.W.; Chen, J.H.; Sun, S.D.; Tang, C.H.; Yang, X.Q.; Wen, Q.B.; Qi, J.R. Physicochemical and structural characterisation of protein isolate, globulin and albumin from soapnut seeds (*Sapindus mukorossi* Gaertn.). *Food Chem.* **2011**, *128*, 420–426. [CrossRef] [PubMed]
6. Sharma, A.; Sati, S.C.; Sati, O.P.; Sati, M.D.; Kothiyal, S.K. Triterpenoid Saponins from the Pericarps of *Sapindus mukorossi*. *J. Chem.* **2013**. Article ID 613190.
7. Upadhyay, A.; Singh, D.K. Pharmacological effects of *Sapindus mukorossi*. *Rev. Inst. Med. Trop.* **2012**, *54*, 273–280. [CrossRef]
8. Suhagia, B.N.; Rathod, I.S.; Sindhu, S. *Sapindus mukorossi* (Areetha): An Overview. *Int. J. Pharm. Sci.* **2011**, *2*, 1905–1913.
9. Shah, M.A.H.; Dutta, K.; Deka, D.C. Fatty acid composition of *Sapindus mukorossi* seed oil. *Adv. Appl. Sci. Res.* **2014**, *5*, 43–50.
10. Kumar, P.; Vijeth, P.F.; Raju, K. A Study on performance and emission characteristics of cotton seed methyl ester, *Sapindous mukorossi* seed oil, and diesel blends on CI engine. *Energy Power* **2015**, *5*, 10–14.
11. Mahar, K.S.; Rana, T.S.; Ranade, S.A. Molecular analyses of genetic variability in soap nut (*Sapindus mukorossi* Gaertn.). *Ind. Crop. Prod.* **2011**, *34*, 1111–1118. [CrossRef]
12. Chen, Y.H.; Chiang, T.H.; Chen, J.H. Properties of soapnut (*Sapindus mukorossi*) oil biodiesel and its blends with diesel. *Biom. Bioen.* **2013**, *52*, 15–21. [CrossRef]
13. Demirbas, A.; Bafail, A.; Ahmad, W.; Sheikh, M. Biodiesel production from non-edible plant oils. *Energ. Explor. Exploit.* **2016**, *34*, 290–318. [CrossRef]
14. Rekik, D.M.; Khedir, S.B.; Moalla, K.K.; Kammoun, N.G.; Rebai, T.; Sahnoun, Z. Evaluation of wound healing properties of grape seed, sesame, and fenugreek oils. *Evid.-Based Complementary Altern. Med.* **2016**. Article ID 7965689.
15. Dakiche, H.; Khali, M.; Boutoumi, H. Phytochemical characterization and *in vivo* anti-inflammatory and wound-healing activities of *Argania spinosa* (L.) skeels seed oil. *Rec. Nat. Prod.* **2017**, *11*, 171–184.
16. Lin, T.Z.; Zhong, L.; Santiago, J.L. Anti-inflammatory and skin barrier repair effects of topical application of some plant oils. *Int. J. Mol. Sci.* **2018**, *19*, 70. [CrossRef]

17. Pai, A.; Rajendra, M.J.; Rao, J.S.; Sudhakar, M. Evaluation of anti microbial, anti oxidant activity and estimation of total flavonoid content in *Sapindus trifoliatus* seed extracts. *Int. J. Pharm. Pharm. Sci.* **2014**, *6*, 550–554.

18. Rodríguez-Hernández, D.; Demuner, A.J.; Montanari, R.M.; Barbosa, L.C.A. Cyanolipids from *Sapindus saponaria* L. seeds oil. *Bol. Latinoam. Caribe Plantas Med. Aromát.* **2016**, *15*, 364–372.

19. Jadon, I.S.; Shukla, R.N.; Goshwami, G.C. Biodiesel from *Sapindus mukorossi* and *Jatropha oils* by transesterification. *Int. J. Pharm. Sci. Invent.* **2012**, *2*, 26–40.

20. Mikolajczak, K.L. Cyanolipids. *Prog. Chm. Fors Orher Lipids.* **1977**, *15*, 97–130. [CrossRef]

21. Srinivasarao, M.; Lakshminarasu, M.; Anjum, A.; Ibrahim, M. Comparative study on phytochemical, antimicrobial and antioxidant activity of *Sapindus mukorossi* Gaertn. and *Rheum emodi* Wall. ex Meissn.: *In vitro* studies. *Ann. Phytomed.* **2015**, *4*, 93–97.

22. Dweck, A.C. Isoflavones, phytohormones and phytosterols. *J. Appl. Cosmetol.* **2006**, *24*, 17–33.

23. Marques, S.R.; Peixoto, C.A.; Messias, J.B.; de Albuquerque, A.R.; da Silva, V.A., Jr. The effects of topical application of sunflower-seed oil on open wound healing in lambs. *Acta Cir. Bras.* **2004**, *19*, 196–209. [CrossRef]

24. Wang, Y.F.; Que, H.F.; Wang, Y.J.; Cui, X.J. Chinese herbal medicines for treating skin and soft-tissue infections. *Cochrane Database Syst. Rev.* **2014**, *25*, CD010619. [CrossRef] [PubMed]

25. Monsuur, H.N.; Boink, M.A.; Weijers, E.M.; Roffel, S.; Breetveld, M.; Gefen, A.; van den Broek, L.J.; Gibbs, S. Methods to study differences in cell mobility during skin wound healing *in vitro*. *J. Biomech.* **2016**, *49*, 1381–1387. [CrossRef]

26. De Moura Sperotto, N.D.; Steffens, L.; Veríssimo, R.M.; Henn, J.G.; Péres, V.F.; Vianna, P.; Chies, J.A.B.; Roehe, A.; Saffi, J.; Moura, D.J. Wound healing and anti-inflammatory activities induced by a *Plantago australis* hydroethanolic extract standardized in verbascoside. *J. Ethnopharmacol.* **2018**, *225*, 178–188. [CrossRef]

27. Zielińska, A.; Nowak, I. Fatty acids in vegetable oils and their importance in cosmetic industry. *Chemik* **2014**, *68*, 103–110.

28. Israel, M.O. Shea Butter: An opposite replacement for trans fat in margarine. *J. Nutr. Food Sci.* **2015**, *S11*, 001. [CrossRef]

29. Alander, J. Shea butter—a multifunctional ingredient for food and cosmetics. *Lipid Technol.* **2004**, *16*, 202–205.

30. Prieto, J.M.; Recio, M.C.; Giner, R.M. Anti-inflammatory activity of β-sitosterol in a model of oxazolone induced contact-delayed-type hypersensitivity. *Bol. Latinoam. Caribe Plant. Med. Aromat.* **2006**, *5*, 57–62.

31. Puglia, C.; Bonina, F. *In vivo* spectrophotometric evaluation of skin barrier recovery after topical application of soybean phytosterols. *J. Cosmet. Sci.* **2008**, *59*, 217–224. [PubMed]

32. Saeidnia, S.; Manayi, A.; Gohari, A.R.; Abdollahi, M. The story of beta-sitosterol—A review. *Eur. J. Med. Plants* **2014**, *4*, 590–609. [CrossRef]

33. Sen, A.; Dhavan, P.; Khukla, K.K.; Singh, S.; Tejovathi, G. Analysis of IR, NMR and antimicrobial activity of β-sitosterol isolated from *Momordica charantia*. *Sci. Secure J. Biotechnol.* **2012**, *1*, 9–13.

34. Moon, E.J.; Lee, Y.M.; Lee, O.H.; Lee, M.J.; Lee, S.K.; Chung, M.H.; Park, Y.I.; Sung, C.K.; Choi, J.S.; Kim, K.W. A novel angiogenic factor derived from Aloe vera gel: beta-sitosterol, a plant sterol. *Angiogenesis* **1999**, *3*, 117–123. [CrossRef]

35. De Castro Campos Pinto, N.; Cassini-Vieira, P.; Souza-Fagundes, E.M.; Barcelos, L.S.; Castañon, M.C.M.N.; Scio, E. *Pereskia aculeata* Miller leaves accelerate excisional wound healing in mice. *J. Ethnopharmacol.* **2016**, *194*, 131–136. [CrossRef]

36. Tsai, M.L.; Huang, H.P.; Hsu, J.D.; Lai, Y.R.; Hsiao, Y.P.; Lu, F.J.; Chang, H.R. Topical *N*-acetylcysteine accelerates wound healing *in vitro* and *in vivo* via the PKC/Stat3 Pathway. *Int. J. Mol. Sci.* **2014**, *15*, 7563–7578. [CrossRef]

37. Mwipatayi, B.P.; Angel, D.; Norrish, J.; Hamilton, M.J.; Scott, A.; Sieunarine, K. The use of honey in chronic leg ulcers: a literature review. *Primary Intention* **2004**, *12*, 107–112.

38. O'Sullivan, S.M.; Woods, J.A.; O'Brien, N.M. Use of Tween 40 and Tween 80 to deliver a mixture of phytochemicals to human colonic adenocarcinoma cell (CaCo-2) monolayers. *Br. J. Nutr.* **2004**, *91*, 757–764. [CrossRef]

39. Lew, W.Z.; Feng, S.W.; Lin, C.T.; Huang, H.M. Use of 0.4-Tesla static magnetic field to promote reparative dentin formation of dental pulp stems cells through activation of p38 MAPK signaling pathway. *Int. Endod. J.* **2019**, *52*, 28–43. [CrossRef]

40. Kumar, S.; Lakshmi, P.K.; Sah, C.; Pawar, R.S. *Sida cordifolia* accelerates wound healing process delayed by dexamethasone in rats: Effect on ROS and probable mechanism of action. *J. Ethnopharmacol.* **2019**, *235*, 279–292. [CrossRef]
41. Zhou, Z.; Chen, J.; Peng, C.; Huang, T.; Zhou, H.; Ou, B.; Chen, J.; Liu, Q.; He, S.; Cao, D.; et al. Fabrication and physical properties of gelatin/sodium alginate/hyaluronic acid composite wound dressing hydrogel. *J. Macromol. Sci. A* **2014**, *51*, 318–325. [CrossRef]
42. Huang, Y.C.; Huang, K.U.; Yang, B.Y.; Ko, C.H.; Huang, H.M. Fabrication of novel hydrogel with berberine-enriched carboxymethylcellulose and hyaluronic acid as an anti-inflammatory barrier membrane. *BioMed. Res. Int.* **2016**, *2016*, 3640182. [CrossRef]

International Journal of
Molecular Sciences

Article

Glucose Tolerance-Improving Activity of Helichrysoside in Mice and Its Structural Requirements for Promoting Glucose and Lipid Metabolism

Toshio Morikawa [1,2,*,†], Akifumi Nagatomo [1,†], Takahiro Oka [1], Yoshinobu Miki [1], Norihisa Taira [1], Megumi Shibano-Kitahara [1], Yuichiro Hori [1], Osamu Muraoka [1,2] and Kiyofumi Ninomiya [1,2]

[1] Pharmaceutical Research and Technology Institute, Kindai University, 3-4-1 Kowakae, Higashi-osaka, Osaka 577-8502, Japan; a-nagatomo@jintan.co.jp (A.N.); tmykoka0325@gmail.com (T.O.); sanmokuhoushin@hokuriku.me (Y.M.); Taira_Norihisa@seiwakasei.co.jp (N.T.); kabazakura2@yahoo.co.jp (M.S.-K.); hori.yuichiro.0208@gmail.com (Y.H.); muraoka@phar.kindai.ac.jp (O.M.); ninomiya@phar.kindai.ac.jp (K.N.)
[2] Antiaging Center, Kindai University, 3-4-1 Kowakae, Higashi-osaka, Osaka 577-8502, Japan
*   Correspondence: morikawa@kindai.ac.jp; Tel.: +81-6-4307-4306; Fax: +81-6-6729-3577
†   These authors contributed equally to this work.

Received: 21 October 2019; Accepted: 13 December 2019; Published: 14 December 2019

Abstract: An acylated flavonol glycoside, helichrysoside, at a dose of 10 mg/kg/day per os for 14 days, improved the glucose tolerance in mice without affecting the food intake, visceral fat weight, liver weight, and other plasma parameters. In this study, using hepatoblastoma-derived HepG2 cells, helichrysoside, *trans*-tiliroside, and kaempferol 3-O-β-D-glucopyranoside enhanced glucose consumption from the medium, but their aglycones and p-coumaric acid did not show this activity. In addition, several acylated flavonol glycosides were synthesized to clarify the structural requirements for lipid metabolism using HepG2 cells. The results showed that helichrysoside and related analogs significantly inhibited triglyceride (TG) accumulation in these cells. The inhibition by helichrysoside was more potent than that by other acylated flavonol glycosides, related flavonol glycosides, and organic acids. As for the TG metabolism-promoting activity in high glucose-pretreated HepG2 cells, helichrysoside, related analogs, and their aglycones were found to significantly reduce the TG contents in HepG2 cells. However, the desacyl flavonol glycosides and organic acids derived from the acyl groups did not exhibit an inhibitory impact on the TG contents in HepG2 cells. These results suggest that the existence of the acyl moiety at the 6″ position in the D-glucopyranosyl part is essential for glucose and lipid metabolism-promoting activities.

Keywords: helichrysoside; acylated flavonol glycoside; glucose tolerance-improving activity; lipid metabolism-promoting activity

1. Introduction

Flavonoids are one of the most abundant classes of secondary plant metabolites. Flavonoids are biosynthesized by the shikimate and acetate-malonate pathways and are comprised of compounds that possess a common C_6-C_3-C_6 skeleton, where two aromatic rings (named ring A and B) are linked via a heterocyclic 4H-pyrane ring (ring C). Modification of the 15-carbon skeleton through different oxidation levels and substituents to ring C gives rise to different classes of flavonoids, such as flavones, flavonols, flavanones, chalcones, dihydroflavonols (flavanonols), isoflavones, aurones, anthocyanidins, leucoanthocyanidines (flavan-3,4-diols), and flavan-3-ols. They naturally occur in not only aglycone forms, but also as glycosylated and/or acylated derivatives and oligomeric and polymeric structures, such as the flavan-3-ol-derived condensed tannins and proanthocyanidins [1–5]. Flavonoid health benefits are well-recognized, such as their antioxidant properties, properties for weight management, cardiovascular disease protection, anti-allergic activity, vascular fragility, prevention of viral and bacterial infections, anti-inflammatory activity, age-related neurodegenerative disease prevention, anti-platelet aggregation effects, and cancer protection, etc. [2–8]. Our studies on bioactive constituents from medicinal and/or food resources have reported several bio-functional properties of flavonoids. These included aldose reductase inhibitory [9–12], anti-platelet aggregation [9], anti-allergic [12–14], anti-inflammatory [12,15–18], aminopeptidase N inhibition [11,17,19], hepatoprotective [20], gastroprotective [21], melanogenesis inhibition [22], and dipeptidyl peptidase-IV inhibitory [23] activities. This paper deals with the practical synthesis and glucose tolerance-improving activity of helichrysoside (**1** = quercetin 3-*O*-(6''-*O*-*trans*-*p*-coumaroyl)-β-D-glucopyranoside), isolated from *Helichrysum kraussii* and *H. stoechas* [24,25] by other research groups. Furthermore, synthetic studies of the related analogs of **1** (**2–15**, Figure 1) were also carried out, as well as characterization of its structural requirements for glucose and lipid metabolism in HepG2 cells. In our previous report, an acylated flavonol glycoside, *trans*-tiliroside (**16** = kaempferol 3-*O*-(6''-*O*-*trans*-*p*-coumaroyl)-β-D-glucopyranoside), isolated from the fruit of *Rosa canina*, was found to suppress visceral fat weight gain and improve glucose tolerance in mice [26]. The structures of **1** and **16** are similar: the former has a *p*-coumaroyl ester at the 6-position in the β-D-glucopyranosyl moiety of quercetin 3-*O*-β-D-glucopyranoside (isoquercitrin, **17**), while the latter has the common acyl group at the same position of kaempferol 3-*O*-β-D-glucopyranoside (**18**).

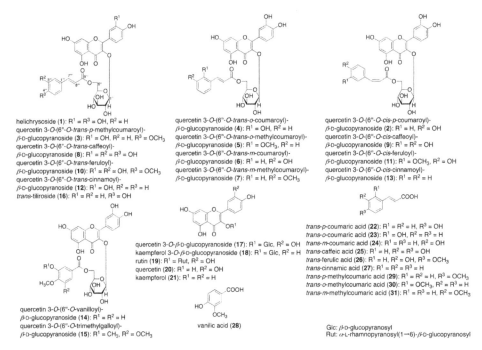

Figure 1. Structures of acylated flavonol glycosides (**1–16**) and related compounds (**17–31**).

2. Results and Discussion

2.1. Synthesis of Acylated Flavonol Glycosides (1–15)

Rutin (**19** = quercetin 3-*O*-α-L-rhamnopyraniosyl(1→6)-β-D-glucopyranoside), constructed with quercetin (**20**) as an aglycone, is one of the most widely distributed naturally occurring flavonoids and has been reported to have several pharmacological activities, such as anti-oxidant, anti-inflammatory, anti-diabetic, anti-adipogenic, and neuroprotective effects, and has been used in hormone therapy [27–30]. In order to achieve the practical synthesis of **1** from **19**, the most inexpensive and commercially available flavonoid, the optimal conditions for enzymatic hydrolysis of the terminal rhamnosyl part were investigated. Therefore, the practical derivation from **19** to **17** was carried out using naringinase (from *Penicillium decumbens*) under an optimal pH and temperature (pH 7 and 50 °C), and the time course of the reaction mixture was monitored by high performance liquid chromatography (HPLC) analysis (Figure S1 and Table S1). As shown in Table 1, the highest content of **17** in the reaction mixture of 2 h was observed. By applying these conditions, a large-scale derivation of **17** (6.50 g and 14.0 mmol, 56.9%) from **19** (15.0 g and 24.6 mmol) was achieved.

Table 1. Peak area ratio of rutin (**19**), quercetin 3-*O*-β–D-glucopyranoside (**17**), and quercetin (**20**) in the reaction mixture.

Reaction Time	Peak Area (%)		
	Rutin (19)	Quercetin 3-*O*-Glc (17)	Quercetin (20)
0 min	99.1	0.0	0.0
5 min	96.6	1.6	0.7
30 min	60.8	30.7	7.5
1 h	29.7	46.3	22.9
1.5 h	16.4	50.1	32.6
2 h	6.3	49.6	43.2
3 h	0.0	40.8	57.7
4.5 h	0.0	25.9	72.5
8 h	0.0	9.0	89.4
24 h	0.0	1.5	95.5

Linearities for **19**, **17**, and **20** in the HPLC analytical condition were calculated as shown in Table S1.

Synthesis of the acylated flavonol glycosides, including helichrysoside (**1–15**) from **17**, using the corresponding acylation reactions, was carried out. Therefore, protection of a phenol group in *p*-coumaric acid (**22**) with *tert*-butyldiphenylsilyl chloride (TBDPSCl) yielded the corresponding silyl ether, **22a**. Acylation of **17** with **22a** in the presence of 1-ethyl-3-(3-dimethylaminopropyl)carbodiimide hydrochloride (EDC·HCl) and 4-dimethylaminopyridine (4-DMAP) in pyridine, followed by deprotection with tetrabutylammonium fluoride (TBAF), provided **1** with a 36.9% yield (Scheme 1).

In a similar procedure to that of **1** [31,32], compounds **3**, **4**, **5**, **6**, **7** [33], **8** [34], **10** [33], **12** [33,35,36], **14**, and **15** were synthesized with **17** and the corresponding organic acids. The *cis*-isomer of **1**, quercetin 3-*O*-(6″-*O*-*cis*-*p*-coumaroyl)-β-D-glucopyranoside (**2**), was derived under a UV lamp in a methanol solution of **1**. Using a similar procedure, quercetin 3-*O*-(6″-*O*-*cis*-caffeoyl)-β-D-glucopyranoside (**9**), quercetin 3-*O*-(6″-*O*-*cis*-feruloyl)-β-D-glucopyranoside (**11**), and quercetin 3-*O*-(6″-*O*-*cis*-cinnamoyl)-β-D-glucopyranoside (**13**) were also isomerized from **8**, **10**, and **12**, respectively. Among these synthetic products, known compounds (**1**, **7**, **8**, **10**, and **12**) were identified by a comparison of their physicochemical data with those of authentic samples or with reported values. The structural determination of new compounds (**2–6**, **9**, **11**, and **13–15**) was elucidated on their spectroscopic properties, including the ^{13}C-NMR data, as shown in Table S2.

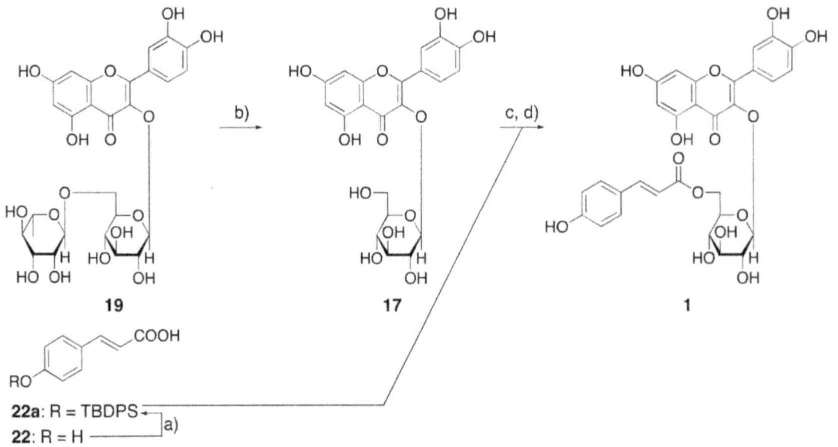

Scheme 1. Reagents and conditions: (**a**) *tert*-butyldiphenylsilyl chloride (TBDPSCl), imidazole/*N*,*N*-dimethylformamide (DMF), 40 °C, 16 h, 76.5%; (**b**) naringinase/H$_2$O, 50 °C, 2 h, 56.9%; (**c**) **22a** (1.2 eq), 1-ethyl-3-(3-dimethylaminopropyl)carbodiimide hydrochloride (EDC·HCl), 4-dimethylaminopyridine (4-DMAP)/pyridine, 50 °C, 12 h; (**d**) tetrabutylammonium fluoride (TBAF)/tetrahydrofuran (THF), r.t., 1 h, 36.9% (two steps from **17**).

*2.2. Effect of Helichrysoside (**1**) on the Liver Triglyceride (TG) Content and Glucose Tolerance Test after 14 Days of Administration in Mice*

Diabetes is characterized by a high incidence of cardiovascular disease and poor control of hyperglycemia caused by insulin resistance (IR). IR can be defined as the inability of insulin to stimulate glucose uptake into the liver, skeletal muscle, or adipose tissue. Hyperglycemia is an important factor contributing to the development of atherosclerosis, and is relevant to the pathophysiology of late diabetic complications. Therefore, improving IR may form part of the strategy for the prevention and management of cardiovascular disease in diabetes [37,38]. We have reported that several anti-diabetogenic therapeutic candidates obtained from natural resources, such as acylated flavonol glycosides from *Sinocrassula indica* [39]; saponins from *Borassus flabellifer* [40]; and thiosugars from *Salacia reticulata*, *S. oblonga*, and *S. chinensis* [41–46], showed the inhibition of postprandial hyperglycemia and/or improvement of glucose tolerance in sugar-loaded animal models. As mentioned above, the structure of **16** isolated from *R. canina* [26] is quite similar to **1**, so we presumed that **1** also exhibits similar anti-diabetogenic activity to **16** in an in vivo study. To continue our search for new candidates of the anti-diabetogenic and/or anti-diabetic principles and to evaluate the anti-diabetogenic effect of **1**, the effect of 14 days of the continuous administration of **1** on glucose tolerance was performed in mice. Following this continuous administration, **1** was found to significantly suppress the increase in blood glucose levels at doses of 1 and 10 mg/kg/day per os (p.o.), at 60 min post glucose loading (Figure 2 and Table S3). The area under the curve (AUC) of blood glucose levels was significantly reduced at the dose of 10 mg/kg/day (p.o.). As indicated in Table S4, the continuous administration of **1** tended to reduce the weights of visceral fat and the liver and the liver TG content, without affecting the food intake and other plasma parameters, including plasma TG, total cholesterol, and free fatty acids (FFA).

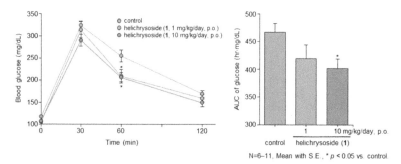

Figure 2. Effect of helichrysoside (**1**) on the glucose tolerance test after 14 days of administration in mice.

2.3. Effects on Glucose Consumption in HepG2 Cells

The liver is one of the tissues important for maintaining blood glucose homeostasis and greatly affects the formation of abnormal glucose tolerance [47]. Since the improving activity of helichrysoside (**1**) in terms of glucose tolerance in mice was observed in the previous section, we investigated the effects of **1** and its related compounds (**16–18** and **20–22**), to clarify the structural requirement of glucose consumption using human hepatoblastoma-derived HepG2 cells. As shown in Table 2, the glucose concentration in the medium was found to be significantly reduced at 6 days pretreatment with **1**, *trans*-tiliroside (**16**), kaempferol 3-O-β-D-glucopyranoside (**18**), and metformin. On the other hand, the desacyl derivative of **1**, quercetin 3-O-β-D-glucopyranoside (**17**); the aglycones of **1** and **16**, quercetin (**20**) and kaempferol (**21**); and *trans-p*-coumaric acid (**22**) did not result in changes in the glucose concentration in the medium. These results suggested that the *p*-coumaroyl moiety at the 6″ position in the D-glucopyranosyl part was essential for promoting glucose consumption. Recent related studies have reported that compounds **17**, **20**, and **21** promoted glucose uptake into muscle and hepatocytes [48–50]. Due to the long-term treatment of test samples of cells in our study, the treatment with compounds **17**, **20**, and **21** showed cytotoxicity at the concentration of 30–100 μM.

Table 2. Effects of helichrysoside (**1**) and related compounds (**16–18** and **20–22**) on glucose consumption in HepG2 cells.

Treatment	Glucose in the Medium (% of Control)(Protein (% of Control))				
	0 μM	3 μM	10 μM	30 μM	100 μM
Helichrysoside (**1**)	100.0 ± 2.6 (100.0 ± 5.4)	94.7 ± 1.1 ** (96.6 ± 2.0)	86.7 ± 1.2 ** (98.3 ± 2.0)	89.3 ± 1.1 ** (102.9 ± 1.5)	82.9 ± 1.5 ** (105.2 ± 1.4)
Trans-tiliroside (**16**)	100.0 ± 6.4 (100.0 ± 4.7)	84.6 ± 0.9 ** (105.4 ± 1.5)	90.1 ± 0.6 ** (102.3 ± 2.7)	96.8 ± 1.7 (103.4 ± 1.9)	79.8 ± 1.0 ** (110.0 ± 1.0)
Quercetin 3-O-Glc (**17**)	100.0 ± 1.1 (100.0 ± 1.3)	100.9± 1.4 (104.0 ± 1.0)	100.6 ± 1.3 (104.1 ± 0.9)	241.7 ± 3.8 ** (47.2 ± 0.6 **)	269.4 ± 5.2 ** (23.1± 1.4**)
Kaempferol 3-O-Glc (**18**)	100.0 ± 3.0 (100.0 ± 3.5)	95.9 ± 0.7 (96.4 ± 2.0)	98.9 ± 2.7 (94.2 ± 1.4 *)	93.4 ± 0.4 ** (100.1 ± 0.4)	92.8 ± 1.1 ** (98.7 ± 1.4)
Quercetin (**20**)	100.0 ± 2.0 (100.0 ± 0.5)	98.6 ± 0.4 (102.0 ± 0.9)	97.2 ± 1.7 (103.4 ± 0.8 **)	105.6 ± 2.0 (98.9 ± 0.6)	249.2 ± 3.9 ** (41.7 ± 0.4 **)
Kaempferol (**21**)	100.0 ± 3.1 (100.0 ± 0.7)	98.4 ± 2.2 (101.0 ± 0.8)	95.2 ± 1.5 (100.7 ± 0.5)	98.1 ± 0.9 (100.3 ± 1.2)	224.4 ± 3.1 ** (55.4 ± 0.5 **)
Trans-p-coumaric acid (**22**)	100.0 ± 3.6 (100.0 ± 3.7)	96.9 ± 1.5 (99.7 ± 0.6)	96.5 ± 0.5 (98.2 ± 1.7)	96.8 ± 1.7 (98.3 ± 0.4)	97.7 ± 1.8 (105.8 ± 1.8 *)
	0 μM	62.5 μM	125 μM	250 μM	500 μM
Metformin	100.0 ± 1.5 (100.0 ± 1.2)	98.9 ± 1.9 (102.0 ± 1.8)	95.1 ± 0.7 (100.9 ± 1.7)	97.7 ± 1.8 (100.5 ± 2.1)	87.5 ± 4.8 * (100.6 ± 2.3)

Each value represents the mean ± S.E. (*n* = 4 or 8); asterisks denote significant differences from the control group, where * *p* < 0.05 and ** *p* < 0.01.

2.4. Effects on Lipid Metabolism in HepG2 Cells

A fatty liver is recognized as a significant risk factor for serious liver diseases [51,52]. A strong causal link has been identified between fatty liver diseases and hyperinsulinemia, caused by insulin resistance [53,54]. Therefore, a fatty liver is considered to be closely associated with obesity and type 2 diabetes [54]. In previous studies on the identification of anti-fatty liver principles from natural medicines, several flavonoids [55–58] were revealed to inhibit lipid accumulation in HepG2 cells. Similarly, we also reported that several megastigmanes [59], diterpenes [60], and limonoids [61] inhibited lipid metabolism in high glucose-pretreated HepG2 cells.

Intracellular TG accumulated in HepG2 cells via increasing the expression of lipogenesis-related proteins, such as sterol regulatory element-binding protein 1c (SREBP-1c) and fatty acid synthase (FAS), when cultured in high glucose-containing medium [55,62]. To characterize this phenomenon, we examined the inhibitory effects of the acylated flavonol glycosides (**1–16**) and related compounds (**17–22**, **24**, **26**, and **28–31**) on (i) high glucose-induced TG accumulation in HepG2 cells and (ii) TG contents in high glucose-pretreated HepG2 cells.

As shown in Table 3, several acylated flavonol glycosides, such as helichrysoside (**1**), quercetin 3-*O*-(6′′-*O*-*cis*-*p*-coumaroyl)-β-ᴅ-glucopyranoside (**2**), quercetin 3-*O*-(6′′-*O*-*trans*-*p*-methylcoumaroyl)-β-ᴅ-glucopyranoside (**3**), quercetin 3-*O*-(6′′-*O*-trimethylgalloyl)-β-ᴅ-glucopyranoside (**15**), and *trans*-tiliroside (**16**), significantly inhibited high glucose-induced TG accumulation in HepG2 cells (% of control at 100 μM: **1** (76.9 ± 2.3%), **2** (80.4 ± 1.2%), **3** (58.2 ± 7.5%), **15** (85.8 ± 4.1%), and **16** (82.3 ± 3.0%)). In contrast, the other acylated flavonol glycosides (**4–14**), related flavonol glycosides (**17–19**), and organic acids, which related to the corresponding acyl groups (**22–31**), did not show significant inhibitory activity up to a concentration of 100 μM. As for the inhibitory effects of the corresponding aglycones, quercetin (**20**, 45.7 ± 0.4% at 100 μM) and kaempferol (**21**, 25.5 ± 1.4% at 100 μM) showed stronger activity than that of the acylated flavonol glycosides, with cytotoxicity under the effective concentrations (data not shown). The structural requirements of the acylated flavonol glycosides were assessed and showed that (1) the acylated flavonol glycosides with a *p*-coumaroyl, *p*-methylcoumaryl, or trimethylgalloyl moiety as the acyl group in the 6′′ position of the D-glucopyranosyl part are essential for the activity, and (2) the glycoside structure contributes to reducing the cytotoxicity.

On the other hand, all the tested acylated flavonol glycosides (**1–16**) and their aglycones (**20** and **21**) were found to significantly inhibit the TG content in high glucose-pretreated HepG2 cells at a concentration of 100 μM, as shown in Table 4. Specifically, the 6′′-*O*-acylated quercetin 3-*O*-β-ᴅ-glucopyranosides structure, having a *trans*- and *cis*-*p*-coumaroyl (% of control at 10 μM: **1** (82.9 ± 1.3) and **2** (86.0 ± 3.2%)), *trans*-*p*-methylcoumaroyl (**3**, 87.4 ± 0.9%), *trans*-*m*-coumaroyl (**6**, 87.5 ± 4.2%), *trans*-*m*-methylcoumaroyl (**7**, 88.4 ± 2.0%), *trans*- and *cis*-cinnamoyl (**12** (87.2 ± 2.1%) and **13** (88.9 ± 1.8%)), and vanilloyl moiety (**14**, 75.0 ± 7.3%), showed potent activities. However, the corresponding flavonol glycosides (**17–19**) and organic acids (**22**, **24**, **26**, and **28–31**) lacked this potency. Based on these results, the following structural requirements can be concluded: the acylated flavonol glycosides with a *p*- or *m*-coumaroyl, *p*- or *m*-methylcoumaryl, cinnamoyl, or vanilloyl moiety with the acyl group in the 6′′ position of the D-glucopyranosyl part are essential for the potent inhibition of TG content in high glucose-pretreated HepG2 cells.

Table 3. Effects of acylated flavonol glycosides (**1–16**) and related compounds (**17–22**, **24**, **26**, and **28–31**) on high glucose-induced triglyceride accumulation in HepG2 cells.

Treatment	TG/Protein (% of Control)				
	0 μM	3 μM	10 μM	30 μM	100 μM
Helichrysoside (**1**)	100.0 ± 1.6	100.9 ± 7.1	96.0 ± 1.5	90.2 ± 2.2	76.9 ± 2.3 **
Quercetin 3-O-(6''-O-cis-p-coumaroyl)-Glc (**2**)	100.0 ± 0.7	102.0 ± 2.1	97.3 ± 2.1	93.2 ± 1.2 *	80.4 ± 1.2 **
Quercetin 3-O-(6''-O-trans-p-methylcoumaroyl)-Glc (**3**)	100.0 ± 4.8	99.8 ± 10.2	107.4 ± 2.3	112.9 ± 2.6	58.2 ± 7.5 **
Quercetin 3-O-(6''-O-trans-o-coumaroyl)-Glc (**4**)	100.0 ± 2.6	104.6 ± 4.7	98.2 ± 3.0	98.3 ± 2.4	93.4 ± 1.2
Quercetin 3-O-(6''-O-trans-o-methylcoumaroyl)-Glc (**5**)	100.0 ± 6.7	84.4 ± 11.7	73.5 ± 12.2	107.6 ± 13.8	125.9 ± 3.6
Quercetin 3-O-(6''-O-trans-m-coumaroyl)-Glc (**6**)	100.0 ± 3.7	97.4 ± 10.9	99.0 ± 2.7	96.4 ± 5.6	106.0 ± 4.8
Quercetin 3-O-(6''-O-trans-m-methylcoumaroyl)-Glc (**7**)	100.0 ± 3.4	108.0 ± 4.5	80.5 ± 10.6	114.2 ± 8.5	92.2 ± 8.5
Quercetin 3-O-(6''-O-trans-caffeoyl)-Glc (**8**)	100.0 ± 0.7	108.4 ± 1.6 *	107.0 ± 1.7 *	103.6 ± 2.3	98.1 ± 1.7
Quercetin 3-O-(6''-O-cis-caffeoyl)-Glc (**9**)	100.0 ± 2.2	102.4 ± 1.8	102.2 ± 1.6	100.7 ± 1.7	93.8 ± 2.2
Quercetin 3-O-(6''-O-trans-feruloyl)-Glc (**10**)	100.0 ± 3.2	104.7 ± 5.3	110.6 ± 2.4	108.4 ± 4.2	114.9 ± 3.6
Quercetin 3-O-(6''-O-cis-feruloyl)-Glc (**11**)	100.0 ± 7.0	104.9 ± 3.3	101.6 ± 2.7	100.3 ± 2.5	92.9 ± 5.2
Quercetin 3-O-(6''-O-trans-cinnamoyl)-Glc (**12**)	100.0 ± 1.3	106.8 ± 3.5	100.6 ± 2.0	102.8 ± 0.9	115.6 ± 2.9 **
Quercetin 3-O-(6''-O-cis-cinnamoyl)-Glc (**13**)	100.0 ± 4.0	106.3 ± 4.1	100.2 ± 3.9	107.8 ± 3.2	121.0 ± 3.1 **
Quercetin 3-O-(6''-O-vanilloyl)-Glc (**14**)	100.0 ± 3.0	96.3 ± 4.5	101.7 ± 2.7	105.9 ± 3.2	104.5 ± 1.3
Quercetin 3-O-(6''-O-trimethylgalloyl)-Glc (**15**)	100.0 ± 2.9	99.7 ± 0.7	96.4 ± 1.1	92.3 ± 3.4	85.8 ± 4.1 **
Trans-tiliroside (**16**)	100.0 ± 2.0	99.1 ± 1.2	95.5 ± 2.0	109.6 ± 3.8	82.3 ± 3.0 **
Quercetin 3-O-Glc (**17**)	100.0 ± 1.1	97.1 ± 1.9	124.5 ± 1.3 **	96.0 ± 3.1	94.3 ± 5.2
Kaempferol 3-O-Glc (**18**)	100.0 ± 3.5	96.8 ± 3.2	95.5 ± 2.0	99.8 ± 1.3	91.9 ± 2.1
Rutin (**19**)	100.0 ± 4.1	102.1 ± 7.6	108.4 ± 3.4	103.9 ± 2.5	103.1 ± 2.6
Quercetin (**20**)	100.0 ± 0.9	99.8 ± 1.1	93.8 ± 0.4 **	82.6 ± 2.4 **	45.7 ± 0.4 **
Kaempferol (**21**)	100.0 ± 1.2	94.2 ± 1.2	100.0 ± 2.4	90.2 ± 2.4 **	25.5 ± 1.4 **
Trans-p-coumaric acid (**22**)	100.0 ± 0.8	98.4 ± 2.9	97.6 ± 3.4	99.6 ± 1.7	102.7 ± 2.1
Trans-o-coumaric acid (**24**)	100.0 ± 1.1	99.1 ± 0.7	97.4 ± 1.7	97.1 ± 1.5	96.2 ± 2.2

Table 3. *Cont.*

Treatment	TG/Protein (% of Control)				
	0 µM	3 µM	10 µM	30 µM	100 µM
*Trans-m-*coumaric acid (**26**)	100.0 ± 1.1	99.2 ± 0.6	97.7 ± 2.1	97.6 ± 1.9	99.6 ± 1.9
*Trans-*caffeic acid (**28**)	100.0 ± 3.8	97.2 ± 1.9	105.1 ± 4.3	99.9 ± 3.3	89.5 ± 4.7
*Trans-*ferulic acid (**29**)	100.0 ± 3.4	95.0 ± 1.8	105.3 ± 4.5	101.9 ± 3.4	102.0 ± 2.6
*Trans-*cinnamic acid (**30**)	100.0 ± 4.7	103.4 ± 2.7	107.1 ± 1.3	100.0 ± 2.5	103.2 ± 5.6
Vanillic acid (**31**)	100.0 ± 2.4	97.2 ± 1.5	100.6 ± 0.7	99.3 ± 2.3	101.3 ± 1.4
	0 mM	0.125 mM	0.25 mM	0.5 mM	1 mM
Metformin	100.0 ± 0.4	86.8 ± 1.5 **	75.6 ± 1.5 **	64.8 ± 1.0 **	61.1 ± 2.8 **

Each value represents the mean ± S.E. ($n = 4$); asterisks denote significant differences from the control group, where * $p < 0.05$ and ** $p < 0.01$.

Table 4. Effects of acylated flavonol glycosides (**1**–**16**) and related compounds (**17**–**22**, **24**, **26**, and **28**–**31**) on the triglyceride content in high glucose-pretreated HepG2 cells.

Treatment	TG/Protein (% of Control)				
	0 µM	3 µM	10 µM	30 µM	100 µM
Helichrysoside (**1**)	100.0 ± 3.5	90.5 ± 0.6	82.9 ± 1.3 *	83.3 ± 4.6 *	62.1 ± 3.6 **
Quercetin 3-O-(6′′-O-*cis-p-*coumaroyl)-Glc (**2**)	100.0 ± 3.7	86.0 ± 0.8 *	86.0 ± 3.2 *	81.6 ± 1.4 **	74.6 ± 2.3 **
Quercetin 3-O-(6′′-O-*trans-p-*methylcoumaroyl)-Glc (**3**)	100.0 ± 2.2	90.3 ± 1.0 **	87.4 ± 0.9 **	83.3 ± 1.5 **	66.4 ± 1.4 **
Quercetin 3-O-(6′′-O-*trans-o-*coumaroyl)-Glc (**4**)	100.0 ± 2.3	93.3 ± 1.5	89.5 ± 2.6 **	79.6 ± 1.6 **	64.5 ± 1.8 **
Quercetin 3-O-(6′′-O-*trans-o-*methylcoumaroyl)-Glc (**5**)	100.0 ± 3.0	94.5 ± 2.7	93.4 ± 1.6	86.4 ± 1.2 **	64.6 ± 2.0 **
Quercetin 3-O-(6′′-O-*trans-m-*coumaroyl)-Glc (**6**)	100.0 ± 1.3	91.3 ± 3.6	87.5 = 4.2 *	83.7 ± 3.1 **	69.8 ± 3.2 **
Quercetin 3-O-(6′′-O-*trans-m-*methylcoumaroyl)-Glc (**7**)	100.0 ± 2.0	91.2 ± 1.9 *	88.4 ± 2.0 **	83.8 ± 1.5 **	76.2 ± 1.5 **
Quercetin 3-O-(6′′-O-*trans-*caffeoyl)-Glc (**8**)	100.0 ± 13.8	91.1 ± 6.0	87.0 ± 5.2	84.2 ± 6.3	65.8 ± 5.4 **
Quercetin 3-O-(6′′-O-*cis-*caffeoyl)-Glc (**9**)	100.0 ± 2.9	95.6 ± 1.4	91.8 ± 2.0	87.4 ± 4.2 *	87.4 ± 4.6 *
Quercetin 3-O-(6′′-O-*trans-*feruloyl)-Glc (**10**)	100.0 ± 7.9	89.2 ± 3.9	94.0 ± 4.3	74.3 ± 5.8 **	75.8 ± 3.7 **

Table 4. Cont.

Treatment	TG/Protein (% of Control)				
	0 µM	3 µM	10 µM	30 µM	100 µM
Quercetin 3-O-(6''-O-cis-feruloyl)-Glc (11)	100.0 ± 10.6	86.8 ± 4.7	90.7 ± 2.2	82.4 ± 4.8 *	77.3 ± 3.5 **
Quercetin 3-O-(6''-O-trans-cinnamoyl)-Glc (12)	100.0 ± 3.4	91.4 ± 2.6	87.2 ± 2.1 *	80.9 ± 2.1 **	68.7 ± 1.3 **
Quercetin 3-O-(6''-O-cis-cinnamoyl)-Glc (13)	100.0 ± 2.1	93.2 ± 0.8	88.9 ± 1.8 **	89.9 ± 0.5 **	82.5 ± 1.0 **
Quercetin 3-O-(6''-O-vanilloyl)-Glc (14)	100.0 ± 9.7	102.5 ± 7.4	75.0 ± 7.3 **	70.2 ± 5.2 **	60.8 ± 6.1 **
Quercetin 3-O-(6''-O-trimethylgalloyl)-Glc (15)	100.0 ± 5.7	92.2 ± 2.0	93.1 ± 1.0	83.7 ± 1.3 **	81.7 ± 3.9 **
Trans-tiliroside (16)	100.0 ± 1.7	98.9 ± 2.9	96.2 ± 1.2	86.1 ± 3.1 **	72.8 ± 3.1 **
Quercetin 3-O-Glc (17)	100.0 ± 2.1	100.9 ± 2.6	100.5 ± 2.5	108.3 ± 1.2	108.0 ± 1.4
Kaempferol 3-O-Glc (18)	100.0 ± 3.2	98.6 ± 3.3	96.0 ± 2.3	88.8 ± 3.3	92.4 ± 5.1
Rutin (19)	100.0 ± 9.2	95.3 ± 4.0	91.8 ± 5.8	99.3 ± 2.7	94.9 ± 7.6
Quercetin (20)	100.0 ± 2.4	92.5 ± 1.1	92.1 ± 3.5	71.5 ± 3.3 **	63.2 ± 0.7 **
Kaempferol (21)	100.0 ± 2.4	103.4 ± 2.8	95.0 ± 4.6	82.8 ± 1.5 **	56.1 ± 3.6 **
Trans-p-coumaric acid (22)	100.0 ± 3.3	95.1 ± 4.5	99.8 ± 4.9	103.7 ± 3.3	118.6 ± 6.2 *
Trans-o-coumaric acid (24)	100.0 ± 2.2	97.2 ± 0.9	93.8 ± 3.3	97.5 ± 4.1	102.4 ± 4.2
Trans-m-coumaric acid (26)	100.0 ± 2.3	93.7 ± 1.0	97.1 ± 3.4	92.1 ± 0.8	94.4 ± 1.7
Trans-caffeic acid (28)	100.0 ± 13.2	89.9 ± 6.6	89.6 ± 0.6	91.1 ± 2.6	97.6 ± 1.4
Trans-ferulic acid (29)	100.0 ± 11.2	88.6 ± 6.3	97.4 ± 3.1	100.5 ± 4.7	104.3 ± 6.6
Trans-cinnamic acid (30)	100.0 ± 3.0	102.8 ± 2.7	99.2 ± 7.0	98.5 ± 2.9	102.0 ± 5.3
Vanillic acid (31)	100.0 ± 9.2	92.9 ± 4.7	98.4 ± 2.8	95.1 ± 8.4	106.7 ± 2.5
	0 µM	0.125 mM	0.25 mM	0.5 mM	1 mM
Metformin	100.0 ± 1.2	92.1 ± 1.4 *	88.6 ± 1.5 **	87.8 ± 2.2 **	81.4 ± 1.4 **

Each value represents the mean ± S.E. ($n = 4$ or 8); asterisks denote significant differences from the control group, where * $p < 0.05$ and ** $p < 0.01$.

Recently, it has been reported that derivatives of **16** activate adenosine 5′-monophosphate-activated protein kinase (AMPK) in 3T3-L1 cells [63] and stimulate glucose transporter (GLUT) 4 translocation in skeletal muscle cells [64]. AMPK is known as a key molecule involved in regulating glucose and lipid metabolism in the liver. From the similarity of the structure, the activities exhibited by **1** and its analogs in this study may have been caused via the same mechanism, but further investigations are needed to clarify the details.

3. Materials and Methods

3.1. Chemicals and Reagents

Rutin and naringinase were purchased from Sigma-Aldrich Co. LLC., St. Louis, MO, USA. DMF, *tert*-butyldiphenylsilyl chloride (TBDPSCl), EDC·HCl, 4-DMAP, TBAF, and tetrahydrofuran (THF) were purchased from Tokyo Chemical Industry Co., Ltd., Tokyo, Japan. Flavonols (**17**, **18**, and **20–21**), organic acids (**22–31**), and other chemicals, unless otherwise indicated, were purchased from Nakalai Tesque Inc., Kyoto, Japan.

3.2. General Experimental Procedures

The following instruments were used to obtain spectroscopic data: specific rotations, Horiba SEPA-300 digital polarimeter (l = 5 cm); UV spectra, Shimadzu UV-1600 spectrometer; IR spectra, Shimadzu FTIR-8100 spectrometer; FAB-MS and high-resolution MS, JEOL JMS-SX 102A mass spectrometer; ESIMS and HRESIMS, Exactive Plus mass spectrometer (Thermo Fisher Scientific Inc., MA, USA); ^{1}H-NMR spectra, JEOL JNM-ECA600 (600 MHz) and JNM-ESC400 (400 MHz) spectrometers; ^{13}C-NMR spectra, JEOL JNM-ECA600 (150 MHz) and JNM-ESC400 (100 MHz) spectrometers, with tetramethylsilane as an internal standard; HPLC detector, Shimadzu SPD-10A*vp* UV-VIS detectors; and HPLC column, Cosmosil 5C$_{18}$-MS-II (Nacalai Tesque Inc.). The following experimental conditions were used for column chromatography (CC): ordinary-phase silica gel CC, silica gel 60N (Kanto Chemical Co., Tokyo, Japan; 63–210 mesh, spherical, neutral), normal-phase thin-layer chromatography (TLC), pre-coated TLC plates with silica gel 60F$_{254}$ (Merck, Darmstadt, Germany; 0.25 mm), with detection achieved by spraying with 1% Ce(SO$_4$)$_2$–10% aqueous H$_2$SO$_4$, and followed by heating.

3.3. Enzymatic Hydrolysis of Rutin (**19**) Monitored by HPLC

A suspension of rutin (**19**, 100.0 mg) in H$_2$O (50 mL) was mixed and stirred at 50 °C in a water bath for a few minutes. Then, naringinase (5.0 mg) was added to the suspension to start the reaction. Aliquots (1 mL) of the reaction mixture after 0, 5, and 30 min and 1, 1.5, 2, 3, 4.5, 8, and 24 h were transferred into a 10 mL volumetric flask and methanol was added to make up the volume, respectively. Each solution was filtered through a syringe filter (0.45 µm), and an aliquot of 1 µL was subjected to the following HPLC analytical conditions.

A series LC-20A Prominence HPLC system (version 3.40, Shimadzu Co., Kyoto, Japan) was equipped with a UV-VIS detector, a binary pump, a degasser, an autosampler, a thermostatic column compartment, and a control module. The chromatographic separation was performed on a Cosmosil 5C$_{18}$-MS-II (3 µm particle size, 150 × 2.0 mm i.d., Nacalai Tesque Inc., Kyoto, Japan) operated at 40 °C with mobile phase A (acetonitrile) and B (H$_2$O containing 0.1% acetic acid). The gradient program was as follows: 0–3 min (A:B = 20:80, v/v) → 10–15 min (90:10, v/v) → 15–25 min (20:80, v/v, hold). The flow rate was 0.2 mL/min with UV detection at 254 nm and the injection volume was 1 µL. The standard curves were prepared with five concentration levels in the range of 25–400 µg/mL (25, 50, 100, 200, and 400 µg/mL, respectively). Linearity for each compound, such as rutin (**19**), quercetin 3-*O*-β-D-glucopyranoside (**17**), and quercetin (**20**), was plotted using linear regression of the peak area versus concentration. The coefficient of correlation (R^2) was used to judge the linearity (Figure S1 and Table S1).

*3.4. Practical Derivation from Rutin (**19**) to Quercetin 3-O-β-D-glucopyranoside (**17**) by Naringinase*

Naringinase (750.0 mg) was added to a suspension of rutin (**19**, 15.0 g, 24.6 mmol) in H_2O (7.5 L), and the mixture was stirred at 50 °C for 2 h. Removal of the solvent from the reaction mixture was carried out under reduced pressure using EtOH as an azeotropic solvent to give a crude product, which, on silica gel CC (500 g, $CHCl_3$/MeOH/H_2O (10:3:0.4, v/v/v)), gave a title compound (**17**, 6.50 g, 56.9%).

*3.5. Synthesis of Helichrysoside (**1**)*

Under an argon atmosphere, imidazole (1.50 g, 22.0 mmol, 3.2 eq) and TBDPSCl (4.54 g, 16.5 mmol, 2.4 eq) were added to a solution of *trans-p*-coumaric acid (**22**, 1.30 g, 6.88 mmol) in dry-DMF (12.0 mL), and the mixture was stirred at 40 °C for 16 h. The reaction mixture was poured into ice-water and extracted with EtOAc, before being washed with brine. The extract was condensed under a reduced pressure to give a white solid, which was dissolved in $CHCl_3$/MeOH (10:7, v/v, 17 mL) and acidified by 1 M HCl until pH 3.0. After stirring at room temperature for 1.5 h, the reaction mixture was condensed under a reduced pressure to give a pale yellow oil, which was crystallized in *n*-hexane/EtOAc (9:1, v/v, 20 mL) to give **22a** (2.12 g, 76.5%).

4-*O-tert*-Butyldiphenylsilyl ether of *trans-p*-coumaric acid (**22a**): ^{1}H NMR (400 MHz, $CDCl_3$): δ 1.10 (9H, s, *tert*-Bu), 6.23, 7.65 (1H each, both d, *J* = 16.0 Hz, H-8 and 7), 6.76, 7.30 (2H each, both d, *J* = 8.7 Hz, H-3,5 and 2,6), [7.37 (4H, m), 7.43 (2H, m), 7.70 (4H, dd, *J* = 1.9, 8.2 Hz), arom.]. ^{13}C NMR (100 MHz, $CDCl_3$): $δ_C$ 127.2 (C-1), 129.8 (C-2,6), 120.3 (C-3,5), 158.1 (C-4), 146.7 (C-7), 114.8 (C-8), 172.3 (C-9), 132.3, 135.4, 127.9, 130.1 (arom. C-1, 2,6, 3,5, 4), 19.4 (CH_3C-), 26.4 (CH_3C-).

Compound **22a** (0.40 g, 0.96 mmol, 1.2 eq), EDC·HCl (0.31 g, 1.60 mmol, 2.0 eq), and 4- DMAP (0.15 g, 1.20 mmol, 1.5 eq) were added to a solution of **17** (0.37 g, 0.80 mmol) in pyridine (4.0 mL), and the mixture was stirred at 50 °C for 12 h. The reaction mixture was condensed under a reduced pressure to give a crude product. Then, a solution of the crude product in THF (5.0 mL) was added to TBAF (*ca.* 1.0 mol/L in THF, 800 μL, 0.80 mmol, 1.0 eq) at room temperature for 1 h. The reaction mixture was quenched in H_2O, and removal of the solvent under a reduced pressure then furnished a residue, which, on silica gel CC (10 g, $CHCl_3$/MeOH/H_2O (10:3:0.4, v/v/v)), gave a title compound (**1**, 0.18 g, 36.9%).

*3.6. Synthesis of **3–8**, **10**, **12**, **14**, and **15***

In a manner similar to that used for **22a** (*vide supra*), *trans-o*-coumaric acid (**24**), *trans-m*-coumaric acid (**26**), *trans*-caffeic acid (**28**), *trans*-ferulic acid (**29**), and vanillic acid (**31**) were derived to yield the corresponding silyl ether derivatives, **24a** (95.1%), **26a** (94.6%), **28a** (393.0%), **29a** (87.3%), and **31a** (98.5%), respectively.

2-*O-tert*-Butyldiphenylsilyl ether of *trans-o*-coumaric acid (**24a**): ^{1}H NMR (400 MHz, $CDCl_3$): δ 1.15 (9H, s, *tert*-Bu), 6.49, 8.53 (1H each, both d, *J* = 16.0 Hz, H-8 and 7), 6.48 (1H, dd, *J* = 1.8, 8.7 Hz, H-3), 6.88 (1H, br dd, *J* = ca. 8, 8 Hz, H-5), 6.96 (1H, ddd, *J* = 1.8, 8.3, 8.7 Hz, H-4), 7.59 (1H, dd, *J* = 1.8, 7.8 Hz, H-6), (7.39 (4H, m), 7.44 (2H, m), 7.72 (4H, dd, *J* = 1.8, 8.3 Hz), arom.). ^{13}C NMR (100 MHz, $CDCl_3$): $δ_C$ 125.0 (C-1), 154.6 (C-2), 119.9 (C-3), 131.5 (C-4), 121.4 (C-5), 127.5 (C-6), 142.3 (C-7), 117.1 (C-8), 172.6 (C-9), 132.2, 135.4, 127.9, 130.1 (arom. C-1, 2,6, 3,5, 4), 19.6 (CH_3C-), 26.5 (CH_3C-).

3-*O-tert*-Butyldiphenylsilyl ether of *trans-m*-coumaric acid (**26a**): ^{1}H NMR (400 MHz, $CDCl_3$): δ 1.12 (9H, s, *tert*-Bu), 6.17, 7.59 (1H each, both d, *J* = 16.0 Hz, H-8 and 7), 6.78 (1H, br d, *J* = ca. 8 Hz, H-4), 6.94 (1H, br s, H-2), 7.04 (br d, *J* = ca. 8 Hz, H-6), 7.10 (dd, *J* = 7.8, 7.8 Hz, H-5), (7.38 (4H, m), 7.44 (2H, m), 7.71 (4H, m), arom.). ^{13}C NMR (100 MHz, $CDCl_3$): $δ_C$ 135.2 (C-1), 119.1 (C-2), 156.0 (C-3), 122.2 (C-4), 129.7 (C-5), 121.5 (C-6), 146.8 (C-7), 117.3 (C-8), 172.1 (C-9), 132.2, 135.5, 127.9, 130.1 (arom. C-1, 2,6, 3,5, 4), 19.5 (CH_3C-), 26.5 (CH_3C-).

3,4-Di-*O-tert*-butyldiphenylsilyl ether of *trans*-caffeic acid (**28a**): ^{1}H NMR (400 MHz, $CDCl_3$): δ 1.14, 1.18 (9H each, both s, *tert*-Bu), 5.48, 7.17 (1H each, both d, *J* = 16.0 Hz, H-8 and 7), 6.39 (1H, d,

J = 8.2 Hz, H-5), 6.53 (1H, dd, J = 1.8, 8.2 Hz, H-6), 6.59 (1H, d, J = 1.8 Hz, H-2), (7.40 (8H, m), 7.45 (4H, m), 7.79 (8H, m), arom.). ^{13}C NMR (100 MHz, CDCl$_3$): δ_C 126.8 (C-1), 119.4 (C-2), 146.5 (C-3), 148.9 (C-4), 120.5 (C-5), 122.3 (C-6), 146.6 (C-7), 114.4 (C-8), 172.0 (C-9), 132.5/132.9, 135.4/135.6, 127.9/128.0, 130.0/130.2 (arom. C-1, 2,6, 3,5, 4), 19.5, 19.5 (CH$_3$C-), 26.6, 26.8 (CH$_3$C-).

4-*O-tert*-Butyldiphenylsilyl ether of *trans*-ferulic acid (**29a**): ^{1}H NMR (400 MHz, CDCl$_3$): δ 1.11 (9H, s, *tert*-Bu), 3.60 (3H, s, -OCH$_3$), 6.23, 7.64 (1H each, both d, J = 16.0 Hz, H-8 and 7), 6.69 (1H, d, J = 8.2 Hz, H-5), 6.86 (1H, dd, J = 1.8, 8.2 Hz, H-6), 6.95 (1H, d, J = 1.8 Hz, H-2), (7.35 (4H, m), 7.41 (2H, m), 7.70 (4H, dd, J = 1.8, 7.8 Hz), arom.). ^{13}C NMR (100 MHz, CDCl$_3$): δ_C 127.7 (C-1), 111.2 (C-2), 150.8 (C-3), 147.9 (C-4), 120.4 (C-5), 122.5 (C-6), 147.1 (C-7), 114.7 (C-8), 172.3 (C-9), 133.1, 135.3, 127.6, 129.8 (arom. C-1, 2,6, 3,5, 4), 19.8 (CH$_3$C-), 26.6 (CH$_3$C-).

3-*O-tert*-Butyldiphenylsilyl ether of vanillic acid (**31a**): ^{1}H NMR (400 MHz, CDCl$_3$): δ 1.12 (9H, s, *tert*-Bu), 3.61 (3H, s, -OCH$_3$), 6.37 (1H, d, J = 9.2 Hz, H-5), 7.47 (1H, dd, J = 1.8, 9.2 Hz, H-6), 7.48 (1H, d, J = 1.8 Hz, H-2), (7.35 (4H, m), 7.41 (2H, m), 7.69 (4H, m), arom.). ^{13}C NMR (100 MHz, CDCl$_3$): δ_C 122.4 (C-1), 113.5 (C-2), 150.4 (C-3), 150.3 (C-4), 119.8 (C-5), 124.0 (C-6), 171.7 (C-9), 132.9, 135.2, 127.6, 129.8 (arom. C-1, 2,6, 3,5, 4), 19.8 (CH$_3$C-), 26.5 (CH$_3$C-).

In a manner similar to that used for the preparation of **1** (*vide supra*), dehydration condensation of **17** (500.0 mg, 1.08 mmol) and **24a**, **26a**, **28a**, **30a**, and **31a** (521.1, 521.1, 521.1, 849.6, 558.6, and 526.3 mg, respectively, 1.29 mmol, 1.2 eq) were conducted to yield the corresponding 6″-*O*-acylated quercetin 3-β-D-glucopyranosides, **4** (134.6 mg, 31.0%), **6** (147.7 mg, 34.0%), **8** (248.5 mg, 35.1%), **10** (176.9 mg, 38.0%), and **14** (130.7 mg, 29.8%), respectively. Syntheses of the 6″-*O*-acylated quercetin 3-β-D-glucopyranosides, **3** (39.0 mg, 20.3%), **5** (63.2 mg, 32.9%), **7** (57.2 mg, 29.8%), **12** (53.2 mg, 33.3%), and **15** (75.2 mg, 32.9%) were also carried out by the dehydration condensation of **17** with *trans-p*-methylcoumaric acid (**23**), *trans-o*-methylcoumaric acid (**25**), *trans-m*-methylcoumaric acid (**27**), *trans*-cinnamic acid (**30**), and trimethylgallic acid, respectively, without the deprotection procedure of the *tert*-butyldiphenylsilyl (TBDPS) ether group.

Quercetin 3-*O*-(6″-*O-trans-p*-methylcoumaroyl)-β-D-glucopyranoside (**3**): A yellow powder, high-resolution positive-ion FABMS: Calcd for C$_{31}$H$_{28}$O$_{14}$Na (M+Na)$^+$: 647.1377. Found: 647.1373. ^{1}H NMR (600 MHz, DMSO-d_6): δ 3.21 (1H, dd, J = 8.9, 9.0 Hz, H-4″), 3.29 (1H, dd, J = 8.8, 9.0 Hz, H-3″), 3.31 (1H, dd, J = 7.4, 8.8 Hz, H-2″), 3.40 (1H, ddd, J = 2.0, 6.9, 8.9 Hz, H-5″), 3.82 (3H, s, -OCH$_3$), (4.30 (1H, dd, J = 2.0, 11.8 Hz), 4.66 (1H, dd, J = 6.9, 11.8 Hz), H$_2$-6″), 5.49 (1H, d, J = 7.4 Hz, H-1″), 6.13, 6.33 (1H each, both d, J = 2.0 Hz, H-6 and 8), 6.17, 7.36 (1H each, both d, J = 16.0 Hz, H-8‴ and 7‴), 6.83 (1H, d, J = 8.4 Hz, H-5′), 6.95, 7.44 (2H each, both d, J = 8.8 Hz, H-3‴,5‴ and 2‴,6‴), 7.53 (1H, dd, J = 2.2, 8.4 Hz, H-6′), 7.55 (1H, d, J = 2.2 Hz, H-2′), 12.60 (1H, br s, 5-OH). ^{13}C NMR (150 MHz, DMSO-d_6): δ_C given in Table S2.

Quercetin 3-*O*-(6″-*O-trans-o*-coumaroyl)-β-D-glucopyranoside (**4**): A yellow powder, high-resolution positive-ion FABMS: Calcd for C$_{30}$H$_{26}$O$_{14}$Na (M+Na)$^+$: 633.1220. Found: 633.1226. ^{1}H NMR (600 MHz, DMSO-d_6): δ 3.22 (1H, dd, J = 8.8, 9.5 Hz, H-4″), 3.28 (1H, dd, J = 8.8, 8.8 Hz, H-3″), 3.30 (1H, dd, J = 7.3, 8.8 Hz, H-2″), 3.40 (1H, ddd, J = 2.2, 6.4, 9.5 Hz, H-5″), (4.07 (1H, dd, J = 6.4, 11.9 Hz), 4.29 (1H, dd, J = 2.2, 11.9 Hz), H$_2$-6″), 5.47 (1H, d, J = 7.3 Hz, H-1″), 6.15, 6.38 (1H each, both d, J = 2.0 Hz, H-6 and 8), 6.34, 7.73 (1H each, both d, J = 16.1 Hz, H-8‴, 7‴), 6.83 (1H, ddd, J = 1.7, 7.8, 8.7 Hz, H-5‴), 6.84 (1H, d, J = 8.2 Hz, H-5″), 6.93 (1H, dd, J = 1.7, 8.3 Hz, H-3‴), 7.22 (1H, ddd, J = 1.6, 8.3, 8.7 Hz, H-4‴), 7.38 (1H, dd, J = 1.6, 7.8 Hz, H-6‴), 7.52 (1H, dd, J = 2.0, 8.2 Hz, H-6″), 7.55 (1H, d, J = 2.0 Hz, H-2″), 12.58 (1H, br s, 5-OH). ^{13}C NMR (150 MHz, DMSO-d_6): δ_C given in Table S2.

Quercetin 3-*O*-(6″-*O-trans-o*-methylcoumaroyl)-β-D-glucopyranoside (**5**): A yellow powder, high-resolution positive-ion FABMS: Calcd for C$_{31}$H$_{28}$O$_{14}$Na (M+Na)$^+$: 647.1377. Found: 647.1381. ^{1}H NMR (600 MHz, DMSO-d_6): δ 3.21 (1H, m, H-4″), 3.33 (2H, m, H-2″, 3″), 3.41 (1H, ddd, J = 2.3, 6.9, 9.5 Hz, H-5″), 3.82 (3H, s, -OCH$_3$), (4.11 (1H, dd, J = 6.9, 12.1 Hz), 4.30 (1H, dd, J = 2.3, 12.1 Hz), H$_2$-6″), 5.48 (1H, d, J = 7.5 Hz, H-1″), 6.07, 6.30 (1H each, both d, J = 2.0 Hz, H-6 and 8), 6.32, 7.70 (1H each, both d, J = 16.1 Hz, H-8‴ and 7‴), 6.83 (1H, d, J = 8.9 Hz, H-5″), 6.98 (1H, br dd, J = ca. 8, 8 Hz, H-5‴), 7.05 (1H, br d, J = ca. 8 Hz, H-3‴), 7.41 (1H, ddd, J = 1.7, 8.2, 8.3 Hz, H-4‴), 7.47 (1H, dd,

J = 1.7, 8.2 Hz, H-6‴), 7.52 (1H, dd, J = 2.3, 8.9 Hz, H-6″), 7.53 (1H, d, J = 2.3 Hz, H-2″), 12.57 (1H, br s, 5-OH). ^{13}C NMR (150 MHz, DMSO-d_6): δ_C given in Table S2.

Quercetin 3-*O*-(6″-*O*-*trans*-*m*-coumaroyl)-β-D-glucopyranoside (**6**): A yellow powder, high-resolution positive-ion FABMS: Calcd for $C_{30}H_{26}O_{14}Na$ (M+Na)$^+$: 633.1220. Found: 633.1226. ^{1}H NMR (600 MHz, DMSO-d_6): δ 3.22 (1H, dd, J = 8.8, 9.0 Hz, H-4″), 3.28 (1H, dd, J = 7.6, 8.9 Hz, H-2″), 3.31 (1H, dd, J = 8.8, 8.9 Hz, H-3″), 3.40 (1H, ddd, J = 2.0, 6.6, 9.0 Hz, H-5″), (4.08 (1H, dd, J = 6.6, 11.9 Hz), 4.30 (1H, dd, J = 2.0, 11.9 Hz), H$_2$-6″), 5.46 (1H, d, J = 7.6 Hz, H-1″), 6.12, 6.33 (1H each, both br s, H-6, 8), 6.24, 7.35 (1H each, both d, J = 16.0 Hz, H-8‴ and 7‴), 6.82 (1H, d, J = 8.4 Hz, H-5′), 6.83 (1H, br d, J = ca. 8 Hz, H-4‴), 6.91 (1H, br d, J = ca. 8 Hz, H-6‴), 6.94 (1H, br s, H-2‴), 7.20 (1H, dd, J = 8.0, 8.0 Hz, H-5‴), 7.52 (1H, dd, J = 2.2, 8.4 Hz, H-6′), 7.54 (1H, d, J = 2.2 Hz, H-2′), 12.57 (1H, br s, 5-OH). ^{13}C NMR (150 MHz, DMSO-d_6): δ_C given in Table S2.

Quercetin 3-*O*-(6″-*O*-vanilloyl)-β-D-glucopyranoside (**14**): A yellow powder, high-resolution positive-ion FABMS: Calcd for $C_{29}H_{26}O_{15}Na$ (M+Na)$^+$: 637.1169. Found: 637.1174. ^{1}H NMR (600 MHz, DMSO-d_6): δ 3.24 (1H, dd, J = 8.9, 9.1 Hz, H-4″), 3.30 (1H, dd, J = 8.8, 8.9 Hz, H-3″), 3.33 (1H, dd, J = 7.4, 8.8 Hz, H-2″), 3.45 (1H, ddd, J = 2.1, 6.9, 9.1 Hz, H-5″), 3.70 (3H, s, -OCH$_3$), (4.13 (1H, dd, J = 6.9, 11.9 Hz), 4.40 (1H, dd, J = 2.1, 11.9 Hz), H$_2$-6″), 5.54 (1H, d, J = 7.4 Hz, H-1″), 6.18, 6.35 (1H each, both d, J = 1.9 Hz, H-6 and 8), 6.70 (1H, d, J = 8.2 Hz, H-5‴), 6.78 (1H, d, J = 8.4 Hz, H-5′), 7.19 (1H, dd, J = 2.0, 8.2 Hz, H-6‴), 7.27 (1H, d, J = 2.0 Hz, H-2‴), 7.51 (1H, d, J = 2.2 Hz, H-2′), 7.53 (1H, dd, J = 2.2, 8.4 Hz, H-6′), 12.58 (1H, br s, 5-OH). ^{13}C NMR (150 MHz, DMSO-d_6): δ_C given in Table S2.

Quercetin 3-*O*-(6″-*O*-trimethylgalloyl)-β-D-glucopyranoside (**15**): A yellow powder, high-resolution positive-ion FABMS: Calcd for $C_{31}H_{30}O_{16}Na$ (M+Na)$^+$: 681.1432. Found: 681.1436. UV (MeOH, nm (log ε)): 259 (3.99), 295 (3.62), 359 (3.77). IR (KBr): 3590, 1701, 1655, 1597, 1503, 1341, 1202, 1075 cm^{-1}. ^{1}H NMR (600 MHz, DMSO-d_6): δ 3.23 (1H, dd, J = 9.1, 9.7 Hz, H-4″), 3.30 (2H, m, H-2″, 3″), 3.50 (1H, ddd, J = 2.4, 7.3, 9.7 Hz, H-5″), (3.67 (6H, s), 3.73 (3H, s), -OCH$_3$), (4.26 (1H, dd, J = 7.3, 11.9 Hz), 4.43 (1H, dd, J = 2.4, 11.9 Hz), H$_2$-6″), 5.49 (1H, d, J = 7.6 Hz, H-1″), 6.10, 6.30 (1H each, both d, J = 2.1 Hz, H-6 and 8), 6.74 (1H, d, J = 8.6 Hz, H-5′), 7.48 (1H, br s, H-2′), 7.49 (1H, br d, J = ca. 9 Hz, H-6′), 12.48 (1H br s, 5-OH). ^{13}C NMR (150 MHz, DMSO-d_6): δ_C given in Table S2.

3.7. Isomerization of **1**, **8**, **10**, *and* **12**

A methanol solution (20 mL) of **1** (100.0 mg, 0.17 mmol) in a Pyrex tube was left standing for 8 h under a UV lamp (short wave) at room temperature. The reaction mixture was condensed under a reduced pressure to give a crude product, which, on HPLC (Cosmosil 5C$_{18}$-MS-II, MeOH–1% aqueous AcOH (55:45, v/v)), gave the *cis*-isomer **2** (25.1 mg) and a recovering compound (**1**, 69.8 mg). Using the similar procedure, a methanol solution (10 mL) of **8**, **10**, or **12** (each 50.0 mg) was isomerized to the corresponding *cis*-isomer **9** (12.2 mg (recovered **8**, 25.8 mg)), **11** (10.8 mg (recovered **10**, 26.9 mg)), or **13** (14.2 mg (recovered **12**, 30.1 mg)).

Quercetin 3-*O*-(6″-*O*-*cis*-*p*-coumaroyl)-β-D-glucopyranoside (**2**): A yellow powder, high-resolution positive-ion FABMS: Calcd for $C_{30}H_{26}O_{14}Na$ (M+Na)$^+$: 633.1220. Found: 633.1226. ^{1}H NMR (600 MHz, CD$_3$OD): δ 3.29 (1H, dd, J = 8.9, 9.0 Hz, H-4″), 3.42 (2H, m, H-3″, 5″), 3.49 (1H, dd, J = 7.3, 8.8 Hz, H-2″), 4.14–4.22 (2H, m, H$_2$-6″), 5.19 (1H, d, J = 7.3 Hz, H-1″), 5.51, 6.69 (1H each, both d, J = 12.8 Hz, H-8‴ and 7‴), 6.18, 6.30 (1H each, both d, J = 1.8 Hz, H-6 and 8), 6.67, 7.49 (2H each, both d, J = 8.6 Hz, H-3‴,5‴ and 2‴,6‴), 6.80 (1H, d, J = 8.7 Hz, H-5′), 7.56 (2H, m, H-2′, 6′). ^{13}C NMR (150 MHz, CD$_3$OD): δ_C given in Table S2.

Quercetin 3-*O*-(6″-*O*-*cis*-caffeoyl)-β-D-glucopyranoside (**9**): A yellow powder, high-resolution positive-ion FABMS: Calcd for $C_{30}H_{26}O_{15}Na$ (M+Na)$^+$: 649.1169. Found: 649.1170. ^{1}H NMR (600 MHz, DMSO-d_6): δ 3.18–3.36 (4H, m, H-2″–5″), 3.71 (3H, s, -OCH$_3$), (4.04 (1H, dd, J = 6.4, 11.9 Hz), 4.19 (1H, dd, J = 2.2, 11.9 Hz), H$_2$-6″), 5.42 (1H, d, J = 7.5 Hz, H-1″), 5.42, 6.58 (1H each, both d, J = 12.8 Hz, H-8‴ and 7‴), 6.20, 6.36 (1H each, both d, J = 1.7 Hz, H-6 and 8), 6.28 (1H, d, J = 2.0 Hz, H-2‴), 6.67 (1H, d, J = 8.5 Hz, H-5‴), 6.82 (1H, d, J = 8.6 Hz, H-5′), 6.98 (1H, dd, J = 2.0, 8.5 Hz, H-6‴), 7.52 (2H, m, H-2′, 6′), 12.59 (1H, br s, 5-OH). ^{13}C NMR (150 MHz, DMSO-d_6): δ_C given in Table S2.

Quercetin 3-*O*-(6''-*O*-*cis*-feruloyl)-β-D-glucopyranoside (**11**): A yellow powder, high-resolution positive-ion FABMS: Calcd for $C_{31}H_{28}O_{15}Na$ (M+Na)$^+$: 663.1326. Found: 663.1330. ^1H NMR (600 MHz, DMSO-d_6): δ 3.19 (1H, m, H-4''), 3.27 (2H, m, H-2'', 3''), 3.36 (1H, ddd, J = 2.3, 6.0, 9.6 Hz, H-5''), 3.71 (3H, s, -OCH$_3$), (4.18 (1H, dd, J = 6.4, 11.9 Hz), 4.19 (1H, dd, J = 1.8, 11.9 Hz), H$_2$-6''), 5.46 (1H, d, J = 7.4 Hz, H-1''), 5.48, 6.65 (1H each, both d, J = 12.8 Hz, H-8''' and 7'''), 6.19, 6.31 (1H each, both d, J = 1.8 Hz, H-6 and 8), 6.72 (1H, d, J = 8.2 Hz, H-5'''), 6.81 (1H, d, J = 8.7 Hz, H-5'), 7.08 (1H, dd, J = 1.8, 8.2 Hz, H-6'''), 7.45 (1H, br d, J = ca. 9 Hz, H-6'), 7.52 (1H, br s, H-2'), 7.59 (1H, d, J = 1.8 Hz, H-2'''), 12.57 (1H, br s, 5-OH). ^{13}C NMR (150 MHz, DMSO-d_6): δ$_C$ given in Table S2.

Quercetin 3-*O*-(6''-*O*-*cis*-cinnamoyl)-β-D-glucopyranoside (**13**): A yellow powder, high-resolution positive-ion FABMS: Calcd for $C_{30}H_{26}O_{13}Na$ (M+Na)$^+$: 617.1271. Found: 617.1277. ^1H NMR (600 MHz, DMSO-d_6): δ 3.14 (1H, dd, J = 8.6, 9.5 Hz, H-4''), 3.25 (1H, dd, J = 7.5, 8.9 Hz, H-2''), 3.28 (1H, dd, J = 8.6, 8.9 Hz, H-3''), 3.33 (1H, ddd, J = 2.3, 6.6, 9.5 Hz, H-5''), (4.07 (1H, dd, J = 6.6, 11.8 Hz), 4.18 (1H, dd, J = 2.3, 11.8 Hz), H$_2$-6''), 5.69, 6.81 (1H each, both d, J = 12.9 Hz, H-8''' and 7''), 6.19, 6.33 (1H each, both d, J = 2.0 Hz, H-6 and 8), 6.82 (1H, d, J = 8.9 Hz, H-5'), 7.27 (4H, m, H-2''',6''', 3''',5'''), 7.43 (1H, m, H-4''), 7.51 (1H, dd, J = 2.0, 8.9 Hz, H-6'), 7.51 (1H, d, J = 2.0 Hz, H-2'), 12.56 (1H, br s, 5-OH). ^{13}C NMR (150 MHz, DMSO-d_6): δ$_C$ given in Table S2.

3.8. Animals

Male ddY mice were purchased from Kiwa Laboratory Animal Co., Ltd., (Wakayama, Japan). The animals were housed at a constant temperature of 23 ± 2 °C and fed a standard laboratory chow (MF, Oriental Yeast Co., Ltd., Tokyo, Japan). All experiments were performed with conscious mice, unless otherwise noted. The experimental protocol was approved by Kindai University's Committee for the Care and Use of Laboratory Animals (KAPR-26-004, 1 April 2014).

3.9. Effects on the Glucose Tolerance Test in Mice

Effects on the glucose tolerance test after 14 days of administration of **1** in mice were determined according to the previously described protocol [26]. A test sample was administrated orally to male ddY mice (11 weeks old and fed a standard laboratory chow) once a day (10:00–12:00) for 14 days. Body weight and food intake were measured every day before administration of the test sample. Fasting for 20 h was carried out after the final administration, and 10% (w/v) glucose solution was intraperitoneally (i.p.) administrated to mice at 10 mL/kg. Blood samples (*ca.* 0.2 mL) were collected in tubes containing 10 units of heparin sodium from the infraorbital venous plexus before (0 h) and 0.5, 1, and 2 h after the loading of glucose. Mice were then killed by cervical dislocation, and the epididymal, mesenteric, and paranephric fat pads were removed and weighed. Plasma glucose, TG, total cholesterol, and FFA levels were determined using commercial kits (Glucose CII-test Wako, Triglyceride E-test Wako, Cholesterol E-test Wako, and NEFA C-test Wako, respectively, FUJIFILM Wako Pure Chemical Corporation, Tokyo, Japan). After removing the liver, ca. 300 mg of liver tissue was cut and homogenized with 9 mL of distilled water. An aliquot of the homogenate (500 μL) was diluted with distilled water (1 mL) and the TG concentration in the suspension was determined using Triglyceride E-test Wako.

3.10. Cell Culture

HepG2 cells (RCB1648, Riken Cell Bank, Tsukuba, Japan) were maintained in Minimum Essential Medium Eagle (MEM, Sigma-Aldrich Co. LLC., St. Louis, MO, USA) containing 10% fetal bovine serum, 1% MEM non-essential amino acids (FUJIFILM Wako Pure Chemical Corporation, Tokyo, Japan), penicillin G (100 units/mL), and streptomycin (100 μg/mL) at 37 °C under 5% CO_2 atmosphere.

3.11. Effects on Glucose Consumption in HepG2 Cells

HepG2 cells were inoculated in a 48-well tissue culture plate (10^5 cells/well in 150 μL/well in MEM). After 20 h, the medium was replaced with 150 μL/well of Dulbecco's Modified Eagle's Medium (DMEM) containing low-glucose (1000 mg/L) and a test sample. Cells were cultured for 6 days, and the medium was replaced every 2 days. The medium was then transferred to 200 μL/well of DMEM containing high-glucose (4500 mg/L) and the cells were cultured. After 20 h, the glucose content in the medium was determined using commercial kits (Glucose CII-test Wako, FUJIFILM Wako Pure Chemical Corporation, Tokyo, Japan). Medium was removed, and the cells were homogenized in distilled water (105 μL/well) by sonication. The protein content in the homogenate was determined using the BCA protein Assay Kit (FUJIFILM Wako Pure Chemical Corporation, Tokyo, Japan). Each test compound was dissolved in DMSO and added to the medium (final DMSO concentration was 0.5%). An anti-diabetic agent, metformin, was used as a reference compound.

3.12. Effects on High Glucose-Induced TG Accumulation in HepG2 Cells

HepG2 cells were inoculated in a 48-well tissue culture plate (10^5 cells/well in 150 μL/well in MEM). After 20 h, the medium was replaced with 150 μL/well of DMEM containing high-glucose and a test sample, which was cultured for 4 days, with medium containing a test sample being replaced every 2 days. Medium was then removed, and the cells were homogenized in distilled water (105 μL/well) by sonication. The TG and protein content in the homogenate were determined using commercial kits (Triglyceride E-test Wako and BCA protein Assay Kit, respectively, FUJIFILM Wako Pure Chemical Corporation, Tokyo, Japan). Data were expressed as the % of control of TG/protein (μg/mg). Each test compound was dissolved in DMSO and was added to the medium (final DMSO concentration was 0.5%). An anti-diabetic agent, metformin, was used as a reference compound.

3.13. Effects on TG contents in High Glucose-Pretreated HepG2 Cells

Effects on TG metabolism-promoting activity in high glucose-pretreated HepG2 cells were evaluated according to the method described previously [61], with slight modifications. HepG2 cells were inoculated in a 48-well tissue culture plate (10^5 cells/well in 150 μL/well in MEM). After 20 h, the medium was replaced with 150 μL/well of DMEM containing high-glucose and cultured for 6 days, with the medium being replaced every 2 days. After accumulation of the lipid, the medium was transferred to 150 μL/well of DMEM containing low-glucose and a test sample, and the cells were cultured. After 20 h, the TG and protein content in the cells were determined by the same manner as described above. Data were expressed as the % of control of TG/protein (μg/mg). Each test compound was dissolved in DMSO and added to the medium (final DMSO concentration was 0.5%). An anti-diabetic agent, metformin, was used as a reference compound.

3.14. Statistics

Values are expressed as means ± S.E. One-way analysis of variance (ANOVA) followed by Dunnett's test was used for statistical analysis. Probability (p) values of less than 0.05 were considered significant.

4. Conclusions

The present study demonstrated that helichrysoside (**1**), an acylated flavonol glycoside, improved glucose tolerance in ddY mice. In the study, using HepG2 cells, helichrysoside (**1**) was shown to significantly enhance glucose consumption in the medium, inhibit high glucose-induced TG accumulation in cells, and promote the effect of TG metabolism in high glucose-pretreated cells. The results from various acylated flavonol glycosides, flavonol glycosides, flavonols, and organic acids indicated that the acyl group at the 6″ position in the D-glucopyranosyl part was essential for the improved glucose tolerance activities. Previous evidence, along with this study, suggests that helichrysoside (**1**) might be considered as a possible candidate for the prevention of glucose and lipid metabolism-related disorders.

Supplementary Materials: Supplementary materials can be found at http://www.mdpi.com/1422-0067/20/24/6322/s1.

Author Contributions: T.M., A.N., O.M., and K.N. conceived and designed the experiments; T.M., A.N., T.O., Y.M., N.T., M.S.-K., Y.H., and K.N. performed the experiments; T.M., A.N., and N.K. analyzed the data; T.M. and A.N. wrote the paper.

Funding: This work was supported by a Grant-in-aid for Scientific Research (KAKENHI), 18K06726 (T.M.), 16K08313 (O.M.), and 18K06739 (K.N.).

Acknowledgments: The authors gratefully thank Division of Joint Research Center, Kindai University for the NMR and MS measurements. We would like to thank Editage (www.editage.com) for English language editing.

Conflicts of Interest: The authors declare no conflicts of interest.

References

1. Symonowicz, M.; Kolanek, M. Flavonoids and their properties to form chelate complexes. *Biotechnol. Food Sci.* **2012**, *76*, 35–41.
2. Santos-Buelga, C.; Feliciano, A.S. Flavonoids: From structure to health issues. *Molecules* **2017**, *22*, 477. [CrossRef] [PubMed]
3. Usman, H.; Abdulrahman, F.I.; Kaita, H.A.; Khan, I.Z.; Tijjani, M.A. Flavonoids: The bioactive phytochemical agent—A review. *Chem. Res. J.* **2017**, *2*, 59–72.
4. Raffa, D.; Maggio, B.; Raimondi, M.V.; Plescia, F.; Daidone, G. Recent discoveries of anticancer flavonoids. *Eur. J. Med. Chem.* **2017**, *142*, 213–228. [CrossRef]
5. Teplova, V.V.; Isakova, E.P.; Klein, O.I.; Dergachova, D.I.; Gessler, N.N.; Deryabina, Y.I. Natural polyphenols: Biological activity, pharmacological potential, means of metabolic engineering (review). *Appl. Biochem. Microbiol.* **2018**, *54*, 221–237. [CrossRef]
6. Mozaffarian, D.; Wu, J.H.Y. Flavonoids, dairy foods, and cardiovascular and metabolic health—A review of emerging biologic pathways. *Circ. Res.* **2018**, *122*, 369–384. [CrossRef]
7. Perez-Vizcaino, F.; Fraga, C.G. Research trends in flavonoids and health. *Arch. Biochem. Biophys.* **2018**, *646*, 107–112. [CrossRef]
8. Harnly, J. Importance of accurate measurements in nutrition research: Dietary flavonoids as a case study. *Food Funct.* **2019**, *10*, 514–528. [CrossRef]
9. Yoshikawa, M.; Murakami, T.; Ishiwada, T.; Morikawa, T.; Kagawa, M.; Higashi, Y.; Matsuda, H. New flavonol oligoglycosides and polyacylated sucroases with inhibitory effects on aldose reductase and platelet aggregation from the flowers of *Prunus mume. J. Nat. Prod.* **2002**, *65*, 1151–1155. [CrossRef]
10. Matsuda, H.; Morikawa, T.; Yoshikawa, M. Antidiabetogenic constituents from several natural medicines. *Pure Appl. Chem.* **2002**, *74*, 1301–1308. [CrossRef]
11. Morikawa, T.; Xie, H.; Wang, T.; Matsuda, H.; Yoshikawa, M. Bioactive constituents from Chinese natural medicines. XXXII. Aminopeptidase N and aldose reductase inhibitors from *Sinocrassula indica*: Structures of sinocrassosides B_4, B_5, C_1, and D_1–D_3. *Chem. Pharm. Bull.* **2008**, *56*, 1438–1444. [CrossRef]
12. Morikawa, T. Search for bioactive constituents from several medicinal foods: Hepatoprotective, antidiabetic, and antiallergic activities. *J. Nat. Med.* **2007**, *61*, 112–126. [CrossRef]
13. Matsuda, H.; Morikawa, T.; Ueda, K.; Managi, H.; Yoshikawa, M. Structural requirements of flavonoids for inhibition of antigen-induced degranulation, TNF-α and IL-4 production from RBL-2H3 cells. *Bioorg. Med. Chem.* **2002**, *10*, 3123–3128.
14. Matsuda, H.; Sugimoto, S.; Morikawa, T.; Matsuhira, K.; Mizoguchi, E.; Nakamura, S.; Yoshikawa, M. Bioactive constituents from Chinese natural medicines. XX. Inhibitors of antigen-induced degranulation in RBL-2H3 cells from the seeds of *Psoralea corylifolia. Chem. Pharm. Bull.* **2007**, *55*, 106–110. [CrossRef]
15. Matsuda, H.; Morikawa, T.; Ando, S.; Toguchida, I.; Yoshikawa, M. Structural requirements of flavonoids for nitric oxide production inhibitory activity and mechanism of action. *Bioorg. Med. Chem.* **2003**, *11*, 1995–2000. [CrossRef]
16. Morikawa, T.; Xu, F.; Matsuda, H.; Yoshikawa, M. Structures of new flavonoids, erycibenins D, E, and F, and NO production inhibitors from *Erycibe expansa* originationg in Thailand. *Chem. Pharm. Bull.* **2006**, *54*, 1530–1534. [CrossRef]
17. Morikawa, T.; Funakoshi, K.; Ninomiya, K.; Yasuda, D.; Miyagawa, K.; Matsuda, H.; Yoshikawa, M. Medicinal foodstuffs. XXXIV. Structures of new prenylchalcones and prenylflavonones with TNF-α and aminopeptidase N inhibitory activities from *Boesenbergia rotunda. Chem. Pharm. Bull.* **2008**, *56*, 956–962. [CrossRef]

18. Morikawa, T.; Wang, L.-B.; Nakamura, S.; Ninomiya, K.; Yokoyama, E.; Matsuda, H.; Muraoka, O.; Wu, L.-J.; Yoshikawa, M. Medicinal flowers. XXVII. New flavanone and chalcone glycosides, arenariumosides I, II, III, and IV, and tumor necrosis factor-α inhibitors from everlasting, flowers of *Helichrysum arenarium*. *Chem. Pharm. Bull.* **2009**, *57*, 361–367. [CrossRef]

19. Morikawa, T.; Xie, H.; Wang, T.; Matsuda, H.; Yoshikawa, M. Acylated flavonol bisdesmosides, sinocrassosides A_3–A_7 and B_3, with aminopeptidase N inhibitory activity from *Sinocrassula indica*. *Chem. Biodivers.* **2009**, *6*, 411–420. [CrossRef]

20. Chaipech, S.; Morikawa, T.; Ninomiya, K.; Yoshikawa, M.; Pongpiriyadacha, Y.; Hayakawa, T.; Muraoka, O. Structures of two new phenolic glycosides, kaempferiaosides A and B, and hepatoprotective constituents from the rhizomes of *Kaempferia parviflora*. *Chem. Pharm. Bull.* **2012**, *60*, 62–69. [CrossRef]

21. Yoshikawa, M.; Morikawa, T.; Funakoshi, K.; Ochi, M.; Pongpiriyadacha, Y.; Matsuda, H. Medicinal foodstuffs. XXXIII. Gastroprotective principles from *Boesenbergia rotunda* (Zingiberaceae)—absolute stereostructures of Diels-Alder type addition prenylchalcone. *Heterocycles* **2008**, *75*, 1639–1650. [CrossRef]

22. Ninomiya, K.; Matsumoto, T.; Chaipech, S.; Miyake, S.; Katsuyama, Y.; Tsuboyama, A.; Pongpiriyadacha, Y.; Hayakawa, T.; Muraoka, O.; Morikawa, T. Simultaneous quantitative analysis of 12 methoxyflavones with melanogenesis inhibitory activity from the rhizomes of *Kaempferia parviflora*. *J. Nat. Med.* **2016**, *70*, 179–189. [CrossRef]

23. Morikawa, T.; Ninomiya, K.; Akaki, J.; Kakihara, N.; Kuramoto, H.; Matsumoto, Y.; Hayakawa, T.; Muraoka, O.; Wang, L.-B.; Nakamura, S.; et al. Dipeptidyl peptidase-IV inhibitory activity of dimeric dihydrochalcone glycosides from flowers of *Helichrysum arenarium*. *J. Nat. Med.* **2015**, *69*, 494–506. [CrossRef]

24. Candy, H.A.; Laing, M.; Weeks, C.M. The crystal and molecular structure of helichrysoside, a new acylated flavonoid glycoside from *Helichrysum kraussii*. *Tetrahedron Lett.* **1975**, *14*, 1211–1214. [CrossRef]

25. Lavault, M.; Richomme, P. Constituents of *Helichrysum stoechas* variety *olonnense*. *Chem. Nat. Compd.* **2004**, *40*, 118–121. [CrossRef]

26. Ninomiya, K.; Matsuda, H.; Kubo, M.; Morikawa, T.; Nishida, N.; Yoshikawa, M. Potent anti-obese principle from *Rosa canina*: Structural requirements and mode of action of *trans*-tiliroside. *Bioorg. Med. Chem. Lett.* **2007**, *17*, 3059–3064. [CrossRef]

27. Fernandes, A.A.H.; Novelli, E.L.B.; Okoshi, K.; Okoshi, M.P.; Di Muzio, B.P.; Guimarães, J.F.C.; Junior, A.F. Influence of rutin treatment on biochemical alterations in experimental diabetes. *Biomed. Pharmacother.* **2010**, *64*, 214–219. [CrossRef]

28. Panchal, S.K.; Poudyal, H.; Arumugam, T.V.; Brown, L. Rutin attenuates metabolic changes, nonalcoholic steatohepatitis, and cardiovascular remodeling in high-carbohydrate, high-fat diet-fed rats. *J. Nutr.* **2011**, *141*, 1062–1069. [CrossRef]

29. Javed, H.; Khan, M.M.; Ahmad, A.; Vaibhav, K.; Ahmad, M.E.; Khan, A.; Ashafaq, M.; Islam, F.; Siddiqui, M.S.; Safhi, M.M.; et al. Rutin prevents cognitive impairments by ameliorating oxidative stress and neuroinflammation in rat model of sporadic dementia of Alzheimer type. *Neuroscience* **2012**, *210*, 340–352. [CrossRef]

30. Chua, L.S. A review on plant-based rutin extraction methods and its pharmacological activities. *J. Ethnopharmacol.* **2013**, *150*, 805–817. [CrossRef]

31. Heřmánková-Vavříková, E.; Křenková, A.; Petrásková, L.; Chambers, C.S.; Zápal, J.; Kuzma, M.; Valentová, K.; Křen, V. Synthesis and antiradical activity of isoquercitrin esters with aromatic acids and their homologues. *Int. J. Mol. Sci.* **2017**, *18*, 1074–1087. [CrossRef]

32. Ren, X.; Shen, L.L.; Muraoka, O.; Cheng, M. Synthesis of quercetin 3-O-[6''-O-(*trans*-*p*-coumaroyl)]-β-D-glucopyranoside. *J. Carbohydr. Chem.* **2011**, *30*, 119–131. [CrossRef]

33. Ishihara, K.; Nakajima, N. Structural aspects of acylated plant pigments: Stabilization of flavonoid glucosides and interpretation of their functions. *J. Mol. Catal. B Enzym.* **2003**, *23*, 411–417. [CrossRef]

34. Calzada, F.; Cedillo-Rivera, R.; Mata, R. Antiprotozoal activity of the constituents of *Conyza filaginoides*. *J. Nat. Prod.* **2001**, *64*, 671–673. [CrossRef]

35. Danieli, B.; Bertario, A. Chemo-enzymatic synthesis of 6''-O-(3-arylprop-2-enoyl) derivatives of the flavonol glucoside isoquercitrin. *Helv. Chim. Acta* **1993**, *76*, 2981–2991. [CrossRef]

36. Gao, C.; Mayon, P.; MacManus, D.A.; Vulfson, E.N. Novel enzymatic approach to the synthesis of flavonoid glycosides and their esters. *Biotech. Bioeng.* **2001**, *71*, 235–243. [CrossRef]

37. Jung, U.J.; Choi, M.-S. Obesity and its metabolic complications: The role of adipokines and the relationship between obesity, inflammation, insulin resistance, dyslipidemia and nonalcoholic fatty liver disease. *Int. J. Mol. Sci.* **2014**, *15*, 6184–6223. [CrossRef]

38. Rodriguez-Araujo, G.; Nakagami, H. Pathophysiology of cardiovascular disease in diabetes mellitus. *Cardiovasc Endocrinol. Metab.* **2018**, *7*, 4–9. [CrossRef]

39. Yoshikawa, M.; Wang, T.; Morikawa, T.; Xie, H.; Matsuda, H. Bioactive constituents from Chinese natural medicines. XXIV. Hypoglycemic effects of *Sinocrassula indica* in sugar-loaded rats and genetically diabetic KK-Ay mice and structures of new acylated flavonol glycosides, sinocrassosides A_1, A_2, B_1, and B_2. *Chem. Pharm. Bull.* **2007**, *55*, 1308–1315. [CrossRef]

40. Yoshikawa, M.; Xu, F.; Morikawa, T.; Pongpiriyadacha, Y.; Nakamura, S.; Asao, Y.; Kumahara, A.; Matsuda, H. Medicinal flowers. XII. New spirostane-type steroid saponins with antidiabetogenic activity from *Borassus flabellifer*. *Chem. Pharm. Bull.* **2007**, *55*, 308–316. [CrossRef]

41. Yoshikawa, M.; Morikawa, T.; Matsuda, H.; Tanabe, G.; Muraoka, O. Absolute stereostructure of potent α-glucosidase inhibitor, salacinol, with unique thiosugar sulfonium sulfate inner salt structure from *Salacia reticulata*. *Bioorg. Med. Chem.* **2002**, *10*, 1547–1554. [CrossRef]

42. Yoshikawa, M.; Pongpiriyadacha, Y.; Kishi, A.; Kageura, T.; Wang, T.; Morikawa, T.; Matsuda, H. Biological activities of *Salacia chinensis* originating in Thailand: The quality evaluation guided by α-glucosidase inhibitory activity. *Yakugaku Zasshi* **2003**, *123*, 871–880. [CrossRef] [PubMed]

43. Matsuda, H.; Yoshikawa, M.; Morikawa, T.; Tanabe, G.; Muraoka, O. Antidiabetogenic constituents from *Salacia* species. *J. Tradit. Med.* **2005**, *22* (Suppl. 1), 145–153.

44. Kobayashi, M.; Akaki, J.; Yamashita, K.; Morikawa, T.; Ninomiya, K.; Yoshikawa, M.; Muraoka, O. Suippressive effect of the tablet containing Salacia chinensis extract on postprandial blood glucose. *Jpn. Pharmacol. Ther.* **2010**, *38*, 545–550.

45. Morikawa, T.; Akaki, J.; Ninomiya, K.; Kinouchi, E.; Tanabe, G.; Pongpiriyadacha, Y.; Yoshikawa, M.; Muraoka, O. Salacinol and related analogs: New leads for type 2 diabetes therapeutic candidates from the Thai traditional natural medicine *Salacia chinensis*. *Nutrients* **2015**, *7*, 1480–1493. [CrossRef] [PubMed]

46. Kabayashi, M.; Akaki, J.; Yamaguchi, Y.; Yamasaki, H.; Ninomiya, K.; Pongpiriyadacha, Y.; Yoshikawa, M.; Muraoka, O.; Morikawa, M. *Salacia chinensis* stem extract and its thiosugar sulfonium constituents, neokotalanol, improves HbA1c levels in *ob/ob* mice. *J. Nat. Med.* **2019**, *73*, 584–588. [CrossRef]

47. Petersen, M.C.; Vatner, D.F.; Shulman, G.I. Regulation of hepatic glucose metabolism in health and disease. *Nat. Rev. Endocrinol.* **2017**, *13*, 572–587. [CrossRef]

48. Huang, X.-L.; He, Y.; Ji, L.-L.; Wang, K.-Y.; Wang, Y.-L.; Chen, D.-F.; Geng, Y.; OuYang, P.; Lai, W.-M. Hepatoprotective potential of isoquercitrin against type 2 diabetes-induced hepatic injury in rats. *Oncotarget* **2017**, *8*, 101545–101559. [CrossRef]

49. Eid, H.M.; Nachar, A.; Thong, F.; Sweeney, G.; Haddad, P.S. The molecular basis of the antidiabetic action of quercetin in cultured skeletal muscle cells and hepatocytes. *Pharmacogn. Mag.* **2015**, *11*, 74–81.

50. Alkhalidy, H.; Moore, W.; Zhang, Y.; McMillan, R.; Wang, A.; Ali, M.; Suh, K.S.; Zhen, W.; Cheng, Z.; Jia, Z.; et al. Small molecule kaempferol promotes insulin sensitivity and preserved pancreatic β-cell mass in middle-aged obese diabetic mice. *J. Diabetes. Res.* **2015**, *2015*, 532984. [CrossRef]

51. Bellentani, S.; Tiribelli, C.; Saccoccio, G.; Sodde, M.; Fratti, N.; De Martin, C.; Cristianini, G. Prevalence of chronic liver disease in the general population of northern Italy: The dionysos study. *Hepatology* **1994**, *20*, 1442–1449. [CrossRef] [PubMed]

52. El-Hassan, A.Y.; Ibrahim, E.M.; Al-Mulnim, F.A.; Nabhan, A.A.; Chammas, M.Y. Fatty infiltration of the liver: Analysis of prevalence, radiological and clinical features and influence on patient management. *Br. J. Radiol.* **1992**, *65*, 774–778. [CrossRef] [PubMed]

53. Marceau, P.; Biron, S.; Hould, F.S.; Marceau, S.; Simard, S.; Thung, S.N.; Kral, J.G. Liver pathology and the metabolic syndrome X in severe obesity. *J. Clin. Endocrinol. Metab.* **1999**, *84*, 1513–1517. [CrossRef] [PubMed]

54. Marchesini, G.; Brizi, M.; Morselli-Labate, A.M.; Bianchi, G.; Bugianesi, E.; McCullough, A.J.; Forlani, G.; Melchionda, N. Association of nonalcoholic fatty liver disease with insulin resistance. *Am. J. Med.* **1999**, *107*, 450–455. [CrossRef]

55. Yuk, T.; Kim, Y.; Yang, J.; Sung, J.; Jeong, H.S.; Lee, J. Nobiletin inhibits hepatic lipogenesis via activation of AMP-activated protein kinase. *Evid. Based Complement. Alternat. Med.* **2018**, *2018*, 7420265. [CrossRef]

56. Hwang, Y.P.; Choi, J.H.; Kim, H.G.; Khanal, T.; Song, G.Y.; Nam, M.S.; Lee, H.-S.; Chung, Y.C.; Lee, Y.C.; Jeong, H.G. Saponins, especially platycodin D, from *Platycodon grandiflorum* modulate hepatic lipogenesis in high-fat diet-fed rats and high glucose-exposed HepG2 cells. *Toxicol. Appl. Pharmacol.* **2013**, *267*, 174–183. [CrossRef]
57. Kawser Hossain, M.; Abdal Dayem, A.; Han, J.; Yin, Y.; Kim, K.; Kumar Saha, S.; Yang, G.-M.; Choi, H.Y.; Cho, S.-G. Molecular mechanisms of the anti-obesity and anti-diabetic properties of flavonoids. *Int. J. Mol. Sci.* **2016**, *17*, 569–600. [CrossRef]
58. Morikawa, T.; Ninomiya, K.; Miyake, S.; Miki, Y.; Okamoto, M.; Yoshikawa, M.; Muraoka, O. Flavonol glycosides with lipid accumulation inhibitory activity and simultaneous quantitative analysis of 15 polyphenols and caffeine in the flower buds of *Camellia sinensis* from different regions by LCMS. *Food Chem.* **2013**, *140*, 353–360. [CrossRef]
59. Muraoka, O.; Morikawa, T.; Zhang, Y.; Ninomiya, K.; Nakamura, S.; Matsuda, H.; Yoshikawa, M. Novel megastigmanes with lipid accumulation inhibitory and lipid metabolism-promoting activities in HepG2 cells from *Sedum sarmentosum*. *Tetrahedron* **2009**, *65*, 4142–4148. [CrossRef]
60. Morikawa, T.; Ninomiya, K.; Xu, F.; Okumura, N.; Matsuda, H.; Muraoka, O.; Hayakawa, T.; Yoshikawa, M. Acylated dolabellane-type diterpenes from *Nigella sativa* seeds with triglyceride metabolism-promoting activity in high glucose-pretreated HepG2 cells. *Phytochem. Lett.* **2013**, *6*, 198–204. [CrossRef]
61. Inoue, T.; Matsui, Y.; Kikuchi, T.; Yamada, T.; In, Y.; Muraoka, O.; Sakai, C.; Ninomiya, K.; Morikawa, T.; Tanaka, R. Carapanolides M–S from seeds of andiroba (*Carapa guianensis*, Meliaceae) and triglyceride metabolism-promoting activity in high glucose-pretreated HepG2 cells. *Tetrahedron* **2015**, *71*, 2753–2760. [CrossRef]
62. Gorgani-Firuzjaee, S.; Meshkani, R. SH2 domain-containing inositol 5-phosphatase (SHIP2) inhibition ameliorates high glucose-induced de-novo lipogenesis and VLDL production through regulating AMPK/mTOR/SREBP1 pathway and ROS production in HepG2 cells. *Free Radic. Biol. Med.* **2015**, *89*, 679–689. [CrossRef]
63. Gan, C.-C.; Ni, T.-W.; Yu, Y.; Qin, N.; Chen, Y.; Jin, M.-N.; Duan, H.-Q. Flavonoid derivative (Fla-CN) inhibited adipocyte differentiation via activating AMPK and up-regulating microRNA-27 in 3T3-L1 cells. *Eur. J. Pharmacol.* **2017**, *797*, 45–52. [CrossRef] [PubMed]
64. Shi, L.; Qin, N.; Hu, L.; Liu, L.; Duan, H.; Niu, W. Tiliroside-derivatives enhance GLUT4 translocation via AMPK in muscle cells. *Diabetes Res. Clin. Pract.* **2011**, *92*, e41–e46. [CrossRef] [PubMed]

International Journal of
Molecular Sciences

Article

Apoptotic-Induced Effects of *Acacia Catechu* Willd. Extract in Human Colon Cancer Cells

Elda Chiaino [1,†], Matteo Micucci [2,†], Miriam Durante [1], Roberta Budriesi [2], Roberto Gotti [2], Carla Marzetti [3], Alberto Chiarini [2] and Maria Frosini [1,*]

[1] Dipartimento di Scienze della Vita, Università di Siena, Via Aldo Moro 2, 53100 Siena, Italy; chiaino@student.unisi.it (E.C.); durante6@unisi.it (M.D.)

[2] Dipartimento di Farmacia e Biotecnologie, Alma Mater Studiorum, Università di Bologna, Via Belmeloro 6, 40126 Bologna, Italy; matteo.micucci2@unibo.it (M.M.); roberta.budriesi@unibo.it (R.B.); roberto.gotti@unibo.it (R.G.); alberto.chiarini@unibo.it (A.C.)

[3] Valsambro S.r.l., Via Cairoli 2, 40121 Bologna, Italy; carla.marzetti@valsambro.it

* Correspondence: frosinim@unisi.it; Tel.: +3905-7723-5355

† The authors contributed equally to this work.

Received: 24 January 2020; Accepted: 16 March 2020; Published: 19 March 2020

Abstract: The research for innovative treatments against colon adenocarcinomas is still a great challenge. *Acacia catechu* Willd. heartwood extract (AC) has health-promoting qualities, especially at the gastrointestinal level. This study characterized AC for its catechins content and investigated the apoptosis-enhancing effect in human colorectal adenocarcinoma HT-29 cells, along with its ability to spare healthy tissue. MTT assay was used to describe the time course, concentration dependence and reversibility of AC-mediated cytotoxicity. Cell cycle analysis and AV-PI and DAPI-staining were performed to evaluate apoptosis, together with ROS formation, mitochondrial membrane potential (MMP) changes and caspase activities. Rat ileum and colon rings were tested for their viability and functionality to explore AC effects on healthy tissue. Quantitative analysis highlighted that AC was rich in (±)-catechin (31.5 ± 0.82 mg/g) and (−)-epicatechin (12.5 ± 0.42 mg/g). AC irreversibly decreased cell viability in a concentration-dependent, but not time-dependent fashion. Cytotoxicity was accompanied by increases in apoptotic cells and ROS, a reduction in MMP and increases in caspase-9 and 3 activities. AC did not affect rat ileum and colon rings' viability and functionality, suggesting a safe profile toward healthy tissue. The present findings outline the potential of AC for colon cancer treatment.

Keywords: *Acacia Catechu* Willd.; colorectal cancer; apoptosis; HT-29 cells; ROS; mitochondrial membrane potential; catechins; polyphenols; natural compounds

---

1. Introduction

Colorectal cancer (CRC) is one of the most common causes of tumour deaths worldwide [1]. In Europe, it is the second and the third most common form of cancer for women and men, respectively. Its occurrence and progression depend on multiple issues, among which family, age, gender and personal history constitute the major risk factors [2]. Standard treatments include surgery and chemotherapy. In the latter case, drugs induce DNA damage or initiate multiple signalling pathways, including cell cycle arrest, DNA repair, etc., leading to cancer cell death. The outcome of chemotherapeutic drugs in patients, however, is related to the cancer subtype, and often the effects of cytotoxicity, drug resistance and adverse reactions constitute overwhelming problems [3].

Natural products continue to provide leads for compounds endowed with pharmacological activities, especially those for treating many types of cancer [4]. A recent report highlighted that 49% of the small molecules approved in the area of cancer from the 1940s to 2014 were natural products or novel structures directly derived from them [5]. These compounds have cytotoxic properties owing to many different mechanisms of action, such as the inhibition of tumour cell growth accompanied by the induction of apoptosis, DNA damage, etc. Furthermore, anticancer drugs have greater potential to kill tumour cells if administered in combination with plant-derived compounds, and hopefully have less adverse effects. To explore this possibility, several clinical trials for various cancers were performed, including those for CRC [6].

Acacia catechu Willd. extracts have been used in traditional medicine for the treatment of several diseases. It possesses hepatoprotective, antipyretic, antidiarrheal, hypoglycaemic, anti-inflammatory, immunomodulatory, antinociceptive, antimicrobial, free radical scavenging and antioxidant activities [7–10]. Moreover, recent studies have demonstrated that *Acacia catechu* Willd. exerts spasmolytic and antispastic activities in vitro by interacting with calcium channels and muscarinic receptors, without affecting *Lactobacilli* and *Bifidobacteria,* the most represented intestinal species, suggesting that it may benefit patients suffering from diarrhoea [11]. *Acacia catechu* Willd. extract contains high amounts of flavonoids, such as flavan-3-ols, (+)-catechin, (−)-epicatechin, (−)-epicatechin-3-*O*-gallate and (−)-epigallocatechin-3-*O*-gallate [12]. These derivatives and related polyphenols possess apoptosis-inducing activity in several cancer cell lines [13]. Thus, this study investigates the effects of a preparation obtained by *Acacia catechu* Willd. heartwood by decoction (AC) on human colorectal adenocarcinoma HT-29 cell line in order to highlight its potential use in cancer therapy. As the capability of AC to spare the viability and functionality of normal tissue may be of clinical interest, this aspect was also investigated in rat ileum and colon rings. The results showed that AC has potential as an anti-cancer agent, as it exhibits irreversible anti-proliferative effects and induces intrinsic apoptosis, while sparing healthy tissue.

2. Results

2.1. AC Chemical Characterization

The decoction of *Acacia catechu* Willd. heartwood was characterized for its catechins content, assuming the most represented monomeric polyphenols as suitable phytomarkers for the herbal drug standardization [11,12]. The applied method, based on HPLC coupled with UV detection [14], showed the ability to resolve and quantify the major catechins in complex matrices; in Figure 1a the representative HPLC chromatogram of a sample of *Acacia catechu* decoction is reported. Identification of the catechins was performed by a comparison of the retention times of the analytical peaks in the sample with those of pure standards. Further confirmation of compounds' identities was achieved by the standard addition method and by comparison of the online UV spectra acquired by the DAD detector. Among the considered monomeric catechins, only catechin ((±)-C) and epicatechin ((−)-EC), were found in the analyzed extract, whereas other major catechins were not detected at the sensitivity level of the method (limit of detection—LOD—within 1–10 µg/g, depending on the compound). By external standard quantitation based on peak area, (±)-C and (−)-EC were found to be 31.5 ± 0.82 mg/g and 12.5 ± 0.42 mg/g, respectively. Further characterization of the sample was carried out by means of a chiral method based on cyclodextrin-modified micellar electrokinetic chromatography (CD-MEKC) which had previously shown the ability to resolve catechin enantiomers [15]. Interestingly, among the major catechins occurring in plant kingdom, catechin is reported to be as the (+)-isomer with (2R, 3S) configuration and labelled as (+)-C. On the other hand, native epicatechin is the (−)-diastereomer (2R, 3R), labelled as (−)-EC. Since the *cis*-related compounds are thermodynamically less stable than the *trans*-related ones, epimerization of (2R, 3R) (−)-EC to the non-native (2S, 3R) (−)-C could easily occur in samples (e.g., processed food and herbal drugs), as was observed in the manufacturing of chocolate from Theobroma cacao [15]. The proposed CD-MEKC method, allowing the enantioresolution of (±)-C, was thus applied to the analysis of the aqueous extract of *Acacia catechu* Willd. decoction. Interestingly, the presence of both the enantiomers, namely, the native (+)-C and the artifact (−)-C, at approximately the same content level was observed (Figure 1b). The latter was assumed as a marker of the epimerization as the consequence of the process applied in decoction preparation (thermal treatment). Analysis of decoction preparations stored during very long-term period (at least two years) at room temperature in the dark, did not show loss of (−)-EC and (+)-C, nor epimerization progression, thus suggesting very high chemical stability of the preparation.

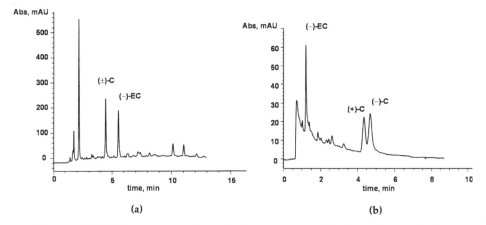

Figure 1. (a) HPLC chromatogram of a sample (aqueous extract) of *Acacia catechu* decoction. The method allows separation of the major catechins; namely, (±)-C, (−)-EC, (−)-ECG, (−)-EGC, (−)-EGCG and (−)-GCG. In the sample, only (±)-C and (−)-EC were found at levels higher than the limit of quantitation. (b) CD-MEKC of the same sample as in A). The method allows for the separation of the major catechins, as in the HPLC method. In addition, enantioseparation of (±)-C was achieved, revealing the presence of a significant amount of non-native (−)-C. HPLC and CD-MEKC conditions are described in the Materials and Methods section.

2.2. AC Induced a Concentration-Dependent, but not Time-Dependent, Irreversible HT-29 Cell Death

Cytotoxic effects towards human colorectal adenocarcinoma HT-29 cells were assessed after 24, 48 and 72 h of AC treatment (0.01–1000 µg/mL) by using an MTT assay. The results showed that HT-29 cell viability was not affected up to 10 µg/mL, whereas it decreased significantly with AC 50 µg/mL (for 72 h), 100 µg/mL (48 h) and 250 µg/mL up to 1000 µg/mL (24 h) (Figure 2a). This effect was concentration-dependent, but not time-dependent, as IC_{50} values among the selected time points were almost comparable (IC_{50} 24 h 199.4 ± 10.3 µg/mL; 48 h, 156.1 ± 11.3 µg/mL; 72 h, 139.5 ± 11.2 µg/mL).

Changes in HT-29 cell morphology mirrored MTT results. At variance with HT-29 untreated cells, which grow normally as tight colonies, those treated with AC (250 and 500 µg/mL, 24 h) showed significant changes in both number and size; displayed larger extracellular spaces; and began to shrink, round and fragment, thus resembling an apoptotic cell's typical appearance. These changes were progressively evident upon the increase in AC concentration, and cytotoxicity grades 2, 3 (250–500 µg/mL) and severe—grade 4 (1000 µg/mL)—occurred (see Figure S1).

To check whether the AC growth-inhibitory effect was reversible, cells were initially exposed to the extract for a 24 h period, following which they were washed thoroughly to remove the treatment, and were cultured in complete drug-free medium for a further period; i.e., 24 or 48 h. AC concentrations of 250 and 500 µg/mL, which caused grade 2 or 3, of toxicity were tested. As reported in (b) of Figure 2, AC caused an irreversible cytotoxic effect at both 250 and 500 µg/mL, as a drastic drop in the viability was evident even after an extra 48 h period of incubation with drug-free medium.

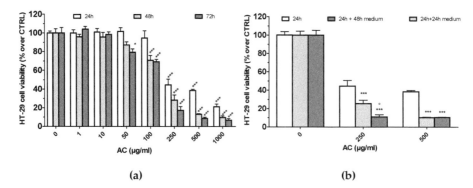

(a)   (b)

Figure 2. (**a**). Human colorectal adenocarcinoma HT-29 cells' viability after treatment with *Acacia catechu* Willd. extract (AC) for 24, 48 and 72 h. Panel B. Reversible or irreversible cytotoxic effect caused by AC. HT-29 cells were treated with AC (250 and 500 µg/mL, 24 h). Afterward, AC was washed off and cells were incubated with fresh serum-containing medium for an additional 24 or 48 h. After each time point, MTT test was performed as detailed in Materials and Methods. In both panels, values are means ± SEMs of 4 or 5 independent experiments in which four points/concentrations/times were run; controls (AC 0 µg/mL) represent untreated cells. Statistical significance was assessed by ANOVA followed by Dunnett post-test. (**a**): * $p < 0.05$, *** $p < 0.001$ vs. controls, same time point. (**b**): *** $p < 0.001$ vs. 24 h AC-treated cells; ° $p < 0.05$ vs. 24 h + 24 h medium-treated cells.

2.3. AC Induced an Apoptosis-Mediated HT-29 Cell Death

To study in more detail the mechanisms causing cell death observed after 24 h of treatment with AC, flow cytometry-mediated cells cycle analysis was performed. AC concentrations of 250 and 500 µg/mL (grade 2 or 3 of toxicity), along with 100 µg/mL—taken as the highest AC safe concentration, were used. A concentration-dependent rise in sub-G0/G1 hypodiploid cells, accompanied by a reduction in those in the G0/G1, was observed upon AC treatment (Figure 3a). While 100 µg/mL did not affect cell cycle distribution, 250 µg/mL increased apoptotic cells (subG0/G1 +9.9%, $p < 0.01$ vs. control), reducing, at the same time, although not significantly, those in G0/G1(-6.4%, $p > 0.05$ vs. control). Accordingly, 500 µg/mL AC had the most striking effect, as subG0/G1 ($+11.5\%$, $p < 0.01$ vs. control), G0/G1 (-23.4%, $p < 0.01$ vs. control) and G2/m ($+13.0\%$, $p < 0.01$ vs. controls) cells were affected. Apoptosis was further investigated with the AV-PI assay (Figure 3b). Challenge with AC caused a marked increase in early apoptotic ($+7.8$ and $+17.8\%$, $p < 0.01$ vs. control for 250 and 500 µg/mL AC, respectively), late apoptotic ($+12.6\%$, $p < 0.01$ vs. control for 500 µg/mL AC) and necrotic HT-29 cells ($+5.0\%$, $p < 0.05$ vs. control for 500 µg/mL AC). This effect was accompanied by progressive reduction in AV- and PI-negative cells, scored as healthy. DAPI staining supported characteristic apoptotic changes elicited by AC, such as chromatin condensation, nuclear pyknosis, elevated number of nuclear body fragments and irregular edges around the nucleus, which increased in a concentration-dependent manner (indicated by asterisk in Figure 3c).

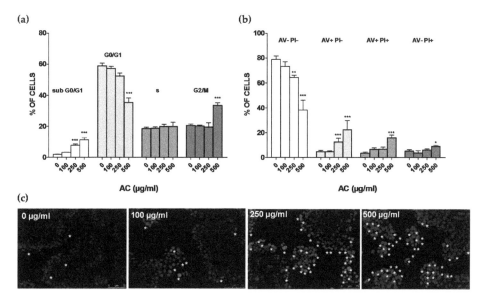

Figure 3. (**a**). *Acacia catechu* Willd. extract (AC)-mediated effects on the human colorectal adenocarcinoma HT-29 cell cycle. Percentages of cells in subG0/G1, G0/G1, s and G2/M phases. (**b**). Apoptotic cells' detection by double staining with annexin V (AV) and propidium iodide (PI). Values are means ± SEMs of four or five independent experiments in which four points/concentrations were run; controls (AC 0 µg/mL) represent untreated cells. * $p < 0.05$, ** $p < 0.01$, *** $p < 0.001$ vs. controls (ANOVA followed by Dunnett post-test). (**c**). DNA condensation and damage assessed by DAPI staining. Asterisks indicate cells with fragmented nuclei and condensed DNA, considered apoptotic. Each photograph was representative of three independent observations (scale bar 75 µm).

2.4. AC Caused ROS Formation along with Loss in Mitochondria Membrane Potential

Many chemotherapy drugs cause cell apoptosis by inducing the formation of ROS, which in turn further stimulate cell apoptosis and DNA damage [16]. For this reason, ROS formation was assessed by monitoring the conversion of the non-fluorescent 2′,7′-dichlorofluorescin to fluorescent 2′,7′-dichlorofluorescein (DCF). Results showed that upon AC treatment, a huge increase in DCF occurred, suggesting a considerable formation of ROS (Figure 4a). This effect, however, was almost comparable between 250 and 500 µg/mL AC concentrations (+166.2 ± 14.3 and +195.5 ± 18.3, respectively). To further support the role of ROS in the cytotoxic effects of AC, the ROS scavenger *N*-acetyl-L-cysteine (NAC, 1 mM) was used. As reported in Figure 4b, HT-29 cells' viability was significantly recovered in the presence of NAC, suggesting that ROS play a key role in AC-mediated HT-29 cell death. As one of the early events in apoptosis consists of the alteration of mitochondrial membrane integrity, changes in the mitochondria membrane potential (MMP) of AC-treated cells were assessed by staining them with R123. This dye selectively enters mitochondria with an intact membrane potential and there is retained, unless MMP is lost, causing R123 to be washed out from the cells. As reported in Figure 4c, intracellular R123 fluorescence decreased significantly by about 50–60% for both 250 and 500 µg/mL AC concentrations.

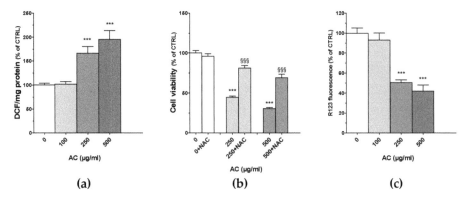

Figure 4. *Acacia catechu* Willd. extract (AC)-mediated effects on 2′,7′-dichlorofluorescein's (DCF) intracellular concentration (**a**); cell viability in the presence of N-acetyl-L-cysteine (NAC) (**b**) and rhodamine 123 (R123) staining (**c**) in human colorectal adenocarcinoma HT-29 cells. NAC (1 mM) was pre-incubated for 2h before the addition of AC (250 or 500 µg/mL). Data are reported as means ± SEMs of at least four independent experiments in which four points/concentrations were run; controls (AC 0 µg/mL) represent untreated cells. *** $p < 0.001$ vs. controls; §§§ $p < 0.01$ vs. the same concentration of AC (ANOVA followed by Dunnett post-test).

2.5. AC-Induced Changes in Caspase Activity

Different pathways of apoptosis are involved in the induction of cell death, including the mitochondria-mediated and the extrinsic receptor-mediated pathways, within which caspase-9 and 8 play essential roles, respectively. These, in turn, activate caspase-3 and fragmentation of DNA [17,18]. To investigate the involvement of these caspases, AC-treated HT-29 cell lysates were used to perform fluorescence assays with specific caspase-3, 8 and 9 substrates.

Caspase-3 plays a central role in apoptotic responses. As shown in Figure 5, the activities of both cleaved caspase-3 and 9 were significantly increased in AC-treated HT-29 cells, in contrast with that of caspase-8, which was not affected by the treatment, suggesting the activation of the mitochondrial pathway, rather than extrinsic receptor-mediated apoptosis pathway.

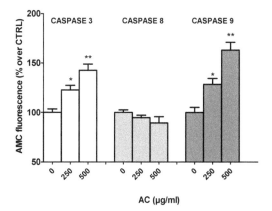

Figure 5. *Acacia catechu* Willd. extract (AC)-mediated effects on caspase-3, 8 and 9 activities in human colorectal adenocarcinoma HT-29 cells. The specific fluorogenic substrates DEVD-AMC (caspase-3), IETD-AMC (caspase-8) and LEHD-AMC (caspase-9) were used, and so was the fluorescence of the AMC-fragment released by active caspases measured at 380 and 460 nm excitation and emission wavelengths, respectively. Data are reported as means ± SEMs of at least three independent experiments in which four points/concentrations were run, and controls (AC 0 μg/mL) represent untreated cells. * $p < 0.05$, ** $p < 0.01$ vs. controls (ANOVA followed by Dunnett post-test).

2.6. AC Does not Affect Viability and Functionality of Healthy Rat Ilia and Proximal Colon Rings

For drugs targeting cancer cells, it is crucial to avoid toxicity to healthy tissues. For this reason, the effects of AC on rat proximal colon tissue viability was assessed.

Ilia were tested as well, as small intestine tissue constitutes the largest part of the gastro-intestinal tract. As in rat ileum and colon rings, a lower amount of AC might be attained in the extracellular milieu with respect to a cell monolayer, AC concentration was raised up to 1000 μg/mL.

Results showed that 24 h of treatment with AC did not change the viabilities of the ilia or proximal colon rings of rats (Figure 6a). Interestingly, the highest concentration of AC did not affect tissue contractility evoked by high potassium-containing solution (Figure 6b), thus suggesting a safe profile of AC toward healthy tissue.

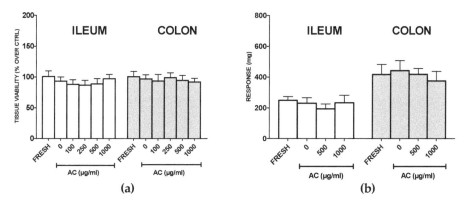

(a)   (b)

Figure 6. Rat ileum and proximal colon rings' viabilities (**a**), and high potassium-evoked contraction (KCl 60 mM) (**b**) after treatment with *Acacia catechu* Willd. extract (AC) for 24 h. Data are reported as means ± SEMs of at least three independent experiments in which four rings/concentrations were run; FRESH and AC 0 μg/mL refer to rings immediately after being explanted or treated with PSS for 24 h, respectively.

3. Discussion

Natural products constitute an important source of new anticancer molecules, thereby driving a novel direction for the prevention and therapy of cancers [6]. Natural product-derived drugs exert anticancer effects by hampering metastasis and angiogenesis and promoting apoptosis, which are the most important features of human cancers [6,18]. Moreover, drugs derived from natural products are generally endowed with better bioactivities and lower toxicity, and some of them have been combined with conventional therapies to enhance cancer cells' susceptibility [19].

This study investigates the apoptosis-enhancing effect of AC on the human colorectal adenocarcinoma HT-29 cell line in order to highlight its potential use in CRC therapy. As a first step, the decoction of *Acacia catechu* Willd. heartwood was characterized for its catechins content, and only catechin (±)-C and epicatechin (−)-EC were found to be present. It is noteworthy that the amounts of these two catechins (total ~40 mg/g) are comparable and even higher than those reported in green tea [20], whose mean contents are in the order of 6 mg/g and 1.5 mg/g for (−)-EC and (±)-C, respectively, as determined in about one hundred analyzed samples [21]. This, together with the observation that the bark extract's catechin content is less subjected to seasonal variation with respect to that in green tea or some fruits [22,23], makes AC a very interesting source of active polyphenols.

Biological assays showed that AC affected HT-29 cell viability in a concentration, but not time dependent fashion. When AC treatment time increased from 24 to 48 and 72 h, in fact, IC_{50} values remained in the range of 190–140 µg/mL AC concentration (i.e., 26–19 µM catechin content). This effect can be explained by considering that treated HT-29 cells undergoing apoptosis after 24 h of treatment (see below) may have progressed into necrosis due to the prolonged incubation with AC. Interestingly, comparable) values for MTT assay, cell cycle analysis and DAPI staining were found in Caco2 cells (see Figure S2), suggesting that this other widely-used colorectal adenocarcinoma cell line, characterized by high homology to enterocytes in the intestinal epithelium, is equally affected by AC.

In the case of cancer cells, is mandatory to investigate whether a cell line may (or may not) be able to restart its proliferating activity upon drug treatment. It is in fact crucial to demonstrate the presence of the so-called "point of no return," a limit line between cell injury and cell death; overtaking that causes irreversible damage. To assess whether AC-mediated cytotoxicity was reversible or irreversible, HT-29 cells were treated for 24 h with the extract, which was then washed off, and incubated with fresh serum-containing medium for an additional 24 or 48 h. The results suggested that AC elicited an irreversible cytotoxic effect against HT-29 cells, since a drastic decrease in the viability occurred even after incubation with drug-free medium for an extra 48 h period. Moreover, flow cytometric analysis and DAPI staining indicated that cytotoxic effects mostly consisted of apoptosis-mediated cell death. Early and late apoptotic, and some necrotic cells were in fact highlighted by AV-PI assay upon AC treatment—confirmed also by cytoplasmic shrinkage, membrane blebbing observed by contrast phase microscopy, DNA fragmentation (DAPI assay) and an increase in sub G0/G1 cells (cell cycle analysis).

Following the induction of apoptosis, perturbation of mitochondrial membrane potential is one of the main and earliest intracellular events. Mitochondria are the key regulators of the mechanisms which control the cell's survival/death balance, since they are the main source of cellular ROS and ATP [6,18]. Consequently, the production of ROS in treated cells was assessed, and results showed that a significant rise in their formation occurred upon AC challenge.

Excessive ROS production is a key negative element that results in the failure of suppression of antiapoptotic factors, thereby further triggering apoptosis. The fluorescent probe R123 was thus used to investigate the effects of elevated ROS production on the function of MMP in treated HT-29 cells. A drop in MMP, leading to the membrane depolarization of the mitochondria, was demonstrated, suggesting that the induction of apoptosis by AC may be associated with the activation of the mitochondrially-mediated pathway. The effects of AC on ROS and MMP, however, were comparable among 250 and 500 µg/mL, indicating that a plateau was reached. This plateau effect was also reported for human colon cancer HT-29 cells exposed to 30–100 µM of EC [24], a concentration comparable to those used in the present study—likewise for human colon carcinoma LoVo cells exposed to very high (500–1000 µM) levels of ECG [25,26].

ROS formation can be explained by considering that AC catechins can auto-oxidize to generate ROS in cell culture medium, and in turn, cause cell death [27,28]. Polyphenols, in fact, have the potential to promote the autoxidation of phenolic hydroxyl groups [29], and that mechanism is at the basis of their antibacterial and anti-cancer activities [28]. In particular, catechins can selectively kill cancer cells by promoting ROS generation over a critical threshold and by mobilization of endogenous chromatin-bound copper ions [30]. Among catechins, EGCG from green tea is one of the most studied, and it has been reported to be active against many types of cancer, including colorectal [31], lung [32], breast [33] and liver [34]. These effects basically arise from its abilities to promote pro-apoptotic effects, inhibit angiogenesis, regulate cellular metabolic pathways, and reduce inflammatory factors [28,35]. EGCG can increase the activities of traditional anticancer treatments [36–38] and reverse drug cell resistance, and this has encouraged its use in clinical trials for treatments of various types of cancer and other diseases [39]. *Acacia catechu* Willd. contains a variety of catechin monomers differently distributed in heartwood, leaves and chunks resin, (−)-EC and (+)-C being reported as the most abundant [12]. Accordingly, the heartwood extract used in the present study showed the presence of (−)-EC and (±)-C, as outlined by the quantitative analysis performed. Their pharmacological properties, although much less investigated with respect to EGCG, include the capability of inducing apoptosis [40], an effect strictly linked to their prooxidant activity [41–43]. Catechins, as previously outlined, can behave as pro-oxidants in the presence of Cu(II), leading to cytotoxic action [41]. As the cellular copper level is considerably elevated in cancer cells [43,44], it is conceivable that in the present experimental conditions, HT-29 cells may be more subjected to electron transfer between copper ions and AC catechins to generate ROS. Since cancer cells, which have altered antioxidant systems, are under constant oxidative stress because of increased rate of growth and metabolism [45,46], further ROS formation generated by AC catechins can overwhelm the HT-29 cells' antioxidant capacity, leading to irreversible damage and apoptosis. This was supported by the fact that the decrease in cell viability was significantly reverted by the ROS scavenger NAC, thereby suggesting that ROS formation may be necessary in AC-mediated effects. The copper-dependent ROS formation could also explain the previously discussed plateau effect, as a further increase in ROS might not occur upon increased AC concentration due to limited copper availability. The possibility that catechins may also induce the production of ROS by different mechanism(s), which could involve the electron transport chain in the mitochondria [47], or catechin-mediated hydrogen-peroxide formation [48], however, cannot be ruled out.

The activation of caspases, a family of cysteine-aspartic-acid specific proteases, is a critical event in the induction of apoptosis, and this ultimately leads to the hallmarks of apoptosis itself, such as chromatin condensation, DNA fragmentation and plasma membrane blebbing [17,18].

The mitochondria-dependent pathway of cell death involves the activation of the downstream caspase-9 via apoptosome formation, which leads to active caspase-3 and 7, the most effective caspases with many cellular targets [17,18]. This hypothesis was confirmed by the fluorimetric caspase assays, which showed increases in caspase-9 and caspase 3 activities following AC treatment.

Apoptosis can occur by the so-called extrinsic pathway as well, mediated by death receptors. This implies the activation of caspase-8, which cleaves and activates the above-mentioned downstream executioner caspases [17,18]. In the present study, however, AC treatment did not affect caspase-8's activity, thereby confirming that the apoptosis induced in HT-29 cells was mediated via the intrinsic mitochondrial pathway and not via the extrinsic, death receptor-linked caspase-8 pathway. Finally, even though intrinsic apoptotic signalling is potentially triggered by oxidative stress in many catechin-treated cancer cells [40–43], the possibility that AC activates apoptosis via a ROS-independent mechanism should be studied further.

Taken all together, the evidence from MTT assays, AV-PI and DAPI staining, cell cycle analysis, ROS production, MMP changes and the activation of caspases 3 and 9, demonstrated AC's promising pro-apoptotic activity towards the human colorectal adenocarcinoma HT-29 cell line via the intrinsic mitochondrial pathway, suggesting that it might be useful as a support to CRC treatment or prevention. Orally administered drugs are exposed to a changing environment, and even if they are planned to target the colon, they will be in direct contact with both the upper part of the GI tract and the colon itself. It is therefore mandatory that healthy tissue is not affected by the treatment. The effects of AC on rat ileum and proximal colon viability and functionality were thus assessed, and results highlighted the safe profile of AC, indicating a selective activity against cancer tissues. This sparing activity was already reported for EGCG and EGC in many cancer cells lines [49–53], and although the precise mechanism is still debated, the lower intracellular copper content of non-malignant cells might constitute the key difference [54]. Finally, AC is endowed with antibacterial activity against Gram-negative (*Escherichia coli, klebsiella pneumoniae, Proteus mirabilis and Pseudomonas aeruginosa*) and Gram-positive bacteria (*Staphylococcus aureus and Streptococcus pneumonia*) [11,55]; at the same time it is ineffective toward *Lactobacilli* and *Bifidobacteria*, the most represented intestinal species. The human gastrointestinal microbiota has a key role in human health, as dysbiosis is associated with various disorders and many types of cancer, including CRC [56]. Thus, the ability of AC to spare microbiota, together with the general safety profile of catechins and epicatechins, increases the therapeutic potential of AC. Moreover, it was recently reported that plasma concentrations of catechin and epicatechin quickly peaked after being orally administered AC in rat, with a rapid and wide distribution in all tissues, especially the intestine [57], reaching amounts comparable to those revealed to be effective in the present study. Thus, by using the translational dose calculation of Reagan–Shaw [58], an extrapolated dose for a man of about 10 mg/kg of catechin and epicatechin is attained, an amount which makes the administration of AC extract feasible for possible future clinical implications.

4. Materials and Methods

4.1. Plant Materials

A preparation obtained from *Acacia catechu* Willd. heartwood by decoction (AC) was supplied by BIO-LOGICA S.R.L. (via della Zecca 1, 40100 Bologna, Italy). The hydroalcoholic fluid extract production from the plant *Acacia catechu* Willd. was obtained by maceration and percolation according to European Pharmacopoeia 8.0. For more insight, please visit Minardi (A. Minardi and figli s.r.l. via Boncellino 18/A 48012 Bagnacavallo (RA) Italy; website, www.minardierbe.it).

4.2. Phytochemical Analysis

4.2.1. Chemicals

Catechins standard references, (±)-catechin hydrate ((±)-C), (+)-catechin ((+)-C), (−)-epicatechin (−)-EC, (−)-epigallocatechin (−)-EGC, (−)-epicatechin gallate (−)-ECG, (−)-epigallocatechin gallate (−)-EGCG, (−)-gallocatechin gallate (−)-GCG, sodium dodecyl sulphate (SDS) and (2-hydroxypropyl)-β-cyclodextrin (HP-βCD, degree of substitution ~0.6). Boric acid, phosphoric acid, sodium hydroxide, trifluoroacetic acid (TFA), acetonitrile (HPLC grade) and all the other chemicals, were purchased from Sigma-Aldrich (Milan, Italy, www.sigmaaldrich.com). Water used for preparation of standard solutions, running buffers and HPLC mobile phases, was purified by a Milli-Q apparatus (Millipore, Milford, MA, USA, www.merckmillipore.com).

4.2.2. HPLC Method

Aliquots of 100 mg of AC decoction were extracted with 10 mL water in an ultrasonic bath at room temperature for 15 min. The filtered solution was diluted 1/1 (v/v), with water and analyzed by HPLC under reversed-phase conditions. A Liquid Chromatograph by Agilent 1050 Ti series (Agilent Technologies, Waldbronn, Germany, www.agilent.com) equipped with a DAD detector (detection was set at 280 nm) was used. The stationary phase was a core-shell type Kinetex PFP (pentafluoro-phenyl) 150 × 4.6 mm (5 µm, 100 Å) by Phenomenex (Castelmaggiore, Bologna, Italy, www.phenomenex.com). The mobile phase was composed of acetonitrile (A) and aqueous TFA 0.1% (v/v) (B) under gradient elution: from 10/90 (A/B) to 20/80 (A/B) in 10 min at the flow rate of 1 mL/min. Sample injections were manually done by a Rehodyne Model 7125 injector (volume 20 µL).

Calibration graphs and sensitivity. According to a previous method [14] the calibration was carried out for the catechins: (−)-ECG (2.5–250 µg/mL), (−)-EGCG (25–500 µg/mL), (−)-EC (5–200 µg/mL), (−)-EGC (10–300 µg/mL), (±)-C (0.3–50.0 µg/mL) and (−)-GCG (2–50 µg/mL) in the concentration ranges given in brackets. Triplicate injections were made for each calibration point and the peak areas of the analytes were plotted against the concentrations of each of corresponding compounds; the determination coefficients were found to be higher than 0.9990. The sensitivity data as limits of detection (LODs) and limits of quantitation (LOQs) were determined by diluting standard solutions till signal-to-noise ratios of 3:1 and 10:1, respectively. The values were in the ranges 0.01–0.1 µg/mL (LOD) and 0.05–0.3 µg/mL (LOQ), depending on the compound.

4.2.3. Capillary Electrophoresis Method (Cyclodextrin-Modified Micellar Electrokinetic Chromatography, CD-MEKC)

Electrophoretic experiments were performed by a $HP^{3D}CE$ instrument by Agilent Technologies. Fused-silica capillaries (50 µm id, 30 cm total length, 8.5 cm length to the detector) were from CM Scientific Ltd. (Ryefield Way Silsden, UK, www.cmscientific.com). The separations were performed at a constant voltage of 15 kV, and the cartridge temperature was 25 °C. The detection was carried out by using the on-line DAD detector, and the quantitation was performed at the wavelength of 200 nm. Hydrodynamic injections were performed at 25 mbar for 5 s. New capillaries were conditioned by flushing sequentially 1M sodium hydroxide, 0.1 M sodium hydroxide and water in the order, for 10 min each. Between the injections the capillary was rinsed with 0.1M sodium hydroxide, water and running buffer for 3 min each.

Borate-phosphate buffer was used as the background electrolyte (BGE); it was prepared at a concentration of 12.5 mM and pH 2.5 by following a standard procedure. The obtained buffer was then supplemented with SDS (90 mM) and HP-βCD (25 mM).

Calibration graphs and sensitivity. According to a previous method [11,15], the calibration was carried out for the catechins: (−)-EC (5.0–300.0 µg/mL), (+)-C and (−)-C (0.3–50.0 µg/mL) in the concentration ranges given in brackets. Triplicate injections were made for each calibration point, and the peak areas of the analytes were plotted against the concentrations; the determination coefficients were found to be higher than 0.9990. The sensitivity data LOD and LOQ were determined by diluting standard solutions till signal-to-noise ratios of 3:1 and 10:1, respectively. The values were for (−)-EC, (−)-C and (+)-C: 0.1 µg/mL (LOD) and 0.4 µg/mL (LOQ).

4.3. Cell Cultures, AC Treatments and Cell Viability Assay

Human colorectal adenocarcinoma HT-29 cells (ATCC® HTB-38™, passages 10–20) were grown in a humidified atmosphere of 95% air and 5% CO_2 at 37 °C as previously reported [59]. AC was prepared immediately before use as 10 mg/mL stock solution in PBS, and pH adjusted to 7.5 before dilution to the desired final concentration. The solution was sterile filtered by passage through a 0.2-micron sterile filter. To assess AC effects, HT-29 cells (5×10^3 cells/well, final volume 200 µL) were treated with the extract (0–500µg/mL) for 24, 48 or 72 h, renewing AC solution every 24 h. To assess the role of ROS in AC-mediated cytotoxicity, N-acetyl-L-cysteine (NAC, 1 mM) was pre-incubated for 2h, and then AC (250 or 500 µg/mL) was added and left for 24 h. At the end of the treatments, MTT (20 µL of 5 mg/mL solution in PBS) was added to each well, and the assay was performed as already described [60]. Reversibility of AC cytotoxicity was tested by treating cells for 24 h with the extract, adding then fresh AC-free culture medium and assessing cell viability after a further 24 or 48 h of incubation [61].

4.4. Cells Morphological Assays

Apoptotic cells experiencing damage in the nuclei are featured by cell shrinkage, membrane blebbing and the presence of apoptotic bodies. In order to monitor these changes caused by AC, HT-29 cells were examined by using a phase-contrast light microscope, and the results were evaluated using the grade scale described in USP 28 (United States Pharmacopeia edition 2005) (grades 0–4) for the assessment of the cytotoxic potentials of the materials as follows: grade 0—no reactivity (discrete intracytoplasmic granules, no cell lysis); grade 1—slight reactivity (no more than 20% of the cells are round, loosely attached and without intracytoplasmic granules; occasional lysed cells are present); grade 2—mild reactivity (no more than 50% of the cells are round and devoid of intracytoplasmic granules; no extensive cell lysis and empty areas between cells); grade 3—moderate (up to 70% of cells are rounded or lysed); grade 4—severe (nearly complete destruction of the cells). [62,63].

4.5. Apoptosis Assays

Flow cytometry techniques, such as cell cycle and sub-G0/G1 population-analysis, and annexin V/propidium iodide (AV/PI) and 4′,6-diamidino-2-phenylindole (DAPI) staining, were applied to identify apoptotic cells. HT-29 cells (5×10^5 cells/well, final volume of 2 mL) were treated with AC for 24 h, and then the analysis was performed by using protocols previously described [62]. Alexa fluor 488™-AV/PI double staining kit (Life Tecnologies Italia, Monza, Italy) was used to detect the externalization of phosphatidylserine in apoptotic cells [64]. Samples were analysed on a FACScan flow cytometer (BD Biosciences, San Jose, CA, USA) by using CellQuest software v. 3.0 (BD Biosciences, San Jose, CA, USA). Viable cells were both AV and PI-negative; cells in early apoptosis were AV-positive and PI-negative; cells in late apoptosis were both AV and PI-positive; necrotic cells were PI-positive and AV-negative. Apoptosis was assessed also by analysing changes in nuclear morphology with the DAPI staining kit (Life Tecnologies Italia, Monza, Italy), as previously described [62].

4.6. ROS Detection

HT-29 cells were seeded into 6-well plates at 5×10^5 cells/well, grown for 24 h under standard conditions and then treated with AC for 24 h. ROS generation was assessed in cells rinsed with PBS and loaded with 10 μM 2′,7′-dichlorofluorescin diacetate (DCFDA) for 10 min at 37 °C, then washed, centrifuged at 13,000× *g* for 5 min and re-suspended in 0.7 mL of PBS. The intracellular fluorescence (504 nm excitation, 529 nm emission, Fluoroskan Ascent fluorimeter, Thermo Labsystems, Helsinki, Finland), was normalized to mg of cellular protein of the samples and expressed as percent of untreated-, control-cells [65].

4.7. Rhodamine-123 Staining

The fluorescent probe rhodamine-123 (R123) was used to check for mitochondria integrity [64]. This dye selectively enters mitochondria with an intact membrane potential and here is retained, unless MMP is lost, thus causing R123 washed out of from the cells. After AC treatment, HT-29 cells were stained with R123 (4 μM) for 10 min at 37 °C in the dark and then thoroughly washed with PBS. Afterward the fluorescence of 10000 single cells/sample was measured by FACScan flow cytometer (BD Biosciences, San Jose, CA, USA) at 505 nm (R123). CellQuest software v. 3.0 (BD Biosciences, San Jose, CA, USA) was used for intracellular fluorescence determination.

4.8. Caspase Activity

At the ends of the treatments, cells were added with 500 μL of caspase lysis buffer (20 mmol/L Hepes/KOH, 10 mmol/L KCl, 1.5 mmol/L MgCl$_2$, 1 mmol/L EGTA, 1 mmol/L EDTA 1, 1 mmol/L DTT, 1 mmol/L PMSF and 10 μg/mL leupeptin, pH 7.5). Afterward, cell lysates (20 μg proteins) were incubated for 1 h at 37 °C with of the following fluorogenic substrates (Enzo Life Sciences, Farmingdale, NY): caspase-9

LEHD-AMC (Ac-Leu-Glu-His-Asp-7-amino-4-methylcoumarin; AMC, 7-Amino-4-methylcoumarin); caspase-3 DEVD-AMC (Ac-Asp-Glu-Val-Asp-7-amino-4-methylcoumarin); caspase-8 IETD-AMC (Ac-Ile-Glu-Thr-Asp-AMC). These were used at 20 μM in 0.25 mL of caspase assay buffer (25 mmol/L Hepes, 0.1% *w/v* CHAPS, 10% *w/v* sucrose, 10 mmol/L DTT, 0.01% *w/v* egg albumin, pH 7.5). The reaction was stopped by adding 0.1% *w/v* ice-cold trichloroacetic acid (0.75 mL) and the fluorescence of AMC fragment released by active caspases was then read (Fluoroskan Ascent fluorimeter, ThermoLabsystems, Helsinki, Finland) at 380 nm and 460 nm (excitation and emission wavelengths, respectively) [66].

4.9. Rat Ileum or Colon Rings

All animal care and experimental protocols conformed to the European Union Guidelines for the Care and the Use of Laboratory Animals (European Union Directive 2010/63/EU, http://ec.europa.eu/environment/chemicals/lab_animals/home_en.htm) and were approved by the Italian Department of Health (666/2015-PR). Male Wistar rats (250–350 g; Charles River Italia, Calco, Italy) were used: 0.5 cm ileum and proximal colon rings were prepared according to the protocols of [67,68]. In particular, rings were placed in a water-jacketed (37 °C) organ bath containing 10 mL of modified Krebs–Henseleit physiological salt solution (PSS) (composition in mM: 118 NaCl, 4.75 KCl, 2.5 CaCl$_2$, 1.19 MgSO$_4$, 1.19 KH$_2$PO$_4$, 25 NaHCO$_3$, and 5.5 glucose, bubbled with a 95% O$_2$–5% CO$_2$ gas mixture, pH 7.4) and mounted on two stainless steel wires, one of which was connected to a force transducer that measured isometric tension in order to evaluate their contractility. Ileum or proximal colon rings were then equilibrated for 90 min under a resting tension of 1.0 g and were contracted by PSS containing high potassium (KCl 60 mM). Contractile isometric tension was recorded and analysed by means of a PowerLab data acquisition system and LabChart 7.3.7 Pro (Power Lab; ADInstruments, Castle Hill, Australia) for rings prepared immediately after their explant ("fresh" controls), and those treated for 24 h with PSS (controls, 0 μg/mL AC) or AC 500-1000 μg/mL [67].

Viability of tissue was also assessed by using MTT assay [69]. Rings were placed in 24 multiwell, one ring/well, and incubated for one hour at 37 °C with 800 μl of MTT solution (0.5 mg/mL). Afterward rings were transferred to a 96 MW (one ring/well) and 800 μL of DMSO added. The plate was stirred for 30 min to allow for the solubilization of the formazan salts formed. Subsequently, 100 μL of supernatant was taken and the absorbance assessed (560–630 nm) by using a plate reader (Multiskan TM GO, Thermo Scientific, Waltham, MA, USA).

4.10. Analysis of Data

Data were collected as quadruplicates from at least four independent experiments. The results were expressed as means ± SEMs. Cell viability was expressed as percentage of untreated cells (controls). Statistical significance was assessed by using ANOVA followed by Dunnett *post test* (GraphPad Prism version 5.04, GraphPad Software Inc., San Diego, CA, USA). In all comparisons, the level of statistical significance (*p*) was set at 0.05.

5. Conclusions

The present study outlines the potential of AC for CRC treatment, as this extract induced cytotoxicity of human colorectal adenocarcinoma HT-29 cells, which was accompanied by increases in apoptotic cells and ROS formation; a reduction in MMP; and increases in caspase-9 and 3 activities. AC did not affect rat ileum and colon rings viability and functionality, suggesting a safe profile toward healthy tissue. Moreover, AC main components are absorbed rapidly and eliminated slowly [57], and this might constitute an added value to the potential use of AC for CRC prevention.

Supplementary Materials: Supplementary materials can be found at http://www.mdpi.com/1422-0067/21/6/2102/s1.

Author Contributions: Conceptualization, R.B. and M.F.; formal analysis, M.F.; investigation, E.C., M.M., M.D., R.G. and C.M.; supervision, M.F.; writing-original draft, M.F.; writing-review and editing, E.C., M.M., M.D., R.B., R.G., C.M., A.C. and M.F. All authors have read and agreed to the published version of the manuscript.

Funding: This research received no external funding.

Acknowledgments: Authors wish to thank Elena Croci and Martina Bartoli for their technical assistance in some of the experiments.

Conflicts of Interest: The authors declare no conflict of interest.

Abbreviations

AC	*Acacia catechu* Willd. heartwood extract
AMC	7-amino-4-methylcoumarin
AV	annexin V
C	catechin
CRC	colorectal cancer
DAPI	4′,6-diamidino-2-phenylindole
DCFDA	2′,7′-dichlorofluorescin diacetate
DEVD-AMC	Ac-Asp-Glu-Val-Asp-7-amino-4-methylcoumarin
EC	epicatechin
ECG	epicatechin gallate
EGC	epigallocatechin
EGCG	epigallocatechin gallate
IETD-AMC	Ac-Ile-Glu-Thr-Asp-7-amino-4-methylcoumarin
LEHD-AMC	Ac-Leu-Glu-His-Asp-7-amino-4-methylcoumarin
MMP	mitochondrial membrane potential
MTT	4,5-dimethylthiazol-2-yl)-2,5-dipheniltetrazolium bromide
PI	propidium iodide
R123	rhodamine-123

References

1. Keum, N.; Giovannucci, E. Global burden of colorectal cancer: Emerging trends, risk factors and prevention strategies. *Nat. Rev. Gastroenterol. Hepatol.* **2019**, *16*, 713–732. [CrossRef] [PubMed]
2. Malvezzi, M.; Carioli, G.; Bertuccio, P.; Boffetta, P.; Levi, F.; La Vecchia, C.; Negri, E. European cancer mortality predictions for the year 2018 with focus on colorectal cancer. *Ann. Oncol.* **2018**, *29*, 1016–1022. [CrossRef] [PubMed]
3. Van der Jeught, K.; Xu, H.C.; Li, Y.J.; Lu, X.B.; Ji, G. Drug resistance and new therapies in colorectal cancer. *World J. Gastroenterol.* **2018**, *24*, 3834–3848. [CrossRef] [PubMed]
4. Harvey, A.L.; Edrada-Ebel, R.; Quinn, R.J. The re-emergence of natural products for drug discovery in the genomics era. *Nat. Rev. Drug Discov.* **2015**, *14*, 111–129. [CrossRef] [PubMed]
5. Newman, D.J.; Cragg, G.M. Natural Products as Sources of New Drugs from 1981 to 2014. *J. Nat. Prod.* **2016**, *79*, 629–661. [CrossRef]
6. Huang, X.M.; Yang, Z.J.; Xie, Q.; Zhang, Z.K.; Zhang, H.; Ma, J.Y. Natural products for treating colorectal cancer: A mechanistic review. *Biomed. Pharm.* **2019**, *117*, 109142. [CrossRef] [PubMed]
7. Burnett, B.P.; Jia, Q.; Zhao, Y.; Levy, R.M. A medicinal extract of Scutellaria baicalensis and *Acacia catechu* acts as a dual inhibitor of cyclooxygenase and 5-lipoxygenase to reduce inflammation. *J. Med. Food* **2007**, *10*, 442–451. [CrossRef]
8. Ismail, S.; Asad, M. Immunomodulatory activity of *Acacia catechu*. *Indian J. Physiol Pharm.* **2009**, *53*, 25–33.
9. Lakshmi, T.; Ezhilarasan, D.; Vijayaragavan, R.; Bhullar, S.K.; Rajendran, R. *Acacia catechu* ethanolic bark extract induces apoptosis in human oral squamous carcinoma cells. *J. Adv. Pharm Technol. Res.* **2017**, *8*, 143–149.
10. Rahmatullah, M.; Hossain, M.; Mahmud, A.; Sultana, N.; Rahman, S.M.; Islam, M.R.; Khatoon, M.S.; Jahan, S.; Islam, F. Antihyperglycemic and antinociceptive activity evaluation of 'khoyer' prepared from boiling the wood of *Acacia catechu* in water. *Afr. J. Tradit Complement. Altern Med.* **2013**, *10*, 1–5. [CrossRef]
11. Micucci, M.; Gotti, R.; Corazza, I.; Tocci, G.; Chiarini, A.; De Giorgio, M.; Camarda, L.; Frosini, M.; Marzetti, C.; Cevenini, M.; et al. Newer Insights into the Antidiarrheal Effects of *Acacia catechu* Willd. Extract in Guinea Pig. *J. Med. Food* **2017**, *20*, 592–600. [CrossRef] [PubMed]

12. Shen, D.; Wu, Q.; Wang, M.; Yang, Y.; Lavoie, E.J.; Simon, J.E. Determination of the predominant catechins in *Acacia catechu* by liquid chromatography/electrospray ionization-mass spectrometry. *J. Agric. Food Chem.* **2006**, *54*, 3219–3224. [CrossRef] [PubMed]

13. Hazafa, A.; Rehman, K.U.; Jahan, N.; Jabeen, Z. The Role of Polyphenol (Flavonoids) Compounds in the Treatment of Cancer Cells. *Nutr. Cancer* **2019**, 1–12. [CrossRef] [PubMed]

14. Fiori, J.; Pasquini, B.; Caprini, C.; Orlandini, S.; Furlanetto, S.; Gotti, R. Chiral analysis of theanine and catechin in characterization of green tea by cyclodextrin-modified micellar electrokinetic chromatography and high performance liquid chromatography. *J. Chromatogr. A* **2018**, *1562*, 115–122. [CrossRef] [PubMed]

15. Gotti, R.; Furlanetto, S.; Pinzauti, S.; Cavrini, V. Analysis of catechins in Theobroma cacao beans by cyclodextrin-modified micellar electrokinetic chromatography. *J. Chromatogr. A* **2006**, *1112*, 345–352. [CrossRef] [PubMed]

16. Wang, X.; Peralta, S.; Moraes, C.T. Mitochondrial alterations during carcinogenesis: A review of metabolic transformation and targets for anticancer treatments. *Adv. Cancer Res.* **2013**, *119*, 127–160. [PubMed]

17. Jan, R.; Chaudhry, G.E. Understanding Apoptosis and Apoptotic Pathways Targeted Cancer Therapeutics. *Adv. Pharm. Bull.* **2019**, *9*, 205–218. [CrossRef]

18. Pfeffer, C.M.; Singh, A.T.K. Apoptosis: A Target for Anticancer Therapy. *Int. J. Mol. Sci.* **2018**, *19*, E448. [CrossRef]

19. Rejhova, A.; Opattova, A.; Cumova, A.; Sliva, D.; Vodicka, P. Natural compounds and combination therapy in colorectal cancer treatment. *Eur. J. Med. Chem.* **2018**, *144*, 582–594. [CrossRef]

20. Saito, S.T.; Welzel, A.; Suyenaga, E.S.; Bueno, F. A method for fast determination of epigallocatechin gallate (EGCG), epicatechin (EC), catechin (C) and caffeine (CAF) in green tea using HPLC. *Food Sci. Technol.* **2006**, *26*, 394–400. [CrossRef]

21. Pasquini, B.; Orlandini, S.; Goodarzi, M.; Caprini, C.; Gotti, R.; Furlanetto, S. Chiral cyclodextrin-modified micellar electrokinetic chromatography and chemometric techniques for green tea samples origin discrimination. *Talanta* **2016**, *150*, 7–13. [CrossRef] [PubMed]

22. Arts, I.C.W.; Van de Putte, B.; Hollman, P.C.H. Catechin Contents of Foods Commonly Consumed in The Netherlands. 1. Fruits, Vegetables, Staple Foods, and Processed Foods. *J. Agric. Food Chem.* **2000**, *48*, 1746–1751. [CrossRef] [PubMed]

23. Gabr, S.; Nikles, S.; Pferschy Wenzig, E.M.; Ardjomand-Woelkart, K.; Hathout, R.M.; El-Ahmady, S.; Motaal, A.A.; Singab, A.; Bauer, R. Characterization and optimization of phenolics extracts from Acacia species in relevance to their anti-inflammatory activity. *Biochem. Syst. Ecol.* **2018**, *78*, 21–30. [CrossRef]

24. Yang, G.Y.; Liao, J.; Kim, K.; Yurkow, E.J.; Yang, C.S. Inhibition of growth and induction of apoptosis in human cancer cell lines by tea polyphenols. *Carcinogenesis* **1998**, *19*, 611–616. [CrossRef]

25. Babich, H.; Krupka, M.E.; Nissim, H.A.; Zuckerbraun, H.L. Differential in vitro cytotoxicity of (−)-epicatechin gallate (ECG) to cancer and normal cells from the human oral cavity. *Toxicol. In Vitro* **2005**, *19*, 231–242. [CrossRef]

26. Tan, X.; Hu, D.; Li, S.; Han, Y.; Zhang, Y.; Zhou, D. Differences of four catechins in cell cycle arrest and induction of apoptosis in LoVo cells. *Cancer Lett.* **2000**, *158*, 1–6. [CrossRef]

27. Hou, Z.; Sang, S.; You, H.; Lee, M.J.; Hong, J.; Chin, K.V.; Yang, C.S. Mechanism of action of (−)-epigallocatechin-3-gallate: Auto-oxidation-dependent inactivation of epidermal growth factor receptor and direct effects on growth inhibition in human esophageal cancer KYSE 150 cells. *Cancer Res.* **2005**, *65*, 8049–8056. [CrossRef]

28. Yang, C.S.; Wang, H. Cancer Preventive Activities of Tea Catechins. *Molecules* **2016**, *21*, 1679. [CrossRef]

29. Shishido, S.; Miyano, R.; Nakashima, T.; Matsuo, H.; Iwatsuki, M.; Nakamura, K.; Kanno, T.; Egusa, H.; Niwano, Y. A novel pathway for the photooxidation of catechin in relation to its prooxidative activity. *Sci. Rep.* **2018**, *8*, 12888. [CrossRef]

30. Farhan, M.; Oves, M.; Chibber, S.; Hadi, S.M.; Ahmad, A. Mobilization of Nuclear Copper by Green Tea Polyphenol Epicatechin-3-Gallate and Subsequent Prooxidant Breakage of Cellular DNA: Implications for Cancer Chemotherapy. *Int. J. Mol. Sci.* **2016**, *18*, 34. [CrossRef]

31. Shin, C.M.; Lee, D.H.; Seo, A.Y.; Lee, H.J.; Kim, S.B.; Son, W.C.; Kim, Y.K.; Lee, S.J.; Park, S.H.; Kim, N.; et al. Green tea extracts for the prevention of metachronous colorectal polyps among patients who underwent endoscopic removal of colorectal adenomas: A randomized clinical trial. *Clin. Nutr.* **2018**, *37*, 452–458. [CrossRef] [PubMed]

32. Rawangkan, A.; Wongsirisin, P.; Namiki, K.; Iida, K.; Kobayashi, Y.; Shimizu, Y.; Fujiki, H.; Suganuma, M. Green Tea Catechin Is an Alternative Immune Checkpoint Inhibitor that Inhibits PD-L1 Expression and Lung Tumor Growth. *Molecules* **2018**, *23*, 2071. [CrossRef] [PubMed]

33. Sinha, D.; Biswas, J.; Nabavi, S.M.; Bishayee, A. Tea phytochemicals for breast cancer prevention and intervention: From bench to bedside and beyond. *Semin Cancer Biol.* **2017**, *46*, 33–54. [CrossRef] [PubMed]

34. Bimonte, S.; Albino, V.; Piccirillo, M.; Nasto, A.; Molino, C.; Palaia, R.; Cascella, M. Epigallocatechin-3-gallate in the prevention and treatment of hepatocellular carcinoma: Experimental findings and translational perspectives. *Drug Des. Devel.* **2019**, *13*, 611–621. [CrossRef] [PubMed]

35. Liu, C.; Li, P.; Qu, Z.; Xiong, W.; Liu, A.; Zhang, S. Advances in the Antagonism of Epigallocatechin-3-gallate in the Treatment of Digestive Tract Tumors. *Molecules* **2019**, *24*, 1726. [CrossRef] [PubMed]

36. Berindan-Neagoe, I.; Braicu, C.; Irimie, A. Combining the chemotherapeutic effects of epigallocatechin 3-gallate with siRNA-mediated p53 knock-down results in synergic pro-apoptotic effects. *Int. J. Nanomed.* **2012**, *7*, 6035–6047.

37. Chen, S.; Zhu, X.; Lai, X.; Xiao, T.; Wen, A.; Zhang, J. Combined cancer therapy with non-conventional drugs: All roads lead to AMPK. *Mini Rev. Med. Chem.* **2014**, *14*, 642–654. [CrossRef]

38. Hsieh, C.H.; Lu, C.H.; Chen, W.T.; Ma, B.L.; Chao, C.Y. Application of non-invasive low strength pulsed electric field to EGCG treatment synergistically enhanced the inhibition effect on PANC-1 cells. *PLoS ONE* **2017**, *12*, e0188885. [CrossRef]

39. Colomer, R.; Sarrats, A.; Lupu, R.; Puig, T. Natural Polyphenols and their Synthetic Analogs as Emerging Anticancer Agents. *Curr. Drug Targets* **2017**, *18*, 147–159. [CrossRef]

40. Bernatoniene, J.; Kopustinskiene, D.M. The Role of Catechins in Cellular Responses to Oxidative Stress. *Molecules* **2018**, *23*, 965. [CrossRef]

41. Farhan, M.; Khan, H.Y.; Oves, M.; Al-Harrasi, A.; Rehmani, N.; Arif, H.; Hadi, S.M.; Ahmad, A. Cancer Therapy by Catechins Involves Redox Cycling of Copper Ions and Generation of Reactive Oxygen species. *Toxins (Basel)* **2016**, *8*, 37. [CrossRef] [PubMed]

42. Hadi, S.M.; Asad, S.F.; Singh, S.; Ahmad, A. Putative mechanism for anticancer and apoptosis-inducing properties of plant-derived polyphenolic compounds. *Iubmb. Life* **2000**, *50*, 167–171. [PubMed]

43. Hadi, S.M.; Bhat, S.H.; Azmi, A.S.; Hanif, S.; Shamim, U.; Ullah, M.F. Oxidative breakage of cellular DNA by plant polyphenols: A putative mechanism for anticancer properties. *Semin Cancer Biol.* **2007**, *17*, 370–376. [CrossRef] [PubMed]

44. Ebadi, M.; Swanson, S. The status of zinc, copper, and metallothionein in cancer patients. *Prog Clin. Biol. Res.* **1988**, *259*, 161–175. [PubMed]

45. Kong, Q.; Beel, J.A.; Lillehei, K.O. A threshold concept for cancer therapy. *Med. Hypotheses* **2000**, *55*, 29–35. [CrossRef]

46. Oberley, T.D.; Oberley, L.W. Antioxidant enzyme levels in cancer. *Histol. Histopathol.* **1997**, *12*, 525–535.

47. Tao, L.; Forester, S.C.; Lambert, J.D. The role of the mitochondrial oxidative stress in the cytotoxic effects of the green tea catechin, (-)-epigallocatechin-3-gallate, in oral cells. *Mol. Nutr. Food Res.* **2014**, *58*, 665–676. [CrossRef]

48. Hong, J.; Lu, H.; Meng, X.; Ryu, J.H.; Hara, Y.; Yang, C.S. Stability, cellular uptake, biotransformation, and efflux of tea polyphenol (-)-epigallocatechin-3-gallate in HT-29 human colon adenocarcinoma cells. *Cancer Res.* **2002**, *62*, 7241–7246.

49. Ahmad, N.; Gupta, S.; Mukhtar, H. Green tea polyphenol epigallocatechin-3-gallate differentially modulates nuclear factor kappaB in cancer cells versus normal cells. *Arch. Biochem. Biophys* **2000**, *376*, 338–346. [CrossRef]

50. Mayanagi, K.; Gaspar, T.; Katakam, P.V.; Kis, B.; Busija, D.W. The mitochondrial K(ATP) channel opener BMS-191095 reduces neuronal damage after transient focal cerebral ischemia in rats. *J. Cereb. Blood Flow Metab.* **2007**, *27*, 348–355. [CrossRef]

51. Mittal, A.; Pate, M.S.; Wylie, R.C.; Tollefsbol, T.O.; Katiyar, S.K. EGCG down-regulates telomerase in human breast carcinoma MCF-7 cells, leading to suppression of cell viability and induction of apoptosis. *Int. J. Oncol.* **2004**, *24*, 703–710. [CrossRef] [PubMed]

52. Rudolfova, P.; Hanusova, V.; Skalova, L.; Bartikova, H.; Matouskova, P.; Bousova, I. Effect of selected catechins on doxorubicin antiproliferative efficacy and hepatotoxicity in vitro. *Acta Pharm.* **2014**, *64*, 199–209. [CrossRef] [PubMed]

53. Yang, C.S.; Wang, H.; Chen, J.X.; Zhang, J. Effects of Tea Catechins on Cancer Signaling Pathways. *Enzymes* **2014**, *36*, 195–221. [PubMed]
54. Parmar, A.; Pascali, G.; Voli, F.; Lerra, L.; Yee, E.; Ahmed-Cox, A.; Kimpton, K.; Cirillo, G.; Arthur, A.; Zahra, D.; et al. In vivo [(64)Cu]CuCl2 PET imaging reveals activity of Dextran-Catechin on tumor copper homeostasis. *Theranostics* **2018**, *8*, 5645–5659. [CrossRef] [PubMed]
55. Dashtdar, M.; Dashtdar, M.R.; Dashtdar, B.; Shirazi, M.K.; Khan, S.A. In-Vitro, Anti-Bacterial Activities of Aqueous Extracts of *Acacia catechu* (L.F.)Willd, Castanea sativa, Ephedra sinica stapf and shilajita mumiyo Against Gram Positive and Gram Negative Bacteria. *J. Pharmacopunct.* **2013**, *16*, 15–22. [CrossRef]
56. Kosumi, K.; Mima, K.; Baba, H.; Ogino, S. Dysbiosis of the gut microbiota and colorectal cancer: The key target of molecular pathological epidemiology. *J. Lab. Precis Med.* **2018**, *3*, 76. [CrossRef] [PubMed]
57. Wang, L.; Shen, X.; Mi, L.; Jing, J.; Gai, S.; Liu, X.; Wang, Q.; Zhang, S. Simultaneous determinations of four major bioactive components in *Acacia catechu* (L.f.) Willd and Scutellaria baicalensis Georgi extracts by LC-MS/MS: Application to its herb-herb interactions based on pharmacokinetic, tissue distribution and excretion studies in rats. *Phytomedicine* **2019**, *56*, 64–73.
58. Reagan-Shaw, S.; Nihal, M.; Ahmad, N. Dose translation from animal to human studies revisited. *Faseb. J.* **2008**, *22*, 659–661. [CrossRef]
59. Terzuoli, E.; Nannelli, G.; Frosini, M.; Giachetti, A.; Ziche, M.; Donnini, S. Inhibition of cell cycle progression by the hydroxytyrosol-cetuximab combination yields enhanced chemotherapeutic efficacy in colon cancer cells. *Oncotarget* **2017**, *8*, 83207–83224. [CrossRef]
60. Bechi, N.; Sorda, G.; Spagnoletti, A.; Bhattacharjee, J.; Vieira Ferro, E.A.; De Freitas Barbosa, B.; Frosini, M.; Valoti, M.; Sgaragli, G.; Paulesu, L.; et al. Toxicity assessment on trophoblast cells for some environment polluting chemicals and 17beta-estradiol. *Toxicol. In Vitro* **2013**, *27*, 995–1000. [CrossRef]
61. Santulli, C.; Brizi, C.; Durante, M.; Micucci, M.; Budriesi, R.; Chiarini, A.; Frosini, M. Apoptotic-induced Effects of Castanea sativa Bark Extract in Human SH-SY5Y Neuroblastoma Cells. *Nat. Prod. Commun.* **2018**, *13*, 887–890. [CrossRef]
62. Brizi, C.; Santulli, C.; Micucci, M.; Budriesi, R.; Chiarini, A.; Aldinucci, C.; Frosini, M. Neuroprotective Effects of Castanea sativa Mill. Bark Extract in Human Neuroblastoma Cells Subjected to Oxidative Stress. *J. Cell Biochem.* **2016**, *117*, 510–520. [CrossRef] [PubMed]
63. Santulli, C.; Brizi, C.; Micucci, M.; Del Genio, A.; De Cristofaro, A.; Bracco, F.; Pepe, G.L.; Di Perna, I.; Budriesi, R.; Chiarini, A.; et al. Castanea sativa Mill. Bark Extract Protects U-373 MG Cells and Rat Brain Slices Against Ischemia and Reperfusion Injury. *J. Cell Biochem.* **2016**, *118*, 839–850. [CrossRef] [PubMed]
64. Durante, M.; Frosini, M.; Fusi, F.; Neri, A.; Sticozzi, C.; Saponara, S. In vitro vascular toxicity of tariquidar, a potential tool for in vivo PET studies. *Toxicol. In Vitro* **2017**, *44*, 241–247. [CrossRef] [PubMed]
65. Riganti, C.; Gazzano, E.; Gulino, G.R.; Volante, M.; Ghigo, D.; Kopecka, J. Two repeated low doses of doxorubicin are more effective than a single high dose against tumors overexpressing P-glycoprotein. *Cancer Lett.* **2015**, *360*, 219–226. [CrossRef] [PubMed]
66. Riganti, C.; Rolando, B.; Kopecka, J.; Campia, I.; Chegaev, K.; Lazzarato, L.; Federico, A.; Fruttero, R.; Ghigo, D. Mitochondrial-targeting nitrooxy-doxorubicin: A new approach to overcome drug resistance. *Mol. Pharm.* **2013**, *10*, 161–174. [CrossRef]
67. Watters, D.A.; Smith, A.N.; Eastwood, M.A.; Anderson, K.C.; Elton, R.A. Mechanical properties of the rat colon: The effect of age, sex and different conditions of storage. *Q J. Exp. Physiol.* **1985**, *70*, 151–162. [CrossRef]
68. Wu, Q.; Harada, N.; Nakamura, A.; Yoshida, M.; Mawatari, K.; Hattori, A.; Li, Q.; Shimohata, T.; Lian, X.; Nakano, M.; et al. NO-1886, a lipoprotein lipase activator, attenuates contraction of rat intestinal ring preparations. *J. Med. Investg.* **2008**, *55*, 61–70. [CrossRef]
69. Contartese, A.; Valoti, M.; Corelli, F.; Pasquini, S.; Mugnaini, C.; Pessina, F.; Aldinucci, C.; Sgaragli, G.; Frosini, M. A novel CB2 agonist, COR167, potently protects rat brain cortical slices against OGD and reperfusion injury. *Pharm. Res.* **2012**, *66*, 555–563. [CrossRef]

MDPI

St. Alban-Anlage 66

4052 Basel

Switzerland

Tel. +41 61 683 77 34

Fax +41 61 302 89 18

www.mdpi.com

International Journal of Molecular Sciences Editorial Office

E-mail: ijms@mdpi.com

www.mdpi.com/journal/ijms

Lightning Source UK Ltd.
Milton Keynes UK
UKHW050624070223
416551UK00004B/416